Agriculture in Economic Development

AGRICULTURE IN ECONOMIC DEVELOPMENT

Edited by

CARL EICHER *and* **LAWRENCE WITT**

Assistant Professor and Professor of Agricultural Economics
Michigan State University

McGRAW-HILL BOOK COMPANY

New York   Toronto   San Francisco   London

AGRICULTURE IN ECONOMIC DEVELOPMENT

19131

CONTENTS

Introduction 1

PART 1. Agriculture and Economic Development in Historical Perspective 7

1. The Place of Agriculture in Economic Development   *William H. Nicholls*   11
2. The Role of Agriculture in Modern Japanese Economic Development
   Kazushi Ohkawa and Henry Rosovsky. 45
3. Agriculture in Regional Economic Growth   *Douglass C. North*. . . 69
4. The Share of Agriculture in a Growing Population   *Folke Dovring* . . 78

PART 2. Measurement Problems in the Agricultural Sector. . . . 99

5. Economic Growth and the Contribution of Agriculture: Notes on Measurement   *Simon Kuznets*. 102
6. A Note on Nonconventional Inputs and Conventional Production Functions
   Glenn L. Johnson 120

PART 3. Theoretical Aspects of Agriculture in Economic Development   125

7. Disguised Unemployment in Agriculture: A Survey   *Charles H. C. Kao,
   Kurt R. Anschel, and Carl K. Eicher*. 129
8. Economic Theory and Agrarian Economics   *N. Georgescu-Roegen*. . 144
9. Economic Theory and Agrarian Reform   *V. M. Dandekar*. 169
10. A Theory of Economic Development   *Gustav Ranis and John C. H. Fei*   181
11. The Ranis-Fei Model of Economic Development: Comment   *Harry T.
    Oshima*. The Ranis-Fei Model of Economic Development: Reply   *Gustav
    Ranis and John C. H. Fei* 195

PART 4. Some Aspects of the Process of Change in Agriculture . . 203

12. Migration from Agriculture: The Historical Record and Its Meaning
    Dale E. Hathway 214
13. Connections between Natural Resources and Economic Growth   *Theodore
    W. Schultz*. 227

14. Comment on "Connections between Natural Resources and Economic
    Growth" *J. H. Dales*   235
15. Patterns of Development in Newly Settled Regions *Robert E. Baldwin*   238
16. The Collective Farm System in Russia: Some Aspects of Its Contribution
    to Soviet Economic Development *Arcadius Kahan*.   251
17. Land Reform and Economic Development *Doreen Warriner*. . . .   272
18. Thoughts on Land Settlement *W. Arthur Lewis*.   299
19. Trade Fluctuations and Buffer Policies of Low-income Countries *Ragnar
    Nurkse*   311
20. International Commodity Arrangements *Gerda Blau*   322
21. Development through Food Grants and Concessional Sales *Lawrence
    W. Witt*   339
22. Programming Changes in Marketing in Planned Economic Development
    N. R. Collins and R. H. Holton.   359
23. Research Costs and Social Returns: Hybrid Corn and Related Innovations
    Zvi Griliches   369
24. Public Purpose in Agricultural Research and Education *Earl O. Heady*   386
25. Reflections on Economic Development Policy *Albert O. Hirschman*. .   393

Selected Bibliography.   399

Name Index   405

Subject Index   409

INTRODUCTION

This book of readings in agricultural development is a reflection of the growing interest of economists and agricultural economists in the relation of the agricultural sector to overall economic development. This book, however, will not provide a blueprint for the development of world agriculture. A more modest goal is in mind. We have sought to bring together some of the ideas that are currently being discussed in the agricultural development field through the inclusion of a number of carefully selected papers and articles. We view the nations in the world as being situated somewhere along a development continuum rather than in developed or underdeveloped categories. As a result, we have selected articles and papers which examine the general process of agricultural change and which should therefore be of interest to readers in all parts of the world today, regardless of their present level of per capita income.

The volume is international in scope; the readings emphasize some of the common tools and approaches in explaining, initiating, and accelerating agricultural change in nations at various points along the development continuum. It is designed to provide a systematic exposure to agricultural development literature and thereby be useful in (1) supplementing senior-level undergraduate and graduate economic development courses in departments of economics in advanced and in less developed countries, (2) serving as a text in agricultural development courses in departments of agricultural economics at home and abroad by complementing materials readily available, (3) serving as a reference book for research and action workers in development, and (4) supplementing texts and case studies used in specialized training courses such as the World Bank's Economic Development Institute in Washington, D.C., and the Institute of Social Studies at The Hague.

It is appropriate to point out the rationale, organization, and criteria used in selecting the articles and papers reprinted. There is no need to underscore the growing intellectual interest in the process of economic development. As this field continues to expand, the general development literature is being made increasingly available on an international level through development journals, books of readings, bibliographies, and abstracts. Topics such as the theoretical aspects of growth and development, wage policies and labor problems in development, and economic history have been fairly adequately covered in books of readings. Moreover, the numerous development texts are serving wider audiences through translations. It is an empirical observation, however, that virtually all the development texts and articles reprinted in books of readings assign little attention to the agricultural sector in the development process. Since this sector in a typical less developed nation occupies half or more of the labor force and generates from one-fourth to one-half of the gross national product, it is important to analyze how agriculture can induce or facilitate overall development and to investigate the equally important adjustments agriculture must make as a consequence of overall development. This structural interdependence of the agricultural and nonagricultural sectors in development is a guiding theme of many of the articles and papers reprinted. Numerous empirical examples of agriculture in United States development are cited in the book and help to illustrate these two facets of overall development, which may enable us to understand better the process of agricultural development in less developed countries.

In view of this background, we have been encouraged by economists to prepare a framework for studying agriculture in relation to overall development and to bring together a group of papers and articles to supplement the standard economic development textbook. That is the first objective of this book.

Agricultural economists are being called on in increasing numbers to give attention both to broad considerations of the agricultural sector in development and to more detailed discussions of marketing, land, or production policy in less developed nations. These are both national and international issues. Agricultural economists have worked to improve the functioning of agriculture in the United States under the labels of farm management, production economics, and marketing for many years; but it is only relatively recently that agricultural economists in universities in advanced countries have turned to an analysis of the interaction between the agricultural sector and the overall economy. T. W. Schultz's *Agriculture in an Unstable Economy* (1945) is an important contribution in this area. Also, agricultural economists are now examining how agriculture can support economic development and studying the adjustments agriculture must make as a consequence of economic development.

Schultz's *Economic Organization of Agriculture* (1953) was a move in this direction. Nicholls, Schultz, Heady, Mellor, Mosher, and many others have been instrumental in helping to shift the agricultural economics profession to a more systematic and long-range interest in research and teaching in the less developed nations. Through this growing interest in international problems, most departments of agricultural economics in the United States now include a course in agricultural development in their graduate and, in some, their undergraduate curriculum. That is the second objective of this book. This book may help the teacher to organize courses in agricultural development which will serve as a *complement* to general development courses rather than as an isolated and independent study. This is an important issue because of the increasing fractionation of development teaching into a wide range of area-oriented, community-development, and regional-development courses. We are suggesting that the economics of agricultural development be taught within the framework of overall economic change and development.

Another important objective of the book is that of bringing together a highly selected list of the major postwar contributions to the literature of agricultural development for students in less developed nations with limited library facilities.

The plan of the volume is as follows. Part 1 analyzes agriculture and economic development in historical perspective: The observed regularities in the development process in the eighteen to twenty-four advanced countries for which quantitative data are available are used to explain their development process, to construct or test growth hypotheses, and to suggest the interaction between agriculture and the overall economy in nations at various points in their history. In Part 2, the measurement problems involved in agricultural development are discussed. In Part 3, we show that agriculture has been rediscovered in the theoretical literature appearing in journals in recent years. These writings are scattered among various journals and thus are not usually included in general development courses. Even though some of the theoretical aspects and models are controversial or nonoperational in development planning, and some are inconsistent with others, it is felt that they should be introduced to the reader. References to the theoretical literature are included in editorial comments and in the bibliography.

We move from economic history, measurement, and theory to applied problems in Part 4. Only a few aspects of initiating and accelerating agricultural change are included. Some of the problems involved in introducing change in agriculture are discussed, as are some of the nonagricultural problems occurring in various parts of the world which influence agricultural development policies in other countries. We stress the interdependence of all nations in the introduction of change.

Attention is also given in Part 4 to agricultural development policy in less developed nations, with the emphasis on moving away from the simplistic notion that land reform, more education, or some other variables are preconditions for development. Instead of looking for obstacles to development and forming policies and plans to remove the obstacles, the editors urge readers to examine Gerschenkron's and Hirschman's comments about expecting the latecomers to skip certain stages and sequences of development rather than follow the same path as the advanced nations. Gerschenkron poses the relevant question: In what way and through what devices can and do latecomers *substitute* for the missing prerequisites?

This volume encompasses only selected aspects of agricultural development and, as a result, does not provide simple answers showing how agricultural development can be initiated and accelerated. Since much of the development literature is either poorly conceived or tied to a specific institutional and cultural setting, we are reprinting only a small number of papers and articles which make an original contribution or which review and criticize our current state of knowledge. Other equally important articles were not included because they were widely available here in other collections or had been translated and reprinted in foreign books or journals. Four original articles were commissioned to fill some gaps in the literature. With the exception of several selections, we reprint complete articles rather than bits and pieces. In some cases original articles were updated.

Since agricultural development occurs within a sociopolitical milieu, community development, institution building, the transfer of technology, and agricultural planning are all influenced by social, cultural, and political variables. However, these influences were not covered in this book because articles making a major contribution were not personally known to the editors or their many advisors.

As an aid to students, we have prefaced each part with editorial comments in order to establish the connection between the part under study and the book as a whole, and to review the rationale for the articles selected. Comments will also serve as a guide to the literature relating to the topics under discussion. A bibliography has been added to aid in preparing courses and undertaking research.

The editors owe a heavy debt to the authors who kindly agreed either to reprint their papers and articles or to prepare original articles, and to publishers who granted us reprinting permission. Individual acknowledgments are made at the beginning of each article. Special thanks, however, are extended to the following people who shared their inventory of the literature and thereby aided in the selection process: James Bonnen, Alexander Eckstein, Bert Hoselitz, Subbiah Kannappan, Saul Katz, Wilfred Malenbaum, John Mellor, Arthur Mosher, William

Nicholls, Martin Pond, Philip Raup, Theodore W. Schultz, and Paul Strassman.

The research for this volume was greatly facilitated by a grant from the Ford Foundation which was administered through the Dean of International Programs at Michigan State University.

We are especially grateful to Charles Kao and William Miller, who assisted in the library research and helped us with a wide variety of tasks to complete this endeavor.

Finally, we wish to thank our wives, Joanne and Lucille, for their enthusiatic support and participation in our international teaching, research, and travel.

part 1

AGRICULTURE AND ECONOMIC DEVELOPMENT
IN HISTORICAL PERSPECTIVE

The four essays reprinted in Part 1 reflect the postwar expansion and growing sophistication of economic history as a field of study. Typically, studies of economic history are not concerned with problems of initiating development. Rather, they are concerned with the search for similarities in the development processes of the eighteen to twenty-four nations which have experienced what Kuznets has labeled "modern economic growth," in order to explain the process of development and to generate and test hypotheses.

Before we turn to the discussion of the four articles reprinted, we think it is important to comment on several studies which have aroused interest and discussion in the field of economic history. Rostow's *revival* of the notion of stages of development in his *Stages of Economic Growth*[1] has been widely debated. Rostow observed the growth processes of nations at various points in their economic history and advanced a theory of development which assumes that all nations will pass through the same five stages of development (traditional, preconditions, takeoff, drive to maturity, and high mass consumption) as they move along the path of economic progress. The danger of moving from an interpretation of the past to a general theory of development has been noted by numerous economists.[2] Rostow's scheme is dominated by uniformity,

---

[1] W. W. Rostow, *The Stages of Economic Growth*, Cambridge University Press, London, 1960.

[2] Among the fairly critical reviews of Rostow's book by economists are Simon Kuznets, *Notes on the Take-off*, a paper presented at the September, 1960, meeting

i.e., the process of development repeats itself from country to country. Gerschenkron's[3] intensive analysis of the growth process in France, Germany, and Russia refutes Rostow's uniformity theme and the Marxian generalization that "the industrially more developed country presents to the less developed country a picture of the latter's future."[4] Gerschenkron contends that this is a half-truth which conceals strategic differences between advanced and less developed nations; in fact, he suggests that the only generalization that can be made is that the latecomers will probably not follow the path of the advanced nations, and that therefore economists should expect less developed nations to skip certain stages of development. Not only does Gerschenkron suggest that nations need not fulfill the preconditions as Rostow outlines them, he also suggests that there should be a fine placed on using words such as "precondition" and "necessary" in historical writing. He submits that historical research should be directed "toward a new question: in what way and through the use of what devices did backward countries *substitute* for the missing prerequisites?"[5]

Economic historians have supplied data to help analyze the issue of whether the agricultural or the industrial sector should be relied upon as the driving force in development. Economic historians generally concur that there are no cases of successful development of a major country in which a rise in agricultural productivity did not precede or accompany industrial development.[6] It is more and more apparent that development over the long run is not likely to occur if it is tied to either an agricultural or an industrial foundation. Today it is recognized that there is no basis for doctrinaire statements that development should be launched with either an agricultural or industrial expansion; instead, "Every economy has an agricultural and a nonagricultural sector, and one of the most important aspects of development is the changing, complex but always intimate relation between the two."[7]

In Selection 1, Nicholls discusses the contributions of agriculture to

---

of the International Economic Association and reprinted in Theodore Morgan, George W. Betz, and N. K. Choudhry (eds.), *Readings in Economic Development*, Wadsworth Publishing Company, Inc., Belmont, Calif., 1963, pp. 201–213; and Goran Ohlin, "Reflections on the Rostow Doctrine," *Economic Development and Cultural Change*, vol. 9, pp. 648–655, July, 1961.

[3] Alexander Gerschenkron's essays over the 1951 to 1961 period are reprinted in *Economic Backwardness in Historical Perspective*, Harvard University Press, Cambridge, Mass., 1962.

[4] *Ibid.*, p. 6, quoting Karl Marx, *Das Kapital*, 1st ed., Preface.

[5] *Ibid.*, p. 358.

[6] See Simon Kuznets, *Six Lectures on Economic Growth*, The Free Press of Glencoe, New York, 1960, pp. 59–60.

[7] A. J. Youngson, *Possibilities of Economic Progress*, Cambridge University Press, London, 1959, p. 284.

overall development and then systematically discusses agriculture's role in the economic development of advanced nations, with implications for *short-run* development policy in less developed countries today. Nicholls contends that Western economists either ignore or seriously underestimate the importance of an "agricultural surplus" in the early stages of growth of presently advanced nations. Nicholls thinks that Western economists' misreading of economic history partially explains why they undervalue the importance of investing in agricultural develop- ment within the *short-run* context of planning in many underdeveloped countries today. Nicholls gives greater precision to his concept of an agricultural surplus in a recent article, "An Agricultural Surplus as a Factor in Economic Development."[8]

The English economic historian, H. J. Habbakkuh, discusses agri- culture's central role in nineteenth-century European economic history in a recent paper.[9]

The reader is directed to Johnston's and Mellor's paper for a discussion of agriculture's contribution to economic development.[10] In Section II of that paper they discuss the product, foreign exchange, labor factor, capital creation, and market contributions which the agricultural sector makes to the development of the nonfarm sector. They do not consider the inverse: the contribution of the nonfarm economy to agricultural de- velopment, which can provide a more or less comparable but different linkage.

Selection 2 by Ohkawa and Rosovsky traces the economic history of Japan, from 1878 to 1917, with a concluding note on the implications of the Japanese development experience for Asian countries today. Ohkawa is often called the "Kuznets of Japan" and is known for his important study, with others, *The Growth Rate of the Japanese Economy Since 1878* (Tokyo, 1957). Rosovsky, a quantitative economic historian at Berkeley, recently published *Capital Formation in Japan, 1868–1940* (Free Press of Glencoe, New York, 1961), which Professor Oshima has called "a bold piece of pioneer work." The reader is especially directed to Chapter Four in Rosovsky's book for a discussion of the relevance of the Japanese development experience for Asian countries today.

Douglass North of the University of Washington is an economic historian who has sparked interest in quantitative research on the

[8] The *Journal of Political Economy*, vol. 71, pp. 1–29, February, 1963.

[9] "Lessons of History," paper presented at the 1962 Conference of the Interna- tional Economic Association, Vienna, to be published by the International Economic Association.

[10] Bruce F. Johnston and John W. Mellor, "The Role of Agriculture in Economic Development," *American Economic Review*, vol. 51, pp. 566–593, September, 1961. See especially Section II. This article reprinted as "El Papel de la Agricultura en el Desarrollo Economico," *El Trimestre Economico*, vol. 30, pp. 279–308, Abril- Junio de 1962.

economic history of the United States in recent years.[11] In the June, 1955, issue of the *Journal of Political Economy*[12] North argued that there is "nothing to prevent population and per capita income from growing in a region whose export base is agriculture." North revised and qualified his position slightly in a 1959 paper which is reprinted as Selection 3; he uses data on regional agricultural export flows in the United States in the nineteenth century and shows that, *under certain conditions,* export agriculture can play a central role in initiating overall growth of a region or a nation. The reader should note that North draws on Baldwin's conception of how the production function of a region influences migration and trade flows (see Selection 15). Vernon Ruttan, in a perceptive review of North's paper, thinks that North has made an important contribution but that he wishes North would revise his position one step further to include "the positive assertion that *the emergence of expanding urban industrial centers is essential to the long-term growth of population and per capita income levels regardless of the original basis for regional growth.*"[13]

Finally, Selection 4 by Dovring is often inaccessible to readers in less developed nations. Dovring uses data from advanced countries to show that although the relative proportion of the labor force engaged in agriculture declined through economic development, the absolute number of people in agriculture increased in early stages of growth of the presently advanced nations and declined only after a relatively long period of time. Dovring concludes that "in most of the less-developed countries today, there is no reason to expect reduction of absolute numbers in the agricultural population within the near future . . . . It will take decades before agriculture ceases to employ and support the majority of the world's population."

[11] Douglass North, "Quantitative Research in American Economic History," *American Economic Review,* vol. 53, pp. 128–130, March, 1963.

[12] "Location Theory and Regional Economic Growth," p. 257.

[13] Vernon W. Ruttan, "Discussion: The Location of Economic Activity," *Journal of Farm Economics,* vol. 41, p. 953, December, 1959.

I. The Place of Agriculture in Economic Development*

WILLIAM H. NICHOLLS

> *"God gives nuts to those who have no teeth."*
> Brazilian proverb

The rapidly growing literature on the history, theory, and policy of economic development has perforce recognized the dominant place of agriculture in the underdeveloped countries and has generally concluded that economic development requires that vast numbers of rural people shift out of agriculture. This literature has also usually agreed that substantial industrialization is necessary if this redundant agricultural population is to find more productive non-agricultural employment, thereby permitting those who remain in agriculture to reorganize their farms into more efficient, larger-scale, mechanized operating units. Within a sufficiently long-run context, these conclusions are beyond cavil for virtually any underdeveloped country. However, as guides to the establishment of short-run planning goals and priorities—particularly as between agricultural and industrial development—they are, in my opinion, often misleading if not completely fallacious.

Instead, I believe that the role of agriculture in economic development depends heavily upon the stage of economic history in which a particular nation finds itself and, especially at the time that economic progress first becomes a major social aspiration, upon the ratio of agricultural land to population. The relative emphasis which public policy gives to agriculture, and the particular forms which agricultural policies take, must

* A paper presented at a Round Table on Economic Development with Particular Reference to East Asia (sponsored by the International Economic Association), held at Gamagori, Japan, Apr. 2–9, 1960. Reprinted by permission of the International Economic Association and the author. This article also appears in the Conference Proceedings entitled *Economic Development with Special Reference to East Asia*, Kenneth Berrill (ed.), 1963. The author is professor of economics, Vanderbilt University.

therefore vary accordingly. Hence, in the present paper, I shall begin with a summary of the important interrelationships between agricultural and industrial-urban development; I shall then seek to discover what lessons we can learn from history as to the role of agriculture in Western economic development; and I shall conclude with an examination of the special problems of agriculture in the overpopulated countries of Asia which aspire to economic development.

INTERRELATIONSHIPS BETWEEN AGRICULTURAL AND INDUSTRIAL-URBAN DEVELOPMENT

Contributions of Agricultural Progress

In a rather fundamental sense, agricultural progress is normally a pre-requisite for industrial development. This is clearly the case in a *closed* economy, where one of the most important pre-conditions of industrial expansion is the achievement of a rate of increase in agricultural productivity which exceeds the concurrent rate of increase in the demand for food. Rising agricultural productivity supports and sustains industrial development in several important ways. First, it permits agriculture to release part of its labor force for industrial employment while meeting the increasing food needs of the non-agricultural sector. Second, it raises agricultural incomes, thereby creating the rural purchasing power needed to buy the new industrial goods and rural savings which may then be mobilized, by direct or indirect means, to finance industrial development. Finally, it enables agriculture to supply the major wage-good (food) of industrial workers at prices favorable to the profitability of new industry.[1]

For an *open* economy, with access to international trade, the contribution of generally rising agricultural productivity to industrial development may be diminished. For then the given nation may find it more economical to import some of its food needs because its comparative advantage lies in non-food production, some of which it may export in exchange for food. For example, it may find that the foreign demand for industrial crops (cotton, jute, rubber), for minerals (tin, copper, petroleum), or even for certain manufactures, is sufficiently large to support substantial exports and even to attract the foreign capital and entrepreneurial talent needed to develop such export industries. Even here, however, rising productivity in the food sector is desirable, both because it may save scarce foreign exchange needed for financing imports of industrial capital and because it contributes to the integration of the dualistic (plantation-peasant) agricultural economy,

[1] Cf. W. Arthur Lewis, *Theory of Economic Growth*, London, Geo. Allen & Unwin, 1955, p. 334.

the existence of which has so often restricted the rate and spread of economic progress. Finally, if agricultural productivity in the food sector is or becomes sufficiently high, the nation may enjoy a food surplus of such magnitude as to permit the export on favorable terms of food itself, with correspondingly favorable effects on the balance of payments and domestic industrialization.

Thus, it is clear that, under all circumstances, increasing agricultural productivity makes important contributions to general economic development and that, within considerable limits at least, it is one of the pre-conditions which must be established before a take-off into self-sustained economic growth becomes possible. So much said, however, it is equally clear that industrial urban development creates conditions much more favorable for increasing agricultural productivity and output.

Contributions of Industrial-Urban Development

As an economy undergoes industrial-urban development, it accelerates the rate of agricultural progress in many important ways. Industrialization increases the demand for wage-goods, of which food is initially most important. The resulting more favorable market for agricultural products tends to break down the relatively stagnant subsistence sector of agriculture, stimulating the production of cash crops on a more specialized and efficient basis, the development of agricultural processing industries, and the integration of the rural and urban economies. Industrialization also makes available to agricultural workers a wider range of consumption goods, raising their level of wants and encouraging greater productive effort; and new and better agricultural production goods, which directly raise agricultural productivity per hectare or per man. Perhaps most important, industrial-urban development makes for more efficient factor markets within agriculture.

By creating more productive non-agricultural employment opportunities, industrialization diverts redundant labor from agriculture, to the benefit of both those who leave and those who remain in agriculture. If the absorption of farm labor into industrial employment proceeds far enough, increasing labor scarcity in agriculture will raise direct or imputed farm wages. As a result, those who continue to work in agriculture must find ways of raising their productivity so that they are worth these higher wages. This they can do if they can increase the scale of farming and the capital-labor ratio. Industrial-urban development facilitates both of these forms of agricultural reorganization. First, in areas which remain almost completely rural, it reduces farm land values as the pressure of population on the land supply is reduced by outmigration, encouraging land consolidation. Second, it increases aggregate financial resources and creates more effective financial institutions, some of the benefits of which redound to the benefit of agriculture. Thus, industrial-urban development creates conditions which—by encouraging the reorganization of agriculture on a more efficient, larger-scale, mechanized basis—are highly favorable to increasing productivity.

Industrial-urban development also creates an intellectual environment which, being less tradition-bound than agriculture, is more favorable to the creation of an entrepreneurial class, to the expansion of new skills, to capital formation and technical innovation, and to declining birth rates. Such an environment contributes to increasing productivity not only in the non-agricultural sector but, both directly and indirectly, in the agricultural sector as well. Furthermore, in a country with a poor agricultural resource base, industrialization may represent a superior alternative to domestic agricultural self-sufficiency, with food imports being paid for by industrial exports. On the other hand, for a country which is relatively efficient in the production of certain agricultural products (or other primary goods) enjoying substantial export markets, domestic industrialization still may contribute significantly to greater stability in its international terms of trade.

The Problem of "Balance"

While rising agricultural productivity and industrial-urban development clearly have much to contribute to each other, and hence to over-all economic growth, the problem of establishing priorities which faces the development planner is a very difficult one. It is easy to say that the answer lies in *balanced* agricultural and industrial development. In practice, however, the underdeveloped country faces the dilemma that, because its economic resources are by definition severely limited, their allocation according to the criterion of balance may spread them so thin that they are below certain crucial minimum levels which must be exceeded if productivity and income are to be raised in any direction. Under such difficult circumstances, it is not possible to avoid policies which seek to promote, in the short run at least, rather different rates of development in (say) the agricultural and industrial sectors. Nonetheless, some consideration of "balance" is unavoidable in the sense of "the minimizing of the waste of productive resources that results when one sector of the economy acts for an unnecessarily long time as the effective limiting factor (bottleneck) on the growth of other sectors."[2]

At any given time, any underdeveloped country is in a position which reflects previous investment decisions and previous development, so that unbalanced investment policies may be needed to complement existing imbalance. The problem is further complicated by the fact that, because economic development is a dynamic process, "external economies" are

[2] Ansley J. Coale and Edgar M. Hoover, *Population Growth and Economic Development in Low-income Countries: A Case Study of India's Prospects,* Princeton Univ. Press, Princeton, New Jersey, 1958, p. 119.

of vital importance. That is, there are certain types of investment which bring substantial benefits to society as a whole without being fully reflected in the direct return to any single firm, industry, or investment sector. Thus, the allocation of investment on the basis of individual estimates of short-run returns on various marginal investment projects (according to static theory) may have a combined effect which is less than the sum of the parts. On the other hand, the allocation of investment which takes into account "external economies" may have a dynamic total effect on the national income which appreciably exceeds the sum of the parts, some of which would yield as single projects too little to appear to warrant the necessary investment. Unfortunately, "external economies" are best promoted by investments which, because of basic indivisibilities, are of relatively large minimum size. This is particularly true of social overhead capital (power, transportation, education, and the like) and of other large-scale investment programs which seek to take the indivisibility (complementarity) of demand into consideration.[3]

Thus, while the principle of balanced agricultural and industrial development appears at first glance to be reasonable enough, it is not easy to put into practice, particularly in countries which are seeking to launch rather than to sustain economic growth. Instead, very difficult choices must be made in any given development plan, whose major objective must be the concentration of extremely scarce resources on certain strategic investments which will remove the most restrictive bottlenecks of the current situation. Recognizing the necessity of choice, economists have fallen into two groups with regard to their judgment as to the relative emphasis which agricultural investment should receive. In the first group are those (e.g., A. E. Kahn, Jacob Viner, and Coale and Hoover) who argue that efforts to increase food supply should receive top priority because of the high demand and great need for additional food or because the highest marginal productivity of capital lies in agriculture.[4] Thus, Coale and Hoover conclude for India that "very substantial progress in that most backward part of the economy (agriculture)" is "a prerequisite to successful development of the . . . economy as a whole" and that "if one sector limits the growth of the other, it is more likely to be a case of agricultural growth limiting nonagricultural than vice versa."[5]

In the second group fall an increasing number of economists (among them Albert Hirschman, Leibenstein, and Higgins) who, while recogniz-

[3] Benjamin Higgins, *Economic Development*, W. W. Norton and Co., New York, 1959, Chapter 16, espec. pp. 400–401 (Singer) and 385–388 (Rosenstein-Rodan).

[4] Harvey Leibenstein, *Economic Backwardness and Economic Growth*, John Wiley, New York, 1957, pp. 261–262.

[5] Coale and Hoover, *op. cit.*, pp. 120, 139.

ing the need for raising agricultural productivity, conclude that it can be accomplished only by giving a "big push" industrialization program top priority. Higgins states this position most baldly in arguing that the only means to a "cumulative improvement in agricultural productivity" is a public policy "designed to make labor relatively scarce in agriculture by simultaneously shifting to a more mechanized and larger-scale agriculture and encouraging a rapid rate of industrialization." Elsewhere he recognizes that such a policy "requires heavy investment in *both* the industrial and agricultural sectors" and warns about the dangers of "industrialization without an agricultural revolution" and "neglect of the agricultural sector." Despite this bow toward agriculture, however, the logic of Higgins' position necessitates emphasis on industrialization since, without it, land consolidation and farm mechanization could hardly increase the scarcity of labor. Leibenstein's position, while more cautiously stated, is quite similar.[6]

While the points of view of these two groups of economists are a matter not of black and white but of different shades of gray, I believe that the second group's position is much the more vulnerable, particularly if it is to be used as the basis for short-run economic planning in over-populated countries. By seriously underestimating the time, effort, and resources required to bring about drastic structural changes in underdeveloped countries, they overlook (and often even deprecate) the short-run potentialities of raising agricultural output with given supplies of land and labor and existing small-scale farming units. By doing so, their conclusions almost amount to saying that the way for an underdeveloped country to become developed is to become developed.

Admittedly, there is probably no underdeveloped country which can at any stage afford to concentrate *all* of its investment on either agricultural or industrial development. However, in my opinion, not until it has succeeded in achieving and sustaining a reliable food surplus (or in at least reducing the food deficit to a magnitude which expanding non-food exports might realistically be expected to cover in the near term) does a shift of emphasis to the large-scale transfer of farm population into non-farm employment and to labor-saving devices in agriculture begin to make sense. I shall return to this important matter later in this paper. Meanwhile, however, let us see what light history has to throw upon the role of agriculture in launching economic development.

AGRICULTURE IN WESTERN ECONOMIC HISTORY

In examining the role of agriculture in Western economic development it is convenient to classify world regions roughly according to their land-population ratios during the immediate pre-industrial period

[6] Higgins, *op. cit.*, pp. 459, 343; Leibenstein, *op. cit.*, p. 264.

of their economic history. We shall do so here, beginning with the regions which were initially underpopulated and ending with those in which overpopulation has been a more serious problem.

The "New" Countries; the Americas and Australasia

With regard to their agricultural base, such "new" countries as the United States, Canada, Australasia, and Argentina were obviously most favorably situated. Initially underpopulated and having an abundance of land, these new countries were soon able to achieve an agriculture characterized by high capital-labor ratios, optimum-sized farming units, and a high rate of capital formation. Under such circumstances, since population growth was a positive asset, large-scale immigration was encouraged, a pervasive spirit of optimism and progress prevailed, and substantial imports of foreign capital (particularly for transportation development which opened up their rich agricultural hinterlands) were attracted. Thus, almost from the very outset, these new countries were able to produce large food and fiber surpluses and were direct beneficiaries of the Industrial Revolution which created ready-made and rapidly growing markets for their agricultural products in England and Western Europe. Finally, by their early attainment of political independence or dominion status, the new countries freed themselves of the restraints on general economic development which the imperial powers of Europe commonly imposed upon their colonies. As a consequence, agricultural productivity was initially high and increased at a steady pace. Thus, agricultural progress was not only clearly a major contributor to their subsequent economic development but was apparently established with a minimum of time, effort, and social hardship.

Even in the new countries, however, initial agricultural development was not always so favorable and, when it was, provided a necessary *but not sufficient* condition for subsequent general economic progress. For example, while initially well-endowed, Brazil failed to make the most of its favorable start. Its agricultural economy took on a dualistic pattern of large commercial plantations and primitive slash-and-burn subsistence farming which does not appear to have been most conducive to general economic development. This outcome was probably due in part to Brazil's serious neglect of social overhead investment (particularly in transportation and education), in part to its failure to develop public land-settlement and immigration policies which might have filled up its frontier regions more expeditiously, and in part to a socio-political structure which unduly favored large landowners and the people of the littoral. Despite its more progressive agriculture, Argentina's general economic development was also long delayed, in part because it suffered historically from an agriculturally-based, oligarchic socio-political structure which had serious deleterious effects on progress. While this landed oligarchy became the main target of the Peron revolution, the latter quickly demonstrated that an industrialization program cannot proceed very far even on the basis of a relatively productive agriculture, if that agriculture is so heavily exploited that it seriously retrogresses.

The relative backwardness of most other Latin American countries (and indeed of the Southern United States) is similarly attributable in considerable part to defective social organization, to war and political instability, and to low investments in social overhead. In addition, most countries of Latin America have been handicapped by having less rich agricultural resources and, perhaps more important, by having such small geographic extent (particularly in Central America and the Caribbean) that domestic markets for most industrial products have been very limited. Exports of particular tropical crops or minerals have usually not been an adequate offset for generally low productivity in domestic food production. While most of these countries are currently experiencing very rapid population growth, most of them can probably support a substantially larger population at rising per capita incomes if their agricultural and industrial sectors are appropriately developed. Since rising agricultural productivity is far less urgent in most of these countries than in the heavy overpopulated Middle and Far East, they are already in a position to put considerable emphasis on industrial development. Nevertheless, agriculture can still become a serious bottleneck if it is neglected in overall development programs.[7]

England and Western Europe

But what was the role of agriculture in Western Europe where, despite the heavy hand of history, the Industrial Revolution began? Here, perhaps too much attention has normally been given to the brief time spans of some 20–40 years during which England and the Western European countries initiated a spectacular acceleration of their economic growth. The revolutionary character of these take-off periods, which began at various dates during 1780–1850, makes it easy to overlook the long periods of evolutionary development which had preceded them. While there were many other factors, agricultural conditions at the outset of the Industrial Revolution were certainly favorable for the launching of economic development. Western Europe had by then enjoyed a long period of agricultural improvements and experimental farming which had introduced high-yielding new crops (e.g., the turnip and potato), had substantially raised yields of traditional staple crops (e.g., wheat), and had greatly improved the efficiency of livestock production.

---

[7] Cf. my article, "Accommodating Economic Change in Underdeveloped Countries," *American Economic Review*, vol. 49 (Papers and Proceedings), pp. 156–168; and my book, *Southern Tradition and Regional Progress*, University of North Carolina Press, Chapel Hill, 1960.

Furthermore, this rising agricultural productivity was initially far from offset by population increase, since the population explosion in Western Europe came after rather than before the take-off periods. The consequence was the growth of towns, marked improvements in transportation, increasing displacement of feudal agriculture by farming for profit, and the creation of a free rural labor class the surplus of which was now available for alternative non-farm employment.

Particularly in England, the landed aristocracy—seeing its traditional socio-political dominance threatened by the rising urban class of merchant capitalists—became more profit-minded, giving new impetus to the enclosure movement by which land was consolidated into larger and more efficient holdings. While the social hardships for those forced off the land were many, there were important ameliorating circumstances. First, England's increasingly efficient agriculture was able to provide sufficient cheap food to meet most of the needs of its rapidly-growing population up to the 1830's. Second, the new urban masses were rapidly absorbed into manufacturing employment as export markets for industrial production burgeoned. Third, with still further population growth, England was able to draw upon the recently settled "new" countries as a source of cheap food imports, thereby permitting it both to achieve even greater industrial specialization and to reallocate its agricultural resources to the more extensive uses for which they were best suited. At the same time, it found that the "new" countries, through their large-scale absorption of British emigrants, offered an effective "safety valve" against population pressure at home. Increasing agricultural productivity does not appear to have been a major source of funds for financing capital formation in England's industrial sector, but it did make possible substantial self-financing of capital formation in the agricultural sector, which was thereby able to continue its upward progress in productivity and efficiency.[8]

To be sure, as first in the field, England reaped the rewards of industrial innovation to a greater extent than did the other Western European nations. Even so, the later take-off periods of France, Belgium, Germany, and Sweden also rested upon a firm base of rising agricultural productivity, despite the fact that unlike England they had little land consolidation. Instead, much of their agriculture continued to be in the hands of small-scale peasant proprietors. Significantly, these peasant proprietors—who so much won the admiration of John Stuart Mill—still succeeded in achieving a considerable degree of efficiency. This rising agricultural productivity—which was facilitated by substantial oppor-

[8] Cf. Paul Mantoux, *The Industrial Revolution in the Eighteenth Century,* Macmillan, New York, 1927, espec. pp. 156, 163, 185, and 187–190; and Bruce F. Johnston, "Agricultural Productivity and Economic Development in Japan," *Journal of Political Economy,* vol. 59 (1951), pp. 505–508 (on Great Britain).

tunities for emigration to the "new" countries, declining rural birth rates, and the increasing availability of imports of cheap food and (even more) of cheap fodder—enabled their agriculture to contribute to and share in at least some of the fruits of subsequent industrialization.

Eastern Europe and Russia

The first real test of the viability of modern capitalistic development under less favorable conditions of time and place was provided by Eastern Europe. Significantly, at the very time (1762) that England was initiating that spectacular burst of energy which was the Industrial Revolution, the Czarist regime was putting the final capstone on the serfdom organization of Russian agriculture by abolishing the service requirements that had formerly been the justification for the nobility's large-scale landholdings. With nearly 80 percent of the Russian population in bondage, there was virtually no incentive or opportunity for improving agricultural production methods which were frozen into a rigid and primitive pattern. During the first half of the nineteenth century, increasing trade with the West revealed other economic patterns and stimulated new ambitions and wants on the part of the landlords and bureaucracy. Some landlords were finding that they could work their land more profitably with hired labor than with unwilling serfs. Others found their traditional obligations to their serfs—for example, the obligation of furnishing them bread at high cost in years of poor crops—sufficiently onerous that they liberated them voluntarily. Under such influences, the feudal social contract began to weaken as landlords took on a more capitalistic outlook.[9]

The disastrous Russian defeat in the Crimean War (1854–56) proved to be the final blow to serfdom, bringing in 1861 the emancipation of the Russian serfs. Certain other Eastern European countries (e.g., Rumania in 1864) soon followed with comparable agrarian reforms. However, these reforms, by sanctioning the separating of the economic interests of landlord and peasants, benefited primarily the capitalistic landlord. Given a condition of substantial agricultural overpopulation, with peasants typically having considerably less land to work than before the agrarian reforms, the substitution of the capitalistic for the feudal formula in the agriculture of Eastern Europe tended merely to increase unwanted leisure. The consequence of applying prematurely to agriculture the marginal principles of profit maximization, in place of the still appropriate traditional principle of maximizing total agricultural

---

[9] Harry Schwartz, *Russia's Soviet Economy*, Prentice-Hall, New York, 1950, pp. 43–45; and Nicholas Georgescu-Roegen, "Economic Theory and Agrarian Economics," *Oxford Economic Papers*, vol. 12 (Feb. 1960), pp. 1–40.

EDITOR'S NOTE: See Selection 8.

output, may have been to diminish agriculture's contribution to the national product. . . . A major effect of the coming of capitalism to a still-feudalistic Eastern Europe was the worsening of the lot of the peasant even as the prosperity of the non-agricultural sector increased.[10]

Nevertheless, the agrarian reforms of the 1860's and after marked a fundamental turning point in most of Eastern Europe. This was particularly true in Russia, which, thanks to its vast geographic extent and basically rich resources, had an enormous economic potential. To be sure, the end of serfdom did not free most Russian peasants from the necessity of remaining in agriculture, both because of the lack of alternative employment opportunities and because they were still bound to the land until they had met their collective obligations for the land-redemption payments required by the agrarian reforms. On the other hand, this land-redemption requirement (plus an increasingly heavy tax burden) forced peasants to raise more crops for sale, thereby facilitating the growth of grain exports to Western Europe by which Russia maintained a favorable balance of trade and serviced its huge capital imports. At the same time, the land-redemption bonds issued to the nobility by the government provided an important source of capital for the development of trade, industry, and transport. Thus, with the active participation of the state in financing a dense railway network and factory construction and in encouraging the aid of extensive foreign capital and technicians, Russia made substantial economic progress during 1885–1913.

Having based much of this progress on extreme exploitation of the peasants, however, the Czarist regime had failed to take fully into account the depths of peasant discontent and resentment. New agrarian reforms of 1903–06 had abolished remaining land-redemption payments and had sought to substitute for the traditional communal-village agriculture a system of consolidated, individually owned farms. The latter policy was well received in the Ukraine and other richer commercial-agricultural areas, which were most aware of both the possibilities of improved agricultural techniques and the pressures of a quarter-century of falling grain prices on world markets. However, there were vast areas of still largely subsistence agriculture where the rapid growth of rural population had intensified peasant distress and the inadequacy of landholdings. In such areas, the Russian government subsidized migration to Siberia and the preparation of land for the new settlers. During 1906–13, this migration is said to have drained off about half the natural increase in these parts of European Russia that were overpopulated. In view of the long neglect of peasant agriculture, however, these policies proved to be too little and too late. As a consequence, the peasants were a major

[10] Georgescu-Roegen, *loc. cit.*, pp. 32–34 [see Selection 8, pp. 160–162]; Schwartz, *op. cit.*, 46–47.

factor in the overthrow of both the Czar and the moderate government that succeeded him in the bloody aftermath of World War I.[11]

At its very outset, the Bolshevik regime abolished land ownership by estate owners, without compensation, but the peasants did not await official implementation, instead distributing among themselves the land and livestock of the estates by direct action. However, during 1918–21, a period of near anarchy under which the entire non-agricultural economy was brought under direct state control, food was requisitioned forcibly from the peasants, often without compensation. The consequence was a rebellious peasantry which so threatened the Soviet regime that it was able to win substantial concessions. The shift from grain confiscation to a lesser grain tax, which left peasants with a substantial grain surplus to sell on the open market, restored incentives to increase farm production. As an offset, however, the peasants drastically reduced the proportion of their grain sold as they increased their food consumption— a trend further encouraged by the shortage of consumer goods and by the violent shift in agriculture's terms of trade to levels distinctly disadvantageous to the rural population. By 1928, having consolidated its control over the non-agricultural sector and preparing to embark upon a program of rapid industrialization, the Soviet regime at last faced up to the problem of channeling more food to the cities.[12]

In choosing the means of achieving this end, however, the Soviet leadership was largely oriented by ideological rather than economic considerations. While the subsequent collectivization of agriculture to some extent reflected the naïve Marxian view that the efficiencies of large-scale organization were as applicable to agriculture as to industry, it was primarily aimed at destroying the independent peasantry which remained the chief potential threat to the Soviet regime. Not only was collectivization shoved down the peasants' throats but the total elimination of the wealthier and more efficient *kulak* class, which produced relatively large grain surpluses, was explicitly a major element in the policy. By 1936 the goal of virtually complete collectivization had been won, but only at the cost of the loss of half of the nation's livestock and much of its other agricultural capital, widespread famine and a reign of terror in which many millions of peasants starved, or were killed or deported to forced-labor camps. Nonetheless, collectivization did permit the Soviet government to extract from the peasantry large quantities of grain at low cost. Through a system of compulsory food collections, the peasants became the residual claimants, to the serious detriment of the quality and quantity of their own food consumption.[13]

[11] This and the preceding paragraph are based on Schwartz, *op. cit.*, pp. 60–64 and 47–50.

[12] *Ibid.*, pp. 100–107

[13] *Ibid.*, pp. 107–110, 280; Johnston, *loc. cit.*, p. 510.

Collectivization also made possible the rapid adoption and more efficient use of the most modern farm machinery and other improved techniques. To be sure, the rapid increase in number of tractors in part merely offset the widespread slaughter of horses occasioned by peasant resistance to collectivization. Furthermore, the rate of farm mechanization outpaced the spread of knowledge about its proper use and maintenance. More important, while mechanization of grain production greatly reduced the labor requirements in cultivation, seeding, and harvesting, there was little reduction in the seasonal peaks in labor requirements for drying and cleaning the grain and handling the straw after harvest. Finally, the combination of clandestine peasant opposition and increasingly coercive methods of control on the collective farms was hardly conducive to maximum efficiency. Thus, by 1938, the average collective farm still provided only 15 acres of sown acreage per peasant family and average annual grain production (on 10 percent more acreage) for 1934–38, according to the most recently revised estimates, approximated no more than the levels of 1925–28 or even of 1913. To be sure, thanks largely to a 15–20 percent drop in the total farm labor force, labor productivity in Soviet agriculture may have increased by 25–30 percent during 1926–38. These gains in agricultural productivity did free many millions for employment in the rapidly expanding industrial sector and, supplemented by a severe squeeze on the food consumption of those who remained in agriculture, offered the principal source for financing Russia's rapid rate of capital formation.[14]

Even if one is willing to ignore the violence with which it wrenched the Soviet economic and social structure and the brutality of its implementation, one must conclude that the Russian collectivization policy produced far from impressive results. That Russia succeeded in feeding its rapidly growing population at even modest per capita levels indicates that it began its drive for economic development with a substantial agricultural surplus. First, it was able to divert once large export surpluses of grain to domestic consumption, although it did not hesitate—in the face of urban food-rationing, famine in the Ukraine, and very unfavorable world prices during the 1930's—to pay for its imports of machinery and technical aid with large grain exports. Second, by causing a sharp drop in meat, milk, and egg production which brought a significant deterioration of the diet, the Soviet policy diverted much more grain from livestock feed to direct human consumption. Finally, through the increasing substitution of tractors for horses, additional grain became available for human consumption. Thus, the circumstances of Russian agriculture at the out-

[14] Schwartz, *op. cit.*, pp. 280, 292–294, 267; Johnston, *loc. cit.*, pp. 509–510; D. Gale Johnson, "Observations on the Economy of the U.S.S.R.," *Journ. Polit. Econ.*, vol. 64 (1956), espec. pp. 199, 194, 200; A. Kahan, "A Note on Estimates of Soviet Grain Output, 1934–38," *Journ. Polit. Econ.*, vol. 64 (1956), pp. 259–260.

set of its industrial revolution were much more favorable than those facing most of today's overpopulated countries in the Middle and Far East.[15]

With the end of the Stalin era, Soviet leadership has been forced to admit its concern about the sad state of its agriculture. In 1953, Khrushchev ruefully noted that during 1940–52 agricultural output had increased only 10 percent while industrial production had more than doubled. Not only has Russia's population increased much more rapidly than its grain production (although as a partial offset Russia has been able to exploit the grain surpluses of its new Eastern European conquests and satellites), but it has been singularly unsuccessful in the area of animal husbandry. With most livestock numbers still below 1928 levels and of very poor quality, production of meat, milk, and eggs is still exceptionally low. Clearly, the efficiency of Soviet agricultural labor is still very unsatisfactory. Johnson has estimated that in 1955, with nearly as many tractors and over six times as many farm workers as the United States had in 1940, Russia produced perhaps a third less farm output. While the limitations of the collective farming system are considerable even in achieving efficient grain production, they may prove to be insurmountable in achieving efficient livestock production. In any case, Russia's recently renewed concern about agricultural policy makes abundantly clear that its problem of agricultural productivity is far from solved.[16]

Some Lessons from the Western Experience

Thus far, we have centered our attention on the more advanced countries of the Western world, whose periods of take-off into economic development had in common a more or less favorable agricultural base from which to start. However, for today's heavily overpopulated countries in Asia, the Western experience is of questionable value as a basis for developmental planning. The unique combination of vast lands and sparse population in the "new" countries can hardly be duplicated. The

[15] Schwartz, op. cit., pp. 312, 327, 508–509, 128; Johnston, loc. cit., p. 195.

[16] Lazar Volin, "Soviet Agricultural Policy After Stalin: Results and Prospects," Journ. Farm Econ., vol. 38 (1956), pp. 275–276; Johnston, loc. cit., pp. 194–195, 197. The facts also suggest that Russia may still have a substantial overpopulation of agriculture which makes the still semi-feudal organization of its agriculture more appropriate than one based more explicitly upon profit-maximizing calculations at the economic margin. For example, Otto Schiller ("Discussion: The Resources and Performance of Soviet Agriculture," Journ. Farm Econ., vol. 38, p. 299), in commenting on the Soviet new-land campaign, argues that, under Soviet conditions, it may pay to produce grain on new lands until the absolute physical limit of cultivation is reached, since the requisite workers must be fed anyway. He is, of course, correct if the opportunity costs of the marginal farm worker in non-agricultural employment are zero (cf. Georgescu-Roegen, loc. cit.). But given Russia's substantial level of industrialization, it would appear to be unlikely that such is any longer the case in the Soviet Union.

long and favorable period of evolutionary development which established the pre-conditions for the Industrial Revolution of Western Europe also had many unique features not likely to be repeated. The experience of Eastern Europe and Russia, where an acceleration of industrial development began under conditions of an overpopulated peasant agriculture, is somewhat more revelant. Certainly, Russian economic development offers an excellent case study for perceiving the advantages and disadvantages of forced-draft structural reorganization of agriculture as a concomitant of rapid industrialization under direct state direction and control.

Even so, the lessons which Western economic history offers for Asian development are general rather than specific. Perhaps the most important lesson is that the existence of a substantial agricultural surplus is a pre-condition for industrial development. Not only in Russia but in England and Western Europe (and more recently in Argentina), industrial development was heavily financed by the exploitation of agriculture and rural people. For present purposes (ignoring any welfare implications), the important fact is that agriculture could be thus exploited only if it first produced a surplus which was there for exploitation. Even Russia started its period of accelerated economic development with per capita incomes and food output well above, and a degree of population pressure far less than, those which most Asian countries face today. The second lesson is that, even given initially favorable agricultural conditions, too long a neglect of policies promoting increased agricultural productivity may have serious repercussions on the rate of general economic progress (France and Russia).

The third lession is that too rapid a restructuring of a small-scale peasant agriculture into large-scale, mechanized farming units is likely to create a surplus labor force not easily absorbed into non-agricultural employment, a pathological rate of urbanization, the reappearance of a feudal agriculture in new forms, and even conscious policies of mass murder or starvation of the people squeezed out of agriculture. Even where this restructuring has involved an increase in the large-scale farming sector on a *private* rather than public basis, as in much of Eastern Europe and pre-Soviet Russia, the effects may have been an increase in unwanted leisure and an actual diminution of the national product.[17]

---

[17] Professor Georgescu-Roegen, a leading student of the economic history of Rumania, insists on both historical and theoretical grounds (*loc. cit.*, pp. 34–36) that such was the impact of Western capitalism in Eastern Europe. As evidence of the effects of "the premature decay of the feudal formula" there he points to the well-known bastion of feudalism, Hungary: "In comparison with all her neighbors also plagued by overpopulation, Hungary stood out by virtue of a better fate of the peasant (in most regions) and a conspicuous economic development in all fields. To a great extent this difference can be attributed to the fact that the Hungarian magnate did not succumb to the capitalist formula as his Polish and Rumanian colleagues had done on a large scale." (cf. Schiller's comments in footnote 16).

The final lesson is that, even after a country has achieved a modern and efficient agriculture, its excessive exploitation through government monopolies as a means of financing industrial development (Peronist Argentina) can cause the agriculture to retrogress seriously to the detriment of the entire economy.

AGRICULTURE'S ROLE IN ASIAN ECONOMIC DEVELOPMENT

As many of Asia's primitive, traditional, and heavily overpopulated countries look hopefully today toward the threshold of economic development, they appear to face almost insurmountable handicaps. Typically, these countries have a long history of colonial exploitation behind them—a status which brought their population explosion during a period in which often thriving handicraft enterprises were decimated and industrialization was actively discouraged by their European masters. Insofar as they were wealthy in certain raw materials, agricultural or mineral, a highly selective foreign development of particular export industries tended to create a few islands of highly capitalistic and efficient plantations and mining enterprises in a vast sea of primitive, small-scale, and overpopulated agriculture. In such a dualistic economy, the highly developed sectors had little spillover effect on the rest of the local economy, with which their ties were extremely tenuous. Hence, as the Asian countries have achieved political independence, they have found themselves with per capita incomes far below those from which virtually any of today's developed countries launched their drive toward economic development. Under these circumstances, many of them have been strongly tempted to emulate the Russian experiment and one (Mainland China) has already begun to do so, as part of an all-out effort to get economic development under way. Before other Asian countries choose the Russian way, however, they might better consider another alternative which is not only more consistent with a modicum of political freedom but may well be more appropriate and effective as judged by more narrowly economic considerations. I refer, of course, to the Japanese experience.

The Japanese Experience

In my opinion, in the entire annals of world economic development, Japan's achievements are without question the most remarkable and impressive in terms of its initial handicaps and, as such, still offer the best model for Asian economic development generally. Johnston has told the agricultural side of the story so well that I need only summarize it briefly here.

Johnston has estimated that during the thirty years between 1881–90 and 1911–20, Japan increased its agricultural output by 77 percent, with the area under cultivation increasing by only 21 percent as compared with increased yields per acre of 46 percent. During the same period, population increased much less (44 percent) while the agricultural labor force fell by about 14 percent. These figures mean that in about thirty years Japan was able to increase per capita food supplies by over 20 percent—and the output per farm worker by 106 percent.[18] Considering the fact that Japan launched its economic development with severe over-population, with per capita incomes probably approximating the low levels of most of today's Asian countries, and with the average farm unit consisting of only 2–3 acres of highly fragmentized land, how was such a remarkable achievement possible?

Johnston attributes this doubling of labor productivity in Japanese agriculture primarily to the expanded use of commercial fertilizers and the selective breeding, propagation, and distribution of rice strains which would respond most favorably to heavy applications of fertilizers. Other factors contributing to the sharp increase in crop yields were improved methods of water and pest control and of cultivating, transplanting, and weeding the growing plants. The resulting remarkable increase in agricultural output was especially impressive because (1) it was obtained with relatively small direct capital outlay, principally for financing fertilizer purchases; (2) it necessitated a minimum of social dislocation, since it was accomplished by largely land-saving methods which could be applied effectively even on existing very small farms with a super-abundance of labor, with a minimum of mechanization; and (3) it reflected an unusual appreciation of the vital importance of knowledge, in that it was made possible by considerable government investment in the social overhead of agricultural research and extension services. By importing foreign agricultural experts and by exporting its own students for study at foreign universities, Japan was able to borrow heavily from the hard-won progress of the more advanced countries. More important, through establishing its own experiment stations, agricultural schools, seed-propagation farms, and extension services, Japan was able to adapt Western knowledge to its own conditions and special environment.[19]

It is important to note in this connection that those who have (often disparagingly) characterized the genius of the Japanese people as their *ability to imitate* have missed the main point. Rather, as their agricultural history demonstrates, it was their respect for knowledge and their intelligent use of knowledge—that is, their *ability to adapt* instead of practicing slavish imitation as so many other underdeveloped countries have done—which are especially noteworthy. On the technical side, Japan's remarkable adaptability has been reflected not only in agricultural production methods but also in the extent to which it has organized new trades efficiently on a cottage industry basis. Thus, in

[18] Johnston, *loc. cit.*, pp. 499–500.
[19] *Ibid.*, pp. 500–501, 512–513.

manufacturing the Japanese have been very successful in "putting out" the production of parts to individual craftsmen or to small workshops, which work to detailed specifications, so that frequently only the assembly of the parts into the final product has been done in central factories. Here as in agriculture, Japanese production methods have been especially well suited to conditions of (particularly rural) overpopulation.[20] Perhaps equally important, on the cultural side, the Japanese adapted their own traditions to the extent, and only to the extent, necessary to sustain economic growth.

All this does not mean, of course, that Japanese agriculture was a major beneficiary of the nation's economic development. Instead, most of the gains in agricultural productivity were siphoned off by heavy land taxes—which substituted fixed money payments for the old feudal levies and increased both farm indebtedness and farm tenancy—in order to finance industrial (and military) expansion. While some of the benefit did go to rural landlords in the form of higher rents, these landlords appear to have used much of their increased incomes to develop small-scale industry in the rural areas. In either case, it is clear that, without the prior increase in agricultural productivity, the financing of Japanese industrial development would not have been possible. Furthermore, rising agricultural productivity contributed to Japanese development in other important ways. First, it minimized the need for using foreign exchange for food imports. Second, by holding down food prices, it reduced the inflationary pressures generated by industrialization and kept wage rates favorably low relative to profits, thereby encouraging industrial production and exports. Finally, it released increasing numbers of workers who were needed in the expanding non-agricultural industries.[21]

While Johnston's analysis probably underemphasizes the contribution of expanding acreage (relative to that of increased yields) in accounting for Japan's agricultural progress, I agree with his conclusion that "the Japanese model is particularly appropriate to Far Eastern conditions."

---

[20] Cf. Lewis, op. cit., pp. 139–140.

[21] Johnston, loc. cit., pp. 502, 504. On the matter of inflation, Lewis (op. cit., p. 407) makes an interesting comparison between the U.S.S.R. and Japan, in both of which "inflation and high taxation have played major roles" in achieving high growth rates. During the decade following 1929, "The U.S.S.R. concentrated its attention upon industrialization, and fought its peasants instead of teaching them how to increase output per acre. . . . This unbalance contributed to a tremendous price inflation" of about 700 percent in a single decade. During the thirty years preceding World War I, "The Japanese were more sensible. Over-all their output increased just as rapidly as that of the U.S.S.R., but they gave equal attention to industry and to agriculture." Even with a consequent doubling of agricultural output per worker and with enormous taxation, however, Japan's price level also doubled during the same period.

For the Japanese experience clearly offsets the commonly held view "that not much can be done to increase agricultural productivity without vast institutional changes in the countryside." Instead, as Lewis adds,

> This is not so. . . . The present institutional framework is in most under-developed countries (but not all) quite adequate for an enormous advance in productivity by means of the introduction of improved technology. Indeed the best hope of raising the standard of living in most of these countries lies in the fact that the backwardness of their agricultural techniques makes possible spectacular advances in production at relatively low cost.[22]

Or again,

> The experience of Japan shows that appropriate expenditure by government (on agricultural research, extension, credit, and roads) can have spectacular effects on the output of peasants, and that agriculture . . . [instead of] acting as a brake on the rest of the economy can be turned into a leader, generating demand for other sectors, and also providing them with capital. But most other governments in this situation have neglected peasant agriculture, with the result that its failure to expand has kept down the rate of growth in other sectors.[23]

The Chinese Example

Malenbaum's recent comparative studies of Chinese and Indian economic development, which indicate better relative performance by Communist China on all fronts, have probably reinforced the tendency of Asian economic planners to look with even greater kindness on the Chinese model than they have already regarded the Russian model. Malenbaum estimates that during 1950–57 aggregate agricultural output rose by 25–30 percent in China, largely because of increased yields per acre; and by only 15–20 percent in India, where increased acreage

[22] Lewis, *op. cit.*, p. 136. At another place (p. 188), Lewis notes that Japan is the only one of the poorer countries to match the American and British rates of one extension worker for every 700 agricultural workers and "also the only one which has had spectacular increase in peasant productivity."

[23] *Ibid.*, p. 279. Some recent calculations of Simon Kuznets, which will be published soon, show the following averages rates of gross domestic capital formation (as a percentage of gross domestic product): 1889–98, 10.3; 1899–1908, 10.9; 1909–18, 12.7; 1919–28, 16.7; 1929–38, 19.7; and 1951–57, 28.8. (Kuznets is inclined to attribute this remarkable performance in part to the almost unchanging simplicity of Japanese consumption patterns, particularly those of the upper classes. Even within Europe, it is significant that the ranks of (say) England, France, Italy, and Spain in per capita real income are inversely correlated with the relative strength of the tradition of conspicuous consumption in the several countries.)

EDITOR'S NOTE: Although the dates are not exactly consistent, this apparently applies to Kuznets' monograph in *Economic Development and Cultural Change*, vol. 9, no. 4, part II, July, 1961.

(most of it irrigated) was at least as important a factor as increased yields. More important, India's agricultural gains appear to have reflected to an unusual degree the effects of unusually favorable weather, failing to show as China has some evidence of persistent upward trend. While the relative allocation of gross investment to industry (including power) was substantially greater in China than in India (and conversely to the tertiary industries such as transport, education, health, etc.), China still allocated slightly more to agriculture than did India. Observing that agriculture "has frequently turned out to be a sector where relatively large returns follow from a unit of new capital—at least . . . where yields per acre are very low initially," Malenbaum adds that "the scope for improvement in agriculture remains large." For example, for rice "the yield per acre in China in 1957 was about half that in Japan; it is generally about twice that in India." He notes that China is accordingly rapidly extending small-scale irrigation, increasing rates of fertilization, and intensifying cultivation, while Indian leadership—which "has increasingly questioned whether a basis for systematic expansion of food-grain output has in fact been established in India"—is giving "ever greater priority" to new programs for agricultural progress.[24]

Malenbaum finds the superiority of China's relative performance in the industrial sector even more impressive than in agriculture and concludes that "For the period as a whole, China seems to have generated a unit of gross-income flows with little more than half the gross investment that was applied in India." He attributes China's superior performance to many factors. It has achieved a far greater standardization of product because of the limited scope of private enterprise and its almost complete powers of product allocation and rationing. It has made extensive use, especially in construction, of a considerable volume of unpaid or underpaid labor on a largely involuntary basis. It has exercised much greater control over savings through heavier taxation of agriculture (which supplies at least 60 percent of total Chinese taxes as compared with only 20 percent in India) and through trading profits derived from its much more extensive state enterprises. It has developed many labor-intensive projects and devices for mobilizing underutilized resources to expand both agricultural and industrial production. It has found means of siphoning out of the rural areas nonmonetized savings in kind which can be monetized or otherwise used to finance capital formation. It has

[24] Wilfred Malenbaum, "India and China: Contrasts in Development Performance," Amer. Econ. Rev., vol. 49 (1959), pp. 293–95, 300. Malenbaum recognizes that India's relatively greater allocation of gross investment to services—insofar as greater investment in social overhead could produce greater returns in the longer run—may be more efficient, given a longer time horizon. However, his data indicate that during 1950–58 China more than overcame India's initial lead in primary-school attendance and nearly closed the gap in the professional training of engineers (ibid., pp. 286, 297, 300–01).

given deliberate attention to the expansion of modern small-scale industries which will encourage regional development and discourage overurbanization. It has been able to export food grains and, through loans from the Soviet Union and other Communist countries, has financed its net import surpluses.[25]

Malenbaum recognizes that Chinese methods "do weigh seriously upon the individual citizen and especially upon a peasantry long proud of its individualism." Furthermore, he argues that the lesson of his comparison is not that totalitarian methods are superior to democratic procedures, but that *democratic governments must define the tasks of growth more realistically and implement them more faithfully.* He concludes that, no less than China, although hopefully by more democratic methods, the governments of other underdeveloped countries must successfully solve such vital problems as structural unemployment, underutilized resources, overurbanization, nonmonetized savings, and investment flows.[26]

Despite the formidable difficulties which the analyst of Chinese economic development faces, the task is of such vital interest and importance that we should all be indebted to Malenbaum for the attempt. Even so, one must marvel at the relative confidence he appears to hold for the basic Chinese data, particularly in view of recent recantations in which the Chinese drastically reduced their previous inflated claims of gains in agricultural output and admitted the failure of their "backyard" iron-production projects. The historical record of Soviet Russian statistics would cast doubt on whether these deflated Chinese claims are as yet deflated enough. Furthermore, insofar as Chinese achievements are real rather than statistical fabrications, they may be in substantial part due to particular economic qualities of ingenuity, energy, resourcefulness, and industry and the absence of economically inhibiting social and religious taboos which the pre-Communist Chinese had long exhibited, particularly as overseas emigrants. Under conditions of far less government compulsion, these qualities might have produced to date at least as favorable results (the recent accomplishments of the free Nationalist Chinese on the severely overcrowded island of Taiwan are not unimpressive). More important, unless the Chinese Communist leadership is wiser and less heavy-handed than seems reasonable to expect, these same qualities could be seriously atrophied or destroyed to the detriment of China's longer-term economic development. Finally, Malenbaum's virtual neglect of the social and political costs of the Chinese experience (a fault to which other analysts of the Chinese economy have been prone) was unfortunate, particularly in view of the already strong proclivity of much of Asian political leadership to view the Soviet model with favor and to overlook the extent to which Japan, Malaya,

[25] *Ibid.*, pp. 298, 303–07, 291, 289.
[26] *Ibid.*, pp. 307–08.

and Hong Kong offer alternative successful models involving much less direct government control.

Because of their very different conditions of time, place, and resources, the heavily overpopulated countries of Asia have probably been wise in rejecting the experience of Western Europe or the "new" countries as the model for their own economic development. However, they have not been so perceptive in choosing the Soviet model, and ignoring the Japanese model, as the basis of their development planning. Of the Asian countries, only Communist China has as yet fully embraced the Soviet model, although Malenbaum's account would suggest that even China has not entirely ignored Japanese experience, particularly in the attention it has given to yield-raising agricultural policies and the development of small-scale industry. But there is little doubt that India and other countries have been strongly influenced by the Communist model, as first developed in Soviet Russia and as more recently adopted in China. The appeal of the Soviet (and now Chinese) model lies in part in the apparent rapidity of Communist economic development and, perhaps in greater part, in the ceaseless propaganda barrage which has exaggerated the gains and concealed the costs and shortcomings of the Communist experience.[27] On the other hand, the appeal of the Japanese model has probably been weakened by the deep enmities which Japan's latter-day imperialism created among her Asian neighbors, a lesson which Communist China currently seems inclined to ignore.

China aside, the Soviet model has been widely influential in encouraging in Asia a strong emphasis on the uneconomic development of heavy industry, which has strong symbolic appeal in most underdeveloped countries; in causing the neglect of agriculture and the rural population in countries which lack the substantial agricultural surplus with which the Soviet Union began its development; and in discouraging adequate recognition and utilization of indigenous private enterprise,[28]

[27] In this connection, it is extremely unfortunate that no careful study has yet been made of the comparative economic progress of Soviet Russia and two of her neighbors, Poland and Rumania, during the two decades following World War I. Since these three countries started from very similar conditions, such a study would throw much needed light on the question of the relative effectiveness of Communist and agrarian regimes in promoting economic development in overpopulated agricultural countries. While Russia might make a better showing on the industrial side, it is at least possible that Poland and Rumania surpassed Russia in terms of growth of real national income. Recent experience in Yugoslavia, under a modified Soviet model, also deserves more careful study than it has yet received.

[28] It is here, undoubtedly, that the Western experience could teach most even under Asian conditions. It is clear, for example, that India's private sector has shown a vigor and dynamism during the period of the Second Five-Year Plan which the latter neither anticipated nor encouraged. On the other hand, some Western economists claim too much in implying that the Western experience has demonstrated for Asian countries the near futility of development planning. One can agree with

which is commonly opposed under the vague and ill-defined "socialist" ideology of much of Asian political leadership. Let us take a look at India in this connection.

The Problem of India

India's First Five-Year Plan (1951–56), while providing substantial outlays for industrialization, clearly recognized that substantial development of agriculture is a precondition of viable industrial development. However, the Second Plan (1956–61) shifted the emphasis strongly toward industrial development, especially the development of heavy industry and the necessary ancillaries such as transport. The relative emphasis on agricultural improvement, education, and roads was significantly reduced. Current draft outlines of the forthcoming Third Plan indicate that the trend in official thinking is toward greater emphasis on public enterprise and heavy industry, a development to be financed by the creation of a state monopoly of wholesale trade in food grains (intended to yield the government a huge trading surplus) and the additional imposition of taxes on agricultural output, other drastic increases in taxation, and large-scale foreign assistance, none of which is to be budgeted for food imports.[29]

In reviewing recent Indian experience, Higgins points out that, almost from the start, the Second Plan was in trouble, particularly in terms of loss of foreign exchange in which an unplanned excess of food imports played a part. But he interprets this experience as "a warning against gradualism" and concludes that, "In terms of what is needed to provide a 'big push' . . . the Second Plan was certainly too small." While he recognized that India's recent experience demonstrates that India planned beyond its capacity, he advocates sufficiently massive foreign assistance to give India the capacity to plan for the requisite "big push." He apparently fully approves India's emphasis on heavy capital-intensive industry, inferentially criticizing the Indian government's industrialization program only on the grounds that, in subsidizing cottage industry unduly, it gave too much weight to maximizing employment relative

---

Bauer that there would be value in educating the underdeveloped countries about "the long history of western economic progress." But he seems to be much too hopeful of the educational value, under such strikingly different conditions, of "a statement of the methods and principles by which North America was turned, within just over a century, from a barren and empty continent into the richest area of the world." (P. T. Bauer, *United States Aid and Indian Economic Development*, American Enterprise Association, Washington, Nov. 1959, pp. 122, 109n.)

[29] Bauer, *op. cit.*, pp. 40, 47, 53, and 98–99. According to Bauer, total capital outlays for elementary education under the Second Plan amount to "about one-half of the cost of one of the steel plants" and, despite a price rise and an approximate doubling of total outlays, are absolutely less than those of the First Plan.

to maximizing output. He also implies that the Second Plan might better have given greater support to the community development program as a means of increasing agricultural productivity. However, given his strong scepticism of the opportunities for agricultural progress in the absence of "a wholesale shift to mechanized commercial agriculture," he must almost exclusively emphasize the importance of far heavier commitments to industrial development. Believing that, "on the basis of comparative advantage, India should probably be an importer of foodstuffs and an exporter of products of heavy industry," Higgins undoubtedly approved whole-heartedly the present directions of Indian development planning.[30]

Even W. Arthur Lewis, who much more than Higgins has emphasized the importance of increasing agricultural productivity as a precondition of economic development in overpopulated countries, lends his authority to the same thesis. Professor Lewis' projections suggest that during 1955–80, India can raise its food output by only 45 percent, with population increasing by the same percentage. Estimating that India will increase its national income by 118 percent and its demand for food by 90 percent during the same period, he sees the need for India to increase its export surplus of manufactures sufficiently to pay for annual food imports worth more than 4 billion dollars by 1980. Lewis supports this view elsewhere in observing that "the fact that an expansion of

[30] Higgins, op. cit., pp. 717–19, 730, 724–25, 719–20, 43. To be sure, Higgins recognizes (pp. 46–47) that, "while India may eventually be able to finance food imports with industrial exports, . . . that day is not yet" and says that in India "the failure to maintain steady growth of agricultural output makes it extremely difficult to obtain steady growth of industrial output, in an economy where the private sector still dominates." Elsewhere (p. 454), he argues that "In the phase when preconditions for take-off are being established, it may make good sense to seize remaining opportunities for raising productivity through fertilizers, seed selection, etc." But he repeatedly (e.g., pp. 341–44, 357, 460–61) asserts that such opportunities are extremely limited. It should not be forgotten that Higgins' central thesis (p. 455) is that "only a rapid change to extensive, mechanized agriculture, with enough industrialization to absorb the population displaced from the rural sector, will assure a take-off into steady growth." (For a critical analysis of this thesis, as applies in Turkey's recent development program, see my article, "Investment in Agriculture in Underdeveloped Countries," Amer. Econ. Rev., vol. 45 Proceedings, pp. 58–73.) Higgins further observes (p. 344) that "a wholesale shift to mechanized commercial agriculture . . . is not an operation to be carried out on a piecemeal private enterprise basis."

Given such views, it seems reasonable to infer that Higgins would favor the policy, increasingly advocated in India, of pooling small agricultural holdings under the management of village councils or cooperative societies. Such an arrangement, which would almost certainly be resisted by Indian peasants, would probably be woefully unsuccessful, hence merely a waystation to collectivization of the land (cf. Bauer, op. cit., pp. 62–63). In any case, it is highly significant that Higgins' 800-page book completely ignores the Japanese experience, which would have seriously undercut his argument of the necessity of simultaneous large-scale reorganization of agriculture and "big push" industrialization.

manufacturing production does not require an expansion of agricultural production if it is backed by a growing export of manufactures is particularly important to those overpopulated countries which cannot hope to increase their agricultural output of food as rapidly as their demand for food however much they try." Such countries as Japan and India must therefore "give urgent attention to increasing the export market for their manufactures since . . . it is the rate of growth of their exports which sets the limit to their internal expansion." This is all the more true since the industrialization of overpopulated countries will quickly outrun the ability of the home market to absorb the increased output of manufactures. It is not easy to capture a larger share of the world market for manufactures although India, which possesses the fuel and ores needed for the metal trades, is in a better position to do so than those countries (e.g., Egypt) whose principal manufactures face a less rapidly expanding demand.[31]

Unlike Higgins, however, Lewis makes clear that the important thing is a proper balance between the growth of manufacturing and agriculture. Overpopulated countries must, in any case, "also strive to increase their agricultural output, since the more they can do so the less they need to rely on pushing their exports of manufactures in the world market." A shortage of foreign exchange often reflects the absence of such a balance, an expansion of either sector increasing the demand for the other, with any deficiency being reflected in a strain on the balance of payments. "If the balance between industry and agriculture is neglected, as in Australia or Argentina, or bungled, as in the U.S.S.R., further progress is held up; the superiority of the development planning of Japan over that of the other countries mentioned stands out clearly in this respect." Thus, a drive to industrialize and develop export markets for manufactures must "be accompanied by a vigorous programme for increasing yields per acre, through greater use of fertilizers, through multiplication and distribution of better types of seeds, through greater conservation and distribution of water, and in all the other ways which Japanese experience has demonstrated to be capable of increasing agricultural output rapidly." Since such opportunities are plentiful in overpopulated countries (and since farm mechanization would do more harm than good), the amount of capital required for a given increase in output is lower in agriculture than in manufacturing in these countries and is also lower than in the more developed countries.[32]

While Lewis thus hedges about his recommendations for an in-

---

[31] W. Arthur Lewis, "India's Economic Prospects for 1980—The Need to Develop Export of Manufactures," *Capital*, Supplement, Dec. 16, 1954, pp. 7ff. (quoted in Coale and Hoover, *op. cit.*, p. 128 n.); and Lewis, *Theory of Economic Growth*, pp. 278–79, 328–29, 351–53.

[32] Lewis, *Theory of Economic Growth*, pp. 279, 388, 328, 205–07, 219–20.

dustrialized India with ample recognition of the importance of agriculture, his precautions are likely to be ignored by those nationalists and Marxists who hold that India's economic progress requires all-out concentration in industrialization. This is all the more likely since, despite his much better balanced approach, Lewis suggests planning goals for India which do not differ radically from those proposed by Higgins. This apparent agreement seems to stem from their common pessimism about the potentialities of expanding Indian food production and an underestimate of the seriousness of India's impending food crisis. Lewis aligns himself with the pessimists by saying that undoubtedly "yields per acre could be increased at the appropriate rates in Asia and Africa for two or three decades, just because current yields are so low; but there are great political and educational obstacles in the way of achieving in most of these countries the sort of results which were achieved in Japan, so we cannot be confident that world food production will increase . . . at the desired rates." (As we have already seen, Lewis estimates that at best Indian food production can just keep pace with its population growth during 1955–80.) If such is the case, Lewis finds hope (and also considerable misgivings) only in the fact that, for at least 25 years or more, the United States "can make up the world's [food] deficits if it pays her to do so."[33]

I believe that Lewis, Higgins, and others of their persuasion are at once unduly pessimistic about the possibilities of expanding India's agricultural productivity and output and unduly optimistic about the extent to which the United States or other advanced countries can make up prospective Indian food deficits. One does not have to accept for India a goal of complete self-sufficiency in food, or to deny that India may ultimately find it to her comparative advantage to pay for some food imports with manufactures, to question the commonly held view that India's current planning should aim at all-out "big-push" industrialization. While it is clear enough that, in overpopulated countries, the fruitful use of labor-saving types of capital investment in agriculture must await a substantial reduction in the farm population and land consolidation, it does not follow (at least in the absence of land collectivization) that most available capital resources should be concentrated on the industrial development needed to absorb the surplus farmers. For one thing, manufacturing (particularly of heavy goods) is usually so capital-intensive that it has a low absorptive capacity in terms of employment.

Another danger of the aggregative approach is its tendency to overlook the fact that, in some very specific but crucial forms, small increments of capital may contribute (as Japan so clearly demonstrated) large increments of agricultural output without a change in the supply

[33] *Ibid.,* pp. 355–56.

of either land or labor. With crop yields as low as India's, I am convinced—on the basis of my brief tour of villages in both South and North India in 1958—that the returns on modest investments in such key limitational factors as fertilizer, improved seeds, insecticides and pesticides, and better cultivation and irrigation practices would be extremely high. While such investments are initially land-saving rather than labor-saving, for a *constant* rural population they would also result in greater output (income) per man as well. To be sure, there is danger that the rural population will expand sufficiently to absorb entirely the greater output resulting from increased crop yields. However, taking Indian population trends fully into account, Coale and Hoover share my more hopeful view by concluding: "On the basis of programs now in operation or envisaged, and the resources available, we find it not unreasonable to look for an approximate doubling of total crop output within the next twenty-five years"—a rate of development which exceeds the most rapid conceivable rate of population growth.[34]

The achievement of so large a potential rate of growth in agricultural production, while entirely feasible, will not come about automatically. Instead, it will require concentrated and sustained effort. Furthermore, the need for such an effort is extremely urgent. The recent report by a Ford Foundation team of outstanding agricultural specialists on India's impending food crisis should offer sobering thought to those who have so confidently recommended "big push" industrialization, with corresponding neglect of agriculture, to Indian and other Asian development planners. This report notes that, starting from a base of 58 million tons of food grains (which in India comprise two-thirds of the average caloric intake) in 1949–50, the First Five-Year Plan set a target of 65.5 million tons by 1955–56 and achieved it easily as a result of greater emphasis on agricultural production and with the help of favorable weather. The Second Five-Year Plan set a target of 80.5 million tons by 1960–61 but at mid-term (1958–59), with very favorable growing conditions, food-grain production was only 70 million tons. With a substantial shortfall already in prospect for the Second Plan, the Ford Foundation report foresees a much wider shortfall of 25 percent by 1965–66, assuming a population of 480 millions (as compared with 360 millions in 1951) and needs of 110 million tons by that time. The report concludes that, unless India triples its present rate of increase in food production, it will face an annual food-deficit of 28 million tons in 1965–66. Emphasizing that "No conceivable programme of imports or

---

[34] Coale and Hoover, *op. cit.*, pp. 80–81 of *ibid.*, Ch. VIII–X for an excellent discussion of agriculture as a part of Indian economic development. Even they consider that "some development of a nonagricultural export surplus is likely to be necessary" to meet India's prospective demand for food imports.

rationing can meet a crisis of this magnitude," the report recommends a Third Plan target of 110 million tons of food grains under an all-out emergency food program to be given the highest priority in the remainder of the Second Plan period and all of the Third Plan period. Then, but *only* then, does the report believe that such a target can be realized.[35]

Quite apart from its implications for India's foreign-exchange position and for the rate of industrialization needed to pay for food imports of such magnitude, the estimated food deficit is well beyond the amounts which the United States might be expected to make up even on a gift basis. It should be emphasized that a deficit of 28 million tons would approach U.S. annual wheat production and would completely exhaust even America's huge storage stocks of wheat within a year and a half. Under such circumstances, if any "big push" is currently called for in India, the Ford Foundation's recommendation of a "big push" for raising agricultural output would appear to be far closer to reality than the present Indian emphasis on "big push" industrialization. Understandably, the Ford Foundation has aroused not only consternation but considerable antagonism among Indian planners, many of whom are not going to abandon easily their dreams of rapid industrial development. Their unrealistic outlook is underlined by the fact, previously mentioned, that early draft outlines of the Third Plan proposed to budget nothing for food imports during 1961–66. This outlook indicates a shocking disregard for the seriousness of India's food production problem, a wholly unreasonable expectation of the magnitudes of agricultural surpluses which the United States might divert to India, or a callous willingness to risk mass starvation as the Soviet and Chinese models have done.

If Indian planners are wise, they will take a careful second look at the criticisms which such minority voices as Vakil and Brahmananda directed at the outset toward the Second Plan. According to Bauer, these Indian economists noted that the Second Plan was obviously modeled on Soviet planning, and warned against not only the political but the economic dangers of using the Soviet experience as a model. Among the economic dangers, they noted that "the composition of available resources was quite different in the Soviet Union and India, especially in the relatively greater abundance of land in the former. They also pointed out that when economic planning in the Soviet Union got under way, *there was already a sizable agricultural surplus,* and the task facing the planners was the diversion of this to the towns and industrial centers, *while in India the surplus is extremely small. This is a very important and relevant difference between the Soviet Union*

---

[35] Ford Foundation Agricultural Production Team (Sherman E. Johnson, Chairman), *Report on India's Food Crisis and Steps to Meet It*, Govt. of India, Ministry of Food and Agriculture and Ministry of Community Development and Cooperation, New Delhi, April 1959, pp. 3–15.

and India, which is very generally ignored both in India and abroad."
Bauer adds that according to Professor Vakil and Dr. Brahmananda,
"on social, political, and economic grounds it would be preferable to
develop agricultural productivity, the manufacture of consumer goods
and the manufacture of cheap equipment for agriculture and the consumer goods industries, following in this more nearly the Japanese
example. In Indian conditions this implies in the industrial sphere the
development of small or medium-scale factory production, rather than
either the massive development of large-scale heavy industry, or the
subsidization of cottage industry." Perhaps we should add that even
the Chinese model (for all its excesses) appears to have observed these
realities to an extent seriously lacking in India's Second Plan.[36]

To sum up, it seems clear that India has not yet fulfilled the most
fundamental precondition for its economic development—the achievement and maintenance of an adequate and reliable food surplus or,
at the very least, the reduction of its food deficit to a magnitude which
expanding manufactures for export might realistically be expected to
cover in the near term. Hence, its present emphasis on industrialization
is decidedly premature. India can and must solve its food problem without further delay. Despite the relative scarcity of land, India has
tremendous opportunities for increasing yields per acre by modest capital expenditures on landsaving techniques and a fuller utilization of her
abundant agricultural labor force. The Ford Foundation team was certainly not overoptimistic in believing that Indian food production per
acre can be doubled if known improvements are adopted in effective
combinations. Favorable to such a goal are low capital-output ratios
in Indian agriculture as compared with those in heavy industry or large
irrigation projects. To be sure, the capital-output ratio for yield-raising
agricultural improvements is higher if the social overhead costs of getting
the improved practices into general use by farmers are taken into account. Thus, some have argued that the emphasis which India's First
Plan gave to increasing agricultural productivity was discredited by its
modest results, discounting the effects of favorable weather. In doing
so, however, they have taken too limited a time horizon to include the
full benefits from given costs. Viewed in this light, India's decision
to reduce its emphasis on agriculture in its Second Plan probably was
not only extremely shortsighted but meant the loss of some of the
valuable cumulative effects which might otherwise have accrued in
the later period from its earlier agricultural investments.

[36] Bauer, *op. cit.*, pp. 50–51, summarizing the conclusions in C. W. Vakil and P. R.
Brahmananda, "Institutional Implications of a Bolder Plan," in Govt. of India, Planning Commission, *Papers Relating to the Second Five-Year Plan*, New Delhi, 1955
[italics added]. Bauer (p. 51n) states that in these Second Plan Papers, only the
experience of Communist China and the Soviet Union is discussed at length.

There is every reason to believe that, like Japan, India can earn very high returns on investments in the discovery, propagation, and financing of land-saving methods through agricultural research and extension services and, in the process, can make a major contribution to its general economic development. If India is to achieve her economic aspirations, and preserve her strongly democratic traditions as well, she will be well advised to reject the Soviet (or even the Chinese) model, instead at last giving the alternative Japanese model the attention it deserves.

CONCLUSIONS

Summary

In this paper, my principal thesis has been that, until underdeveloped countries succeed in achieving and sustaining (either through domestic production or imports) a reliable food surplus, they have not fulfilled the fundamental precondition for economic development. We saw how the "new" countries had such a food surplus from the outset and that England and Western Europe were able to initiate industrial revolution because an agricultural revolution had already provided a domestic food surplus which sufficed until, through expanding exports of manufactures, they could supplement their rapidly increasing food needs by imports. We also noted that Russian economic progress was made possible by an initially substantial food surplus but that, having neglected further agricultural progress, Russia now faces an important agricultural crisis despite its remarkable industrial development.

Turning to the more difficult problem of the seriously overpopulated countries of Asia, we reviewed the development experience of Japan and Communist China. We particularly emphasized the intelligent way in which Japan, with a minimum of structural disturbance to an agricultural economy characterized by land shortage and a labor surplus, established policies which created a food surplus which became the basis for its spectacular economic development. We also saw how Communist China, faced with similar problems, has more recently sought to solve them by adoption of the totalitarian Soviet model. While China may have achieved considerable success at the severe cost of personal liberty and a violent wrenching of the economic structure, it at least seems to have recognized the importance of achieving an agricultural surplus and, in adapting the Soviet model to its own special conditions, appears to have been not unmindful of important elements in the successful Japanese experience. Finally, we examined recent Indian development planning and found it seriously wanting because it has sought to emphasize large-scale industrialization without first solving the problem of serious food deficit and a redundant rural labor force.

Dangers of Overemphasis on Longrun and Macro-economic Analysis

I believe that India's recent experience is well worth careful study as an example of perilous economic advice, not only from indigenous planners but too often from Western advisers as well. In a sufficiently longrun context, it is clear enough that there must be a large-scale transfer of farm population into nonfarm employment and to labor-saving devices in an agriculture composed of much enlarged farming units. In making shortrun planning goals and establishing near-term priorities, however, overpopulated countries may use this model at their peril. Such a model necessarily emphasizes the importance of industrialization, confirming the usual nationalistic biases of indigenous political leadership while diverting attention from the clear and present dangers of food shortages. Furthermore, it encourages the substitution of compulsion for persuasion and the creation of pathological over-urbanization as an alternative to the lesser evil of rural underemployment. Thus, one does not have to question the *longrun* validity of the Lewis-Higgins policy goals for the India of 1980 to argue that 1965 comes first. Admittedly, shortrun policies should be as consistent as possible with longrun goals. But, until the preconditions of economic development are fully met, consistency is not necessarily a virtue. Nor is Higgins' advice that, in allocating resources in underdeveloped countries, "planning must be based on 'shadow prices' as they would prevail *after* a drastic structural change has been achieved"[37] as sound as it might first appear.

Economic advice to underdeveloped countries has not only been faulty because it emphasized the longrun to the neglect of the shortrun; it has also been faulty in being too global and macro-economic in approach, to the neglect of precise and detailed knowledge (for example, of the technological, economic, and socio-psychological relationships in agriculture and village life) of a micro-economic character. The typical macro-economic approach has certain important virtues in terms of its overall perspective, its emphasis on major inter-sector relationships, and its dynamic rather than static view of economic development. But, I believe that Japanese experience and the repeated testimony of agricultural specialists prove that Higgins is demonstrably wrong in arguing for the rural sector that "although the elasticity of substitution of labor for capital may be high, the elasticity of substitution of capital for *land* is low. Relatively small amounts of investment in tools, irrigation, seed selection, and fertilizer could bring the marginal productivity of capital

[37] Higgins, *op. cit.*, p. 357. On the same page, he also states, "Thus economic development requires raising productivity per man-day—not per acre—in the peasant agriculture sector." This view overlooks the fact that many land-saving, yield-raising agricultural techniques can do both.

down to zero, given the present ratio of labor to land. It may well be that in some underdeveloped countries the marginal productivity of both land and capital is close to zero in the rural sector." Upon the basis of this dubious argument about the low substitutability of capital for land, he is able to conclude that "the only way to raise the marginal productivity of capital is to increase the ratio of land to labor a good deal"—not from 2 to 3 acres but to 20 or 200 acres "so that mechanization becomes profitable."[38] If the choice of the agriculture of the underdeveloped countries is so much a matter of "all or nothing" as Higgins concludes, their future is indeed black. Fortunately, much more modest and less drastic choices also exist which Higgins largely ignores.

Shortcomings of Marginal-productivity Principles

As a valuable antidote to such typical but highly questionable advice, economic planners in the underdeveloped countries might well study very carefully Professor Georgescu-Roegen's analysis of the economics of an overpopulated agriculture. His analysis is not only important because it emphasizes vital aspects of the development problem which most economists have overlooked but because he almost uniquely combines a very high level of theoretical competence with a thorough knowledge of peasant agriculture. According to Georgescu, "where the geo-historical conditions of an economy are such that *all available resources* must be used in production as long as they increase output, the argument regarding the superiority of the large-scale production is poor economics." He correctly observes that "most underdeveloped agrarian economies are poor not only because of the insufficiency of land, but also because of a chronic dearth of capital." More important, he emphasizes that, unless "the 'equilibrium' price of labor is at least equal to the minimum of biological subsistence," the standard general-equilibrium model based on marginal-productivity principles "has only meager economic relevance." In overpopulated countries, the fact that the marginal productivity of unskilled peasant labor is zero is fully consistent with the appropriateness of maximizing *total* net output, with some workers (e.g., the gleaners of European feudalism) earning more than their specific contribution to output.[39]

Georgescu finds in leisure a key element differentiating advanced from overpopulated countries. In advanced countries, "leisure time is allocated by an opportunity choice and . . . its price obviously is identical with that of labor." In overpopulated economies, however, leisure

---

[38] *Ibid.*, pp. 342–43. Strangely enough, Higgins' description of the post-war development of East Germany would appear to fit closely the probable outcome for India if his broader advice were followed there, without concomitant attention to land-saving techniques in its peasant agriculture.

[39] Georgescu-Roegen, *loc. cit.;* Section II. [EDITOR'S NOTE: Selection 8.]

is not an economic good, in the sense of resulting from a choice between greater leisure and greater real income. Instead, leisure is economically *unwanted*, having a value of zero even though labor has a positive "price." Thus, while the usual practice of excluding leisure from the national income seriously understates the economic progress of advanced economies, it is wholly appropriate for measuring the level of economic progress in the overpopulated economies. Consequently, the overpopulated economy will operate efficiently only if some laborers earn more than their own marginal productivity since such a "feudal formula" maximizes both material output and national welfare. Only after labor productivity curves have shifted upward sufficiently to equate the marginal productivity of labor with its wage rate can capitalist development proper begin and the application of marginal principles become appropriate. In moving from the one phase to the other—that is, from a situation of unwanted leisure to one in which leisure is strictly another economic good—an overpopulated country must usually pass through a phase (which Marx considered a basic feature of capitalism) where the working class has no leisure at all.[40]

If the principles of marginal productivity theory are adopted prematurely—whether under a capitalist or socialist regime—by an overpopulated economy, the effect will be to increase unwanted leisure while diminishing the national (material) output. From the Marxist viewpoint, the premature disappearance of feudalism is justified on the grounds that it is an earlier fulfillment of what must inexorably come. Hence, the Soviet Russian prejudice in favor of large-scale mechanized farms whose size, being far greater than the optimum compatible with overpopulation, uses labor inefficiently. (However, the recent Chinese experience indicates some awareness of this danger, in that the feudal formula still seems in full force as the attempt is made to eliminate leisure entirely as a necessary part of the transition to a situation in which marginal principles may ultimately become appropriate.) Georgescu recognizes that the feudal formula of using labor until its marginal productivity is zero, while quite suitable for a small family-operated farm or shop, is hardly practicable for large-scale production units. In the latter, the use of labor beyond the point where its marginal productivity equals the wage rate would destroy the main criterion of managerial efficiency and the principal sanction against loafing—matters which are easily solved in the close confines of the family and the cultural patterns of the village.[41]

Thus, it is a basic feature of overpopulated countries that enterprises (particularly agricultural) operated by feudal formula exist side by side with others managed according to marginal-productivity principles.

[40] *Ibid.*, Section IV.
[41] *Ibid.*, Section IV.

Under such circumstances, Georgescu argues, national output will not only fall short of its maximum but national welfare will fall short of its optimum (at which employment is maximized), for neither of these goals can be achieved without the marginal productivity of labor falling below the minimum of subsistence. Furthermore, the premature abandonment of the feudal formula in agriculture may not only reduce food production below its physical maximum, thereby undermining the meager food surplus needed to sustain industrial-urban development; but may destroy the basis for expanding that food surplus which is the initial principal source for financing capital formation. Such a step will also have serious effects even on the "capitalistic" industrial sector by forcing too rapid a rural exodus into the cities, bringing irresistible social pressures to use labor beyond the margin even in factory production; and by artificially forcing industrial wages upward toward the subsistence level, overprice labor relative to capital and encourage methods of industrial production which are unduly capital-intensive. For such reasons, since factor prices bear little resemblance to the corresponding marginal productivities, the use of marginal principles in fixing investment criteria in overpopulated countries is almost certain to give almost completely inappropriate results.[42]

A Final Word

I have summarized Georgescu's penetrating and pathbreaking analysis at such length because I believe that it emphasizes important truths which most Western economists and Asian economic planners have almost completely ignored. I not only consider that Georgescu's theoretical analysis is wholly sound but that it strongly supports my own policy conclusions, based largely upon historical-empirical rather than theoretical grounds. On either basis I believe that the wisdom of the Japanese experience, and the dangers of the Communist model (except as modified in certain significant ways by China), are fully confirmed. It is to be hoped that India and other overpopulated Asian countries will learn these lessons in time to avoid serious economic and political blunders in their near-term planning. It is elementary that one has to learn to walk before he can run. In urging the contrary, particularly in matters of food and agricultural policy in the overpopulated countries, too many Western economists have done a serious disservice to a majority of mankind.

[42] *Ibid.*, Section IV.

2. The Role of Agriculture in Modern Japanese Economic Development*

KAZUSHI OHKAWA AND HENRY ROSOVSKY

I

Japan is a relative late-comer to modern economic development, and still remains the only industrialized country in Asia. These features have undoubtedly left their mark on Japanese economic growth. Recently, efforts have been made to give a clearer quantitative picture of this growth, and even though certain vague points still remain, we believe that it is now possible to provide a more thorough sectoral analysis.

Perhaps the most outstanding feature of Japanese development is its rapidity, or what is even more important, the sustained character of the growth process.[1] What are the crucial factors which led to the economic breakthrough in the nineteenth century and made for sustained rapid growth in the ensuing period? The purpose of our paper is to supply a partial but relevant answer to this question: a study of the role of agriculture in modern Japanese economic development. This necessarily becomes a two-fold problem. Firstly, we outline the main features of Japanese agricultural development in its role as one of the major sectors of the economy. Secondly, we examine the relationships between agriculture and the other sectors during the growth process.

The discussion that follows attempts to accomplish these aims within certain clearly defined limits. Observations are generally macro-sectoral, and sub-sectoral material is introduced only for specific illustrations. Historically, we try to compare two rather long periods: period I, from the Meiji Restoration to World War I, and period II, from World War

* From *Economic Development and Cultural Change*, vol. 9, part 2, October, 1960, pp. 43–68, with corrections added. Copyright 1960 by the University of Chicago. Reprinted by permission of the authors and The University of Chicago Press. The authors are professor of economics at Hitotsubashi University, Tokyo, and professor of economics at the University of California, Berkeley, respectively.

[1] For general background, see Kazushi Ohkawa and Others, *The Growth Rate of the Japanese Economy Since 1878* (Tokyo: Kinokuniya Bookstore Ltd., 1957), especially part II, Bruce F. Johnston, "Agricultural Productivity and Economic Development in Japan," *Journal of Political Economy*, LIX, 6 (Dec. 1951), and Henry Rosovsky, "Japanese Capital Formation: The Role of the Public Sector," *Journal of Economic History*, XIX, 3 (Sept. 1959).

I to World War II. In spite of the sustained character of growth in Japan, the relative position of major sectors in the economy changed considerably. As we will show, World War I marked a distinct structural change especially pronounced in the relations between agriculture and industry. A third period might have been considered: the years after World War II to the present. But this would have required an extensive discussion of the land reform and the peculiar nature of the postwar economic recovery, and both topics deserve separate and extensive analysis. We therefore confine ourselves to periods I and II, and try to add international comparisons at the end.

II

The analysis starts with a study of the period from 1878 to 1917. (Before 1878 statistical deficiencies are nearly insurmountable.) Our attention will primarily focus on two aspects of agricultural progress: output and productivity. Throughout these pages the term "productivity" is used in a conventional way, simply meaning product per worker or per unit area. These may be considered neutral measures and are of equal importance to all types of economic development. Within this framework we will deal with three principal questions:

1. What happened to output and productivity during the period?
2. What developments took place in the structure of the producing unit?
3. How did the changing pattern of factor combinations affect output and productivity?

Although there exist statistical hurdles in analyzing changes in Japanese agricultural output, the overall picture is very clear. The expansion rate of food crops was high enough to outstrip the growth rate of population. Gross and net output of agriculture in real terms increased steadily throughout the period. The annual growth rate of net output from 1878 to 1917 averaged about 2.3 percent, while the growth rate of gross output was somewhat higher.[2] These observations can be verified with the data supplied in Table 1.

Turning next to productivity, let us first look at land productivity, obtained by dividing net output by arable land. If we assume yields per unit to have been 100 in 1878–82, they rose to 180 by 1913–17. (See Table 2.) It must be remembered that during this period the area of arable land increased from 4,524 thousand hectares in 1884 to 6,084 thousand hectares in 1920. But this is an increase of only 35 percent,

---

[2] Our discussion is based on data fully presented in Ohkawa and Others, part II. By net output we mean gross output minus intermediate goods. Real term series result from dividing money values by an agricultural price index. It must be noted that the use of Japanese statistics before the 1920's inevitably involves errors and biases, and it is not an easy matter to ascertain the direction of these departures from reality.

TABLE 1. AGRICULTURAL OUTPUT, 1878–1917*
(*Five Year Averages*)

Year	Rice: total output† (million bushels)	Rice: yields (bushels/ hectare)	General agricultural production index‡	Agricultural gross output (million ¥, 1928–32 prices)	Agricultural net output (million ¥, 1928–32 prices)
1878–82	147.53 (100)	59.72 (100)	100	960 (100)	825 (100)
1883–87	167.64 (113)	63.93 (107)	112	1,088 (113)	934 (113)
1888–92	192.87 (130)	70.38 (117)	123	1,349 (140)	1,089 (131)
1893–97	186.87 (126)	67.36 (112)	129	1,420 (147)	1,196 (144)
1898–02	210.70 (142)	74.30 (124)	147	1,688 (175)	1,432 (173)
1903–07	229.58 (155)	79.56 (133)	158	1,842 (191)	1,517 (183)
1908–12	250.91 (170)	84.87 (142)	176	2,129 (221)	1,722 (208)
1913–17	274.00 (185)	89.68 (150)	198	2,306 (240)	1,829 (221)

* Figures in parentheses show the series as relatives, 1878–82 = 100.

† Rice production figures are shown separately because it was the most important crop. Rice production statistics are generally conceded to be most reliable.

‡ The overall index of agricultural production, still classified as a tentative result by the Ministry of Agriculture, is included for general reference purposes.

SOURCES: Rice Output Yields—Japan, Nōrinshō, *Nōrin tōkei, 1868–1953* (Statistical Tables of Agriculture and Forestry), (1955), Tables 9 and 18; Production Index— *Nōrin tōkei geppō* (Monthly Review of Agriculture and Forestry Statistics), (May 1946); Gross and Net Output: Ohkawa and Others, pp. 58 and 72.

compared to an 80 percent increase in land productivity. This shows that gains in productivity were more important than new land in achieving output increases, and suggests that land-saving technological innovations were of great importance. We will have to return to this matter below.

TABLE 2. INCREASES IN LAND AND LABOR PRODUCTIVITY, 1878–1917
(*Five Year Averages*)

Year	Land productivity (net output/ arable land)	Labor productivity (net output/ labor force)	Labor force (thousands)
1878–82	¥ 17.3 (100)	¥ 53.0 (100)	15,573 (100)
1883–87	20.5 (118)	60.2 (113)	15,511 (99)
1888–92	22.2 (128)	70.4 (132)	15,466 (99)
1893–97	23.8 (137)	77.7 (146)	15,397 (98)
1898–02	28.3 (163)	93.5 (176)	15,303 (98)
1903–07	28.5 (164)	99.9 (188)	15,184 (97)
1908–12	30.5 (176)	115.2 (217)	14,490 (93)
1913–17	31.2 (180)	125.2 (236)	14,613 (93)

SOURCE: Computed from Table 1. Labor Force estimates based on unpublished results of Ohkawa.

Estimating labor productivity is a very hazardous undertaking in the Japanese case mainly because the term "labor force" is conceptually and statistically treacherous. There are several estimates for the labor force and for the gainfully occupied population in agriculture, but it is still not possible to accept the figures with full confidence. Using the latest and best computations, shown in Table 2, the results are as follows: labor productivity (net output/labor force) increased annually by 2.6 percent. The trend was not entirely uniform; towards the end of the period increases in labor productivity tended to become slower. Available sources indicate that between 1898 and 1917 there took place a small decline in the number of persons gainfully occupied in agriculture. Thus, increases in net output associated with a reduction in the labor force suggest that technological development took a mild labor-saving form.

What are the implications of these output and productivity changes? They can be understood only in conjunction with other macro-economic data. In terms of domestic events, the expansion of output was almost large enough both to supply the needed food for a rapidly growing urban population, and to meet the increased food demand stemming from a rise in real per capita income. As shown in Table 3, Japan was a

TABLE 3. BALANCE SHEET OF AGRICULTURE PRODUCTS
(Five Year Averages)*

Year	Domestic supply	Domestic demand	Supply − demand
1878–82	431	420	+ 11
1883–87	333	326	+ 7
1888–92	460	463	− 3
1893–97	632	663	− 31
1898–02	959	1,058	− 99
1903–07	1,230	1,425	−195
1908–12	1,501	1,754	−253
1913–17	1,787	2,186	−399

* Unit: Million Y.
SOURCE: Domestic Supply—Ohkawa and Others, p. 58; Domestic Demand—Seiichi Tōbata and Kazushi Ohkawa (eds.), *Nihon no keizai to nōgyō* (The Japanese Economy and Agriculture), (Tokyo: Iwanami Shoten, 1956), ch. iv, sec. 1, Table 4.2.

net exporter of agricultural products until the 1890's; after that she became a moderate importer of food.[3]

During the period total population grew at rates which varied from 0.8 to 1.3 percent per year, while the income elasticity for food has been

[3] The figures of Table 3 tend to overstate the imports of food crops. Japan became an especially heavy importer of certain industrial crops in the twentieth century; e. g. cotton.

estimated to have been about 0.6 to 0.7, a high figure as compared with later periods.[4] Per capita real income increased at about an annual rate of 2 percent.[5] Taken together, these data indicate that the demand for food increased at an annual rate of about 2 percent, and that this increase was largely met by output expansion, slight increases in arable land, and a small reduction in the labor force.[6] In this sense, excepting short-term fluctuations, the forces of demand and supply for food were in near equilibrium during the initial phases of Japanese industrialization. The terms of trade between agriculture and the other sectors lend support to this conclusion. From 1878 to 1917, they remain extremely steady, as shown below, except for cyclical fluctuations.

TABLE 4. TERMS OF TRADE BETWEEN URBAN AND RURAL SECTORS
(*Five Year Averages*)*

Year	Price index of non-agricultural commodities (N)	Price index of agricultural commodities (A)	N/A
1878–82	44	44	100
1883–87	33	30	107
1888–92	34	34	100
1893–97	41	44	92
1898–02	53	56	94
1903–07	63	66	95
1908–12	68	70	97
1913–17	82	77	106

* 1928–32 = 100.
SOURCE: Computed from Ohkawa and Others, p. 130.

We have shown that Japanese agriculture grew in harmony with the other sectors of the economy. In so doing, agriculture made a necessary contribution to rapid industrialization and urbanization. Inflationary pressures stemming from a shortage of food must have been minimal, and many underdeveloped areas today must envy this situation.

So far we have stressed the domestic role of Japanese agriculture, but, as is well known, its contribution was also notable in the expansion of international trade. Increases in output and quality improvement of such commercial products as silk cocoons and tea leaves were, in the

---

[4] Tōbata and Ohkawa, chapter 4, section 1, pp. 166 ff. [see citation in Table 3.] This calculation is based on aggregate time series; family budget studies have shown slightly different results.

[5] Ohkawa and Others, p. 24.

[6] Rate of population increase + rate of per capita income increase × income elasticity for food = rate of increase of food demand.

early years, the primary basis for the rapid growth of semi-manufactured exports, such as raw silk and tea. Raw silk in particular remained an important export item even after World War I. The function of agriculture as an earner of foreign exchange was extremely important to the economic development of the country. In the absence of foreign loans, export surpluses were required to import foreign capital goods to be used in the modernization of industry. Before World War I these export surpluses largely originated in agriculture.

III

The industrial revolution in Japan was not preceded or accompanied by an agricultural revolution of the *Western type.*[7] There was, as we have seen, a rapid expansion of agricultural output combined with speedy industrialization, and "revolutionary changes" took place in a matter of decades. However, the increases in output and productivity were based on the traditional patterns of rural organization inherited, in the main, from the Tokugawa period. The small family farm, averaging about 1 hectare per household, the distribution between peasant proprietors and tenants, high rents in kind—all of these characteristics were maintained during the period. At the same time, there was no strong trend of land consolidation, and this preserved the scattered holdings of tiny plots of ground, nor was there evidence of a rural exodus to the urban areas by a *newly created* landless peasant class. During the early period of industrialization necessary increases in the labor force did indeed come from the rural areas. But laborers were usually young and left singly. There was only very little movement in terms of family units, and no formation of an agricultural proletariat.[8] Thus, a fairly typical Asian type of agriculture remained in existence and was utilized to promote impressive increases in productivity, while Western technology was making rapid progress in manufacturing.

Let us very briefly turn to some of the statistical evidence which supports the views expressed here. The records indicate that there were 5,437,000 farm households in 1884, and 5,573,000 in 1920—a very small increase. For size of holdings, only a comparison between 1908 and 1917 is possible. In 1908, 69.9 percent of farm households had holdings of less than 1 hectare; 25.9 percent held between 1 and 3 hectares, and 4.2 percent owned over 3 hectares. In 1917 these percentages were 69.8,

[7] The term "agricultural revolution" is, at best, vague, and not all Western countries went through agricultural revolutions of the Western type. Here we only wish to underline the fact that no radical reorganization of the producing unit took place shortly before or after the Restoration. Earlier in the Tokugawa period, as Thomas C. Smith has clearly shown, a very peculiar type of agricultural revolution did take place. Cf. *The Agrarian Origins of Modern Japan* (Stanford: Stanford University Press, 1959).

[8] See Tōbata and Ohkawa, ch. iii, section 1, pp. 123 ff. and section 2, pp. 153–55.

26.3, and 3.9 respectively, and can be taken as some indication that the concentration of tiny holdings remained more or less unchanged.[9]

The statistics on tenancy are more complicated. In 1903—the year in which consistent time series begin—44.5 percent of the arable land was cultivated by tenants. In 1917 tenants cultivated 46.2 percent of the land. Some partial surveys taken in the nineteenth century indicate that tenancy increased in the early years of Meiji: from 34.2 percent in 1883 to 40 percent in 1892. The number of pure tenants (having no land of their own) increased as well, from 19.2 percent in 1883 to 27.6 percent in 1915.[10] These numbers indicate that some landholders could not adapt themselves to the new money economy and tax system. Undoubtedly there was some rural instability exemplified by the transfer of land ownership from peasants to landlords. But these changes were not radical. They were carried out in keeping with the existing system of productive organization, and left the majority of owner-cultivators untouched.

What were the causes of rural stability? It is not easy to be precise about these matters, and we can only try to suggest a few causal possibilities. The strength of the family system and an orientation towards farming as a way of life inherited from the ancestors no doubt strengthened the commitment towards one's own land. Motivations of this kind require strong incentives to pull rural inhabitants to urban districts, especially in family or household units. Even the individuals who do move will usually retain close ties with their families still located on the land.

Is it possible that the Japanese rate of industrial growth was not rapid enough to make the kinds of inroads into the agricultural population which would have upset the traditional labor-intensive organization of production? In view of the comparatively rapid rate of industrialization —matched by very few Western countries—there must be a better way of stating the problem. It would be more correct to say that population in the rural areas grew so quickly that no other methods could be adopted. In other words, the surplus over and above the replacement population was just capable of being absorbed by the non-agricultural sectors.

The inherited system of land tenure which was based on the small proprietor helped to reinforce these tendencies. It explains in part the absence of a large rural proletariat, such as exists in India, ready to flow into the cities with dependents. Even Japanese peasants who owned no land became traditional tenants and did not normally work for a money wage. In fact, landlordism helped to raise output and speeded tech-

[9] *Ibid.*, Chapter ii, section 3, pp. 110 ff. and Japan, Nōrinshō, *Nōrin tōkei, 1868–1953* (1955), table 3.

[10] *Ibid.*, table 9, and Japan, Nōshōmushō, *ōshōmushō N tōkeihyō* (Statistical Yearbook of the Ministry of Agriculture and Commerce), 1886 and 1895.

nological changes through selected methods which fitted into the traditional system of tenancy.

Thus, the situation in Japan during early industrialization came to be characterized by stability or unchanged organization of the rural community, side by side with rapid progress in agricultural productivity.

IV

The previous analysis implies that there must have been key improvements in Japanese agricultural practice in keeping with the small unit of production. Broadly speaking, two kinds of improvement took place in combination. The first kind took the form of land improvement, including better irrigation and drainage facilities and the reclamation of some arable land—mostly paddy rice fields. The second kind of improvement encompassed superior seeds, better methods of crop cultivation, and increased input of manures and fertilizers. The latter type of technological advance required increases in working capital rather than lumpy investment in fixed capital such as machinery or livestock. As such, these were methods of improvement within the reach of the small family unit. On the other hand, land improvement projects and reclamation required capital and labor beyond the reach of the individual farmer, and were carried out principally by landlords and the government.[11]

Quantitative data which can be used as evidence for the above assertions are, in the nature of things, a trifle indirect. Shishido's agricultural input index, reproduced below as Table 5, shows the very rapid increase in fertilizer input as against rather slow advances for energy input. In addition, fragmentary data from 1890 to 1908, based on farm household surveys, indicate proportionately rising fertilizer and seed input, as well as a rising proportion of commercial fertilizers replacing such things as night soil and barnyard manure.[12] We believe that the increased use of better seeds and commercial fertilizers were most responsible for the rise in output, even though the cost ratio to net output in agriculture was still very small during the period.[13]

[11] Before World War I, farm mechanization was virtually non-existent in Japan. See Japan, Ministry of International Trade and Industry, *Japan: Farm Machinery*, 1957, pp. 9–10. On land reclamation and comparative fertilizer input, see S. Nasu, *Land Utilization in Japan* (Tokyo: Institute of Pacific Relations, 1929), pp. 103 ff. and 161 ff.

[12] Ohkawa and Others, pp. 61–62, Saitō's figures show that in 1890, 45 percent of fertilizers were purchased. The proportion rose to 53 percent by 1908. Obviously these were long-run trends which had started before the Restoration.

[13] *Ibid.* About 14 percent in 1890 and 16 percent in 1908. It should be clear that these improvements mainly affected the cultivation of rice. If there had been a greater degree of agricultural diversification the capital requirements would have been quite different. Diversification probably required a different national level of per capita income and radically altered consumer tastes.

Before World War I the incentives for investment in agriculture were not lacking. Landlords received a high rent in kind, and were interested in raising and stabilizing yields. Nominally rents were set on the basis of absolute amounts, rather than as a share of output, but the final rent paid tended to fluctuate in accordance with yield changes. These factors encourage entrepreneurship. Furthermore, during almost the entire period, the price of rice rose *pari passu* with the general price level, and this must have been an incentive to one and all to improve practices of cultivation. Also, the land tax burden was lessened with greater production. At this time, absentee owners were rare in Japan. Most land-

TABLE 5. AGRICULTURAL INPUT INDEX
(*Five Year Averages*)*

Year	Fertilizer†	Energy†
1878–82	100	100
1883–87	109	97
1888–92	171	95
1893–97	239	99
1898–02	597	104
1903–07	1,494	102
1908–12	2,792	112
1913–17	3,997	119

* 1878–82 = 100.
  † Energy input is represented only by draft animals because power machinery was virtually unused. The fertilizer index shows deflated values of purchased fertilizers.
  SOURCE: Tōbata and Ohkawa, Chapter 2, Section 2.

owners lived in the rural districts and frequently acted as leaders in introducing new methods suited to particular local conditions.[14] The State also played an important role in developing locally suited technology. Local and Central Government established experimental stations and extension services, and provided technical and general education through organization and support of the school system.

Two indices, cited in Table 6, can be used to support the assertions concerning private incentives. Until the 1890's, we can show that the share of rents increased; after that it seems to have declined slightly. These figures imply that in the process of expanding rice output, the marginal gains of the early period went primarily to the landlords. In the later years of our period of analysis, the trend changed in favor of the tenants. In effect, both sides had periods of real gains.[15] We can also

[14] For an interesting and amusing discussion of these and other points pertaining to landlords, see R. P. Dore, "The Meiji Landlord: Good or Bad?," *The Journal of Asian Studies*, XVIII, 3 (May, 1959).
  [15] In fact, the rent share index is cited only to indicate relative changes, and it should not be concluded that the implications for the tenants were necessarily adverse during any period. Winter crops are not included in these computations, and the fruits of these went almost exclusively to the tenants.

TABLE 6. RELATIVE SHARE OF RICE YIELDS AND VALUE OF PADDY FIELDS
(*Ten Year Overlapping Averages*)

Year	Rent paid yields %	Index of paddy field value in terms of rice price
1878–87	59	100
1883–92	62	104
1888–97	68	131
1893–02	68	153
1898–07	63	147
1903–12	60	150
1908–17	58	183

SOURCE: Tōbata and Ohkawa, p. 268.

see that paddy land value, in terms of the rice price, exhibited a steady upward trend, which can be taken as evidence of a continual strong demand for arable land.

V

Let us now examine the characteristics and progress of agriculture during the next major phase of Japanese economic development: from 1918 to 1940. We have stated earlier that the years around World War I marked a structural change in the relation between the primary and the other sectors of the economy. Now we will attempt to document this change, and to substantiate the thesis that agriculture shifted from being a dynamic supporter of development to a relatively passive position.

Our analysis in this part will focus on the following questions:

1. What happened to output and productivity during the period?

2. How are the changes in output and productivity reflected in the agricultural production pattern?

3. How can we characterize the changing role of agriculture in the overall process of economic development?

These are broad questions, and the empirical underpinnings for unambiguous answers are not always secure. But it is possible to draw the broad trends with sufficient clarity.

It is generally recognized that the outbreak of World War I made a great and favorable impact on the growth rate of the Japanese economy. Japan's national income grew more quickly than in any preceding modern period, and there were no serious retardations until the end of the 1930's. The figures of Table 7 give a panoramic view of the three broad industrial sectors of the economy, and the data are presented in such a manner as to allow a contrast between the pre and post 1913–17 period. Certain conclusions are obvious. The net output of real income produced by the primary sector continued to increase for the entire period under discussion, but after World War I the rate of acceleration decreased. In contradistinction, the growth acceleration of secondary and tertiary industry continued to increase during the same period.

An adequate explanation of these differential growth patterns would, of course, involve almost all of modern Japanese economic history. Our

TABLE 7. REAL NET OUTPUT BY INDUSTRIAL SECTOR*

Year	Primary industry	Secondary industry	Tertiary industry
1882–92	1,150 (100)	356 (100)	664 (100)
1893–97	1,467 (128)	528 (148)	892 (134)
1898–02	1,757 (153)	793 (223)	1,177 (177)
1903–07	1,791 (156)	803 (226)	1,354 (204)
1908–12	2,040 (177)	1,037 (291)	1,820 (274)
1913–17	2,025 (176)	1,479 (415)	2,150 (324)
1913–17	2,025 (100)	1,479 (100)	2,150 (100)
1918–22	2,409 (119)	1,826 (123)	2,977 (138)
1923–27	2,551 (126)	2,253 (152)	4,529 (211)
1928–32	2,552 (126)	3,373 (228)	6,463 (300)
1933–37	2,862 (141)	4,713 (318)	7,420 (345)
1938–42	3,156 (156)	7,050 (477)	8,534 (397)

* Figures in parentheses are relatives. Unit: Million Ұ.
SOURCE: Computed from Ohkawa and Others, p. 17.

TABLE 8. AGRICULTURAL OUTPUT, 1913–1942*

Year	Rice: total output (million bushels)	Rice: yields (bushels/ hectare)	General agricultural production index	Agricultural gross output (million Ұ 1928–32 prices)	Agricultural net output (million Ұ 1928–32 prices)
1913–17	274.00 (100)	89.68 (100)	100	2,306 (100)	1,829 (100)
1918–22	292.24 (107)	97.22 (108)	106	2,517 (109)	1,975 (108)
1923–27	287.69 (105)	93.95 (104)	109	2,524 (109)	1,901 (104)
1928–32	299.92 (114)	97.49 (109)	124	2,756 (120)	2,109 (115)
1938–42	315.02 (115)	99.50 (111)	125	2,985 (129)	2,305 (126)

* See notes to Table 4.
SOURCE: See Table 4.

limited purpose is to understand the developments in agriculture, and we can gain a lot of insight by examining the data of Table 8, which should be looked at in conjunction with Table 1. What do we see? The per hectare yields and total output of rice grow much less impressively, and the same is true of the three macroagricultural series: the general production index for agriculture, and net and gross output.

No matter what output measure is chosen, the statistics reveal a rather dramatic change.

The same situation pertains when we turn from output to productivity. As the figures of Table 9 show—and they should be contrasted with Table 2—land and labor productivity increases moved at a much slower pace compared to the pre-World War I period. Both net output and labor productivity grew at annual rates of less than 1 percent, and it will be recalled that growth rates in the previous period were well over 2 percent.

TABLE 9. INCREASES IN LAND AND LABOR PRODUCTIVITY, 1913–42
(*Five Year Averages*)

Year	Land productivity (net output/ arable land)	Labor productivity (net output/ labor force)	Labor force (thousands)
1913–17	¥ 31.2(100)	¥125.2(100)	14,613(100)
1918–22	32.8(105)	137.4(110)	14,235(97)
1923–27	31.6(101)	134.8(108)	14,103(96)
1928–32	37.4(120)	148.6(119)	14,192(97)
1933–37	38.3(123)	159.9(128)	14,414(99)

SOURCE: Net Output—see Table 4; Arable land—Japan. Ministry of Agriculture and Forestry, *Statistical Tables of the Ministry of Agriculture and Forestry, 1868–1953,* p. 10; Labor Force, Tōbata and Ohkawa, p. 415 (based on Hemmi's computations).

The most significant measures of economic growth, and of the relative position of a sector within the economy, must necessarily be put into per capita terms. This is done in Table 10 where we show real income per gainfully occupied person in relative figures. The data must be interpreted with care because indices of this type can be misleading. For Table 10 we chose an arbitrary base period (1913–17 = 100) which allows a comparison between the pre and post World War I period. The figures show only this: from 1878 to 1917 real income per gainfully occupied person in agriculture grew at more or less the same rates as real income in the service industries, and slightly more slowly than real income in manufacturing. From 1918 to 1942 the growth of real income in agriculture, in relative terms, falls far behind that of the other sectors. The table cannot show the differences in the absolute level of real income between sectors. In 1878–82, real income per gainfully occupied person in primary industry average ¥ 57; in secondary industry the equivalent income was ¥ 132, and in tertiary ¥ 156. In 1913–17 the incomes were ¥ 129, ¥ 339, and ¥ 333 respectively, and in 1938–1942 they stood at ¥ 220, ¥ 928, and ¥ 838, in the same order.[16] These results are, of course, fully consistent with the relative figures.

[16] See Ohkawa and Others, p. 20.

TABLE 10. REAL INCOMES PER GAINFULLY OCCUPIED PERSON (RELATIVES)
(*1913–17 = 100*)

Year	Primary industry	Secondary industry	Tertiary industry
1878–82	44.1	38.9	46.8
1883–87	45.7	49.1	59.8
1888–92	51.9	53.1	59.2
1893–97	65.8	63.1	68.1
1898–02	78.3	79.7	78.5
1903–07	81.3	70.2	78.5
1908–12	96.1	78.9	94.1
1913–17	100.0	100.0	100.0
1918–22	125.4	116.0	117.4
1923–27	134.0	136.7	154.1
1928–32	134.0	202.8	202.8
1933–37	151.0	231.8	220.4
1938–42	170.4	274.0	251.7

SOURCE: Computed from Ohkawa and Others, p. 20.

VI

What are the implications of these changes for the economy as a whole? First of all, it meant that the supply of food could no longer keep up with the demand for food. During the period, let us say from 1918 to 1942, population grew at rates which varied from 1.2 to 1.5 percent per year.[17] The average was probably slightly above 1.3 percent—a significant increase over the earlier period. Per capita real income increased at a faster pace, but there seems reason to assume some fall in the income elasticity of food products. On the other hand, we have indicated that the rate of output expansion was now very much reduced. A large deficit is obvious, and the evidence is produced in Table 11. Once again a comparison should be made with Table 3, and the new situation will be clearly apparent.

TABLE 11. BALANCE SHEET OF AGRICULTURAL PRODUCTS
(*Five Year Averages*)*

Year	Domestic supply	Domestic demand	Supply – demand
1913–17	1,787	2,186	– 399
1918–22	4,062	5,263	–1,201
1923–27	3,902	5,607	–1,705
1933–37	3,277	4,977	–1,700

* Unit: Million Y.

SOURCE: Supply—computed from Ohkawa and Others, p. 58; Demand—computed from Tōbata and Ohkawa, p. 173.

[17] *Ibid.*, p. 19.

Perhaps the most remarkable change occurred in the net import of Japan's principal food crop item. Imports of rice (from Korea and Taiwan) increased sharply immediately after the War, and continued to grow until the end of the 1930's, as shown in the long time-series of Table 12.

TABLE 12. BALANCE SHEET FOR RICE
(*Five Year Averages*)*

Year	Import	Export	Import − export
1878–82	31	250	−219
1883–87	31	339	−308
1888–92	565	855	−290
1893–97	1,027	694	333
1898–02	2,040	575	1,465
1903–07	5,383	307	5,076
1908–12	3,687	393	3,285
1913–17	3,385	686	2,699
1918–22	6,305	428	5,877
1923–27	10,008	1,052	8,956
1928–32	10,378	959	9,419
1933–37	13,220	713	12,507
1938–42	13,406	800	12,606

* Unit: Thousand Koku = 4,960 bushels.
SOURCE: Tōbata and Ohkawa, p. 80.

The creation of Korea and Taiwan as major rice suppliers for the Japanese domestic market was the result of deliberate government policy, inspired in part by the outbreak of the "rice revolt" of 1918, and strengthened in subsequent years. In that year, because of the growing secular shortage of rice, the retail price of this all-important commodity stood at almost a record high, causing serious difficulties for the livelihood of the common people. Only a large and organized import program could prevent an economic and social crisis. In this sense, the "rice revolt" assumes the proportion of an epochal turning point in the development of Japanese agriculture. It represents a shift from the period of agricultural "balanced growth" to the period of agriculture as a retarded or depressed sector.[18]

[18] The term: "balanced growth" is used in a somewhat special sense. It indicates that sectoral productivity levels grew at more or less equal rates. Lack of balance in Japan meant more rapid productivity gains in industry than in agriculture. Increases in population which could not be absorbed in the non-agricultural sectors created a situation of low productivity and rural overemployment.

Our conclusions do not imply that continued growth in agriculture was necessary to achieve a better allocation of resources. It is obvious that in the period after World War I opportunities for investment were much more attractive outside of agriculture, and that by means of the ordinary expansion of international trade

Government policy, helped by the activities of private enterprise, succeeded to the extent that ever larger quantities of rice (similar to indigenous quality) were imported from Taiwan and Korea, meeting the increased domestic demand, and keeping the retail price of rice almost parallel to the general price movement. But this situation was not without dangerous implications for domestic agriculture. Japanese rice farmers suffered a great deal from the competition of these overseas suppliers, because the cost of production of the colonial territories was lower, largely due to the (purposely?) depressed standard of living in these areas. Competition was particularly damaging in the late 1920's and early 1930's when a number of bumper crops in Japan caused a situation of temporary over-supply.

The changing output-cost relationships in domestic agriculture (Table 13) reveal the general slow-down of productivity from still an-

TABLE 13. OUTPUT-COST RELATIONSHIPS IN AGRICULTURE
(1933–37 = 100)

Year	Production index (a)	Cost index (b)	Real cost per unit (b)/(a)
1878–82	37.1	89.4	2.41
1883–87	44.5	89.5	2.01
1888–92	52.8	91.0	1.72
1893–97	58.6	91.4	1.56
1898–02	68.0	91.7	1.35
1903–07	75.3	94.2	1.24
1908–12	87.6	96.8	1.10
1913–17	100.0	100.0	1.00
1918–22	110.0	103.7	0.94
1923–27	115.8	106.3	0.91
1928–32	126.0	110.1	0.87
1933–37	134.0	114.5	0.85
1938–42	135.9	122.9	0.90

SOURCE: Tōbata and Ohkawa, p. 95. Based on data supplied by Mr. Shishido.

other facet, and prove that Taiwanese and Korean imports must have been prejudicial to the welfare of the domestic farmer. A number of conclusions can be deduced from these data. Production gains were much larger than cost increases until World War I. In the ensuing pe-

Japan could import food because she exported more manufactured products. We wish to underline, however, that precisely this type of development produced as a side effect an agricultural sector which was retarded and overpopulated. Rapid population growth, more than any other factor, made this inevitable.

For a more detailed discussion of the residual or overemployment problem in agriculture, see Kazushi Ohkawa, "Economic Growth and Agriculture," *The Annals of the Hitotsubashi Academy*, VII, 1 (October 1956).

riods, costs and increases in production rose at nearly equal speeds. Consequently, real costs per unit in agriculture seemed to have reached a plateau in the 1920's and 1930's. It is also clear that the cost of land improvements rose steeply after 1900. Taking that year as 100, an index of real improvement costs reaches 214 by 1931–34.[19] The Japanese farmer, given the prevailing system of cultivation, had reached his most efficient method of production in the 'teens of the twentieth century, and now he was not able to make further impressive gains. Under these circumstances, most agriculturists were virtually defenseless against lower-cost colonial producers.

What once had been a source of great strength in Japanese economic development now became a limiting factor in the process of continued growth. The entire traditional agricultural complex which had served Japan quite well since the early changes of the Tokugawa Era, and which had been spectacularly successful during Meiji and part of Taishō, now entered a far less brilliant period. Perhaps the greatest problem lay in the fact that major changes were politically, socially, and culturally quite impossible. The production structure of domestic agriculture—a pattern of small holdings and landlordism—despite internal and external pressures, had to be maintained for many reasons, and we will call attention to some of the economic forces which stood in the way of further progress.

First of all, one must notice that the size of the farm labor force remained almost unchanged after the first census of 1920. At the same time, the area of arable land also remained nearly constant. Thus, nothing took place which could make the factor proportions (mainly the man-land ratio) more favorable. No doubt it is also significant that the nature of landownership was in the process of transition. Absentee ownership was increasing, and the landlord-entrepreneur was fading away.[20] Landlord interest was shifting from production to marketing, and their collective efforts came to be concentrated on maintaining the price of rice. Their efforts were not too successful in spite of sizable government expenditures.

To a large extent, all of the above mentioned factors are only symptoms of more deep-seated structural problems arising in the Japanese economy at this time. The unchanging size of the agricultural labor force resulted from population pressure and the inability of the secondary and tertiary sectors to aborb a greater share of the rural surplus. The relative decline of rural output and productivity probably grew out of even more chronic difficulties. Within the prevailing production function, further gains were necessarily slow and small. When Japan started

    [19] See Tōbata Seiichi, *Nihon nōgyō no tenkal katei* (The Development Process of Japanese Agriculture), (Tokyo: Iwanami Shoten, 1938), Table 45, p. 260.
    [20] See Dore, "The Meiji Landlord," *Journal of Asian Studies,* XVIII, 3.

on the road to modernization there were areas in the economy where, to use Ranis' apt expression, "slack"—in this case "excess labor on the land and reserves of productivity in the land"—could be taken up.[21]

By the end of World War I, barring major structural changes, the slack in agriculture was no longer present. There can thus be no doubt that a fundamental change had taken place in the dynamic role of agriculture sometime in the second decade of this century. An important transition in urban-rural economic relations was a matter of record.

All of these contentions are well reflected in the changes of the macro-economic structure: It is most evident in the *relative retardation* of agricultural labor productivity. If we make an index of the primary/secondary productivity ratio, taking the 1913–17 ratio as a base, the prewar period would average 100 to 120, while 1928–42 would be as low as 60 to 70.[22]

VII

In discussing the changing role of agriculture in Japanese economic development, especially when attempting to observe the economic facets of urban-rural relationships, we have so far ignored at least two important problems. The first has to do with the human factor—movement of the labor force to cities and sources of entrepreneurship—and this topic has been covered by others. The second problem deals with investment flows from the rural to the urban regions. Agriculture was a source of savings in the economy, and these savings were translated into investment, i.e. capital formation. At this juncture, it is almost impossible to provide a quantitative discussion of these investment flows. The data are not adequate, and we will therefore approach the issue indirectly.

We begin with the widely accepted assumption that large savings in agriculture could be and were in fact used for purposes of industrialization. The rationale of this assumption can be illustrated theoretically. Let us suppose that for the pre World War I period the average growth rate of the economy was about 3.5 percent per year, and that the average capital coefficient was around 3 or 4. Then the average ratio of savings in the economy would be 10 to 14 percent—that is, simply the product of the growth rate and the capital coefficient. (We believe the figures to be close to reality.) The growth rate of net output in agriculture, as shown previously, was 2.3 percent per year during the relevant period, and it can be reasonably supposed that the capital coefficient of this

---

[21] G. Ranis, "The Financing of Japanese Economic Development," *The Economic History Review*, XI, 3 (April 1959), p. 440.

[22] Computed from Ohkawa and Others, pp. 29–31.

sector was lower than the national average.[23] This means that the *required* investments in agriculture were smaller than the savings generated by this sector—if the savings ratio was at least as large as the national level—and the resulting surplus could have been siphoned off to the non-agricultural sectors.[24]

Good evidence that the facts are in rough correspondence with the theory lies in the operation of the famous Meiji land tax. In an earlier section, we stressed the maintenance of high rents in kind in the face of steadily increasing agricultural productivity. A traditional landlord system and the device of the land tax allowed the government to exploit the existing situation by transferring income from one sector of the economy to the other.[25] It is not necessary to provide a detailed description of this tax, enacted in 1873. Let us only remind ourselves that, during a critical stage of Japanese economic development, the land tax was the main source of government revenue; its weight in the central government revenue structure is shown in Table 14.

The changing role of agriculture comes out clearly in these data. Until 1913–17, the land tax—though steadily declining in significance—was absolutely the most important source of government revenue. The agricultural land tax formed 80 or 90 percent of the general land tax, and thus the main source of revenue had to be the net product of the farms. An income tax enacted into law in 1888 played only a minor role before World War I. It became important as agriculture faded out of the picture as the primary source of revenue, and as a dynamic force of further development.

The heavy burdens which the rural areas were required to shoulder during the course of development come out even more obviously in Table 15. Here we use Tsunematsu's estimates of the relative direct tax burden—central and local—on income produced, dividing the economy

[23] We indicated previously that the key improvements in Japanese agriculture were not especially capital using. Certainly they were less capital using than Western industrial technology which was being adopted in the secondary sector.

[24] In the initial stages of Japanese industrialization, foreign capital, on the whole, played a minor role. The Meiji Government borrowed considerable sums of money from great merchants, and in this way used some of the capital accumulation dating back to feudal times. The new government also established a modern banking and credit system in order to facilitate the creation of funds for industrialization. Also, the inflationary process, especially during the early period, by creating forced savings contributed to the intricate process of capital formation. All of these points, worthy of further study, are well beyond the limits of our paper. Here we only wish to stress that, in addition to the devices discussed above, the transfer of rural income and savings to the urban sector played a continuous and fundamental role in overall capital formation.

[25] For an analysis dealing with almost the same problem and reaching similar conclusions, see Ranis, "Financing Japanese Development," *Economic History Review*, XI, 3.

TABLE 14. COMPOSITION OF MAIN CENTRAL GOVERNMENT TAXATION REVENUE*
(*Five Year Averages*)†

Year	Income tax		Land tax		Business tax		Customs duty		Total
		%		%		%		%	
1888–92	1,091	2.4	38,446	85.6	740	1.6	4,654	10.4	44,941
1893–97	1,599	3.3	38,679	80.4	1,335	2.8	6,483	13.5	78,096
1898–02	5,520	7.8	44,632	63.2	6,058	8.6	14,414	20.4	70,624
1903–07	19,907	15.5	71,579	55.8	15,710	12.3	33,835	26.4	141,031
1908–12	34,071	18.3	79,541	42.9	25,033	13.5	46,691	25.3	185,337
1913–17	51,249	26.0	73,983	37.6	25,334	12.9	46,245	23.5	196,811
1918–22	187,276	47.4	73,936	18.3	57,226	14.2	85,686	21.1	404,124
1923–27	206,692	45.0	71,204	15.5	58,835	12.3	122,264	26.7	459,218
1928–32	177,568	42.9	65,121	15.8	48,290	11.7	122,414	29.6	413,393
1933–37	267,695	49.4	58,175	10.7	62,132	11.5	153,751	28.4	541,753

* Revenue other than from the four main taxes—the so-called "miscellaneous revenue"—is excluded from the table. Before World War I it accounted for about 30 to 40 percent of total revenue; after the War its share rose to from 45 to 50 percent.

† Unit: Thousand ¥.

SOURCE: Tōbata and Ohkawa, p. 375. Calculated from data provided by Tsunematsu.

TABLE 15. DIRECT TAX RATIO TO INCOME PRODUCED
AGRICULTURE VERSUS NON-AGRICULTURE

Year	Agriculture		Non-agriculture	
	Direct tax (thous. ¥)	Ratio (%)	Direct tax (thous. ¥)	Ratio (%)
1883–87	63,552	22.1	9,548	3.0
1888–92	58,479	15.5	9,779	2.3
1893–97	65,626	12.4	13,167	2.0
1898–02	99,050	12.1	35,378	3.2
1903–07	113,582	11.2	79,313	5.4
1908–12	153,441	12.5	132,196	6.4
1913–17	167,660	12.9	145,441	4.5
1918–22	295,672	9.2	431,081	5.4
1923–27	304,217	10.5	506,203	5.2
1928–32	205,450	9.7	421,311	4.3
1933–37	197,325	7.8	559,235	4.2

SOURCE: Tōbata and Ohkawa, p. 381. Computed from data supplied by Tsunematsu.

into two sectors: agriculture and non-agriculture. It may be surprising to note that the direct tax ratio remained considerably higher in agriculture during the period. A very high tax rate was imposed on agriculture during the early years of development, while a very low rate prevailed outside; it is true, however, that the weight of the burden declined with time. The persistence of the agricultural tax load stems from heavy local tax rates, applied in rural prefectures, which were not reduced when productive capacity lagged.

By way of summary, let us take a brief look at the expenditure side of the government budget, concentrating on subsidies. Throughout the relatively long period of Japanese development, the government played a very important role, especially as an investor.[26] Subsidies were one method of government investment. While other methods (mainly direct investment) were quantitatively more important, subsidies do indicate to some extent the economic priorities of the regime. These changing priorities are apparent in Table 16, where we show the distribution of subsidies by industrial sectors.

TABLE 16. SECTORAL COMPOSITION OF SUBSIDIES
(*Total* = *100*)

Year	Primary sector	Secondary sector	Tertiary sector	Miscellaneous
1891	. . .	58.8	2.3	37.9
1901	. . .	51.9	28.7	17.8
1911	0.8	38.0	30.9	30.3
1921	0.6	19.6	32.8	47.1
1931	10.8	40.2	10.9	38.1
1941	20.0	10.8	40.9	28.4

SOURCE: Nakayama Ichirō (ed.), *Nihon keizai no kōzō bunseki*, part ii, p. 159.

Throughout the entire period, the secondary and tertiary sectors were the main recipients of government subsidies. Manufacturing, shipping, armaments, and social overhead capital all received extensive support. More significant from our point of view is the varying picture in the primary sector. Until the 1920's practically no subsidies (although plenty of other help) were allotted to agriculture; after all, it was one of the major sources of surplus in the economy. But then the income flow seems to be reversed as agriculture begins to get some financial support from the government. We believe that the changing distribution of subsidies is symptomatic of a structural change in the traditional capital flow. In a sense the economy had turned a full circle. In the early period of development there was a net flow of capital from the rural to the urban areas. We think that this flow may have been reversed sometime after World War I. Admittedly this must remain a highly conjectural conclusion, and requires further detailed investigation before it can be accepted with the proper degree of confidence.

[26] See Rosovsky, "Japanese Capital Formation," *Journal of Economic History*, XIX, 3.

VIII

How does the Japanese experience fit the international pattern of development? In this section we will try to examine certain aspects of this question for the entire period of analysis: that is, from 1868 to the 1940's. International comparisons are technically and substantively intricate. Comparable and otherwise adequate series are in extremely short supply, and all too often a great deal of guesswork is involved. This is especially true for long-term comparisons. To minimize these problems our comparisons are restricted to a few basic and broad issues.

In common with all other developing countries, during Japanese industrialization there took place a decline in the relative share of income produced and labor employed in agriculture. The percentage of national income produced in the primary sector fell from 64 in 1878–82, to 36 in 1913–17, to 17 in 1938–42. The percentage of the labor force engaged in agriculture was 76, 59, and 44 during the same periods.[27] Both of these measures indicate a rather rapid transformation when compared to the data available for Europe.

Let us first consider the matter of income shares. European data are unfortunately unavailable for the period which would correspond to the initial phase of Japanese development. Beginning in the 1880's, when Kuznets' series start, we note that income produced in agriculture accounted generally for 40 to 50 percent of national income. By 1940, the European range lay between 27 percent (Italy) and 13 percent (Sweden)—excluding the United Kingdom.[28] Two conclusions follow: the income share of agriculture decreased at a much more rapid tempo in Japan than in Europe, and, perhaps more important, the relative position of Japanese agriculture in terms of income produced had reached the average European levels even before World War II.

The average European share of labor force in agriculture was much lower than in Japan. Around 1940 it ranged from 25 to 35 percent (leaving out certain extreme cases).[29] This naturally requires the conclusion

---

[27] Ohkawa and Others, pp. 26–27. The figure for 1878–82 has been tentatively revised to 76 percent from the previous 82 percent. See Kuzushi Ohkawa, "Yūgyō jinkō (1872–1920) no suikei—nōgyō jinkō" (Survey of the Gainfully Employed Population in Agriculture, 1872–1920), Hitotsubashi University Institute of Economic Research Working Papers, 1958.

[28] Simon Kuznets, "Quantitative Aspects of the Economic Growth of Nations—II, Industrial Distribution of National Product and Labor Force," *Economic Development and Cultural Change*, supplement to Vol. V, No. 4 (July 1957), Appendix Table 2.

[29] *Ibid.*, Appendix Table 4. It might not be out of place to point out here that statistics dealing with the occupational breakdown of the labor force are frequently unreliable. For example, the Japanese figures classify as agricultural labor many persons who engage in so-called "by-employment" (usually small industry or services) and whose major source of income, especially on a household basis, may be from secondary or tertiary employment.

that the relative level of per capita income in Japanese agriculture was much lower than the average level in Europe. And indeed this is hardly surprising in view of the structural difficulties of Japanese agriculture which were encountered in the period preceding World War II.[30]

These brief comparisons suggest a number of questions which may serve to clarify the differences between the Japanese and the European patterns. First of all, what effect could have been expected from the economic level prevailing in Japan when she started to industrialize? The issue of "initial conditions" is frequently raised by economists when they consider the possibilities of economic development in currently backward areas. Often there is the feeling that the Western experience with industrialization is only of highly limited applicability because pre-industrial economic levels in Europe were much higher. These are complex problems, and the lack of data rarely allows quantitative analysis. In the case of Japanese agriculture, however, it may be possible to say something about the initial stages with the aid of productivity figures. At this time, of course, agriculture was the most important sector in the economy and therefore represents quite well the average economic level.

Let us look at levels of productivity prevailing in Asia today, and those which prevailed in Japan during the Meiji Era. The *Yearbook of Food and Agricultural Statistics* (1957) of the FAO cites the following national paddy yield averages for 1954–56 in bushels/hectare: China (Taiwan) 134.2, China (Mainland) 121.0, Malaya 98.5, Indonesia 84.8, Burma 74.5, Thailand 66.1, India 63.7, Philippines 58.8, and Japan 208.7. We know that Japanese paddy field yields were approximately 63 bushels/hectare in 1878–82, and it seems safe to assume that yields fluctuated between 60 and 70 bushels/hectare in the first decade of

[30] It may be of interest to make a few comparisons with the most recent and important case of agricultural take-off in Asia: the experience of Communist China. This has become possible with the recent authoritative study by Choh-Ming Li, *Economic Development of Communist China* (Berkeley: University of California Press, 1958). He shows that in 1956, 40 percent of China's NNP was produced by agriculture (p. 110). Japan had reached nearly the same level by 1908–12 (Ohkawa and Others, p. 26), but China descended from 49.7 percent to 40.0 percent in four years, while this took Japan about fifteen years. The current ratio of net to gross output in Chinese agriculture is around 74 percent. This is roughly equivalent to the Japanese level in 1942 (Li, pp. 86–87, and Ohkawa and others, p. 64). These differences seem largely due to the greater degree of mechanization in present Chinese practice. Li estimates the food grain output growth rate to be about the same as that of population, i.e. 2.5 percent annually (p. 72). We have already shown that the pre-World War I rates in Japan were on the same level *with much lower population growth.* No simple analogy can be attempted between Meiji Japan and Communist China. It is, however, quite clear that the social costs of Japanese development were lower. Similar growth of output was achieved without collectivizations, communes, and other social strains.

Meiji.[31] In other words, the level of rice farming land productivity at the beginning of Japanese economic development was similar to the current levels of Southeast Asia. It is reasonable to suppose that this was also true for labor productivity.

It is much more difficult to compare Japanese and Western productivity levels during the initial phases of development because the main crops were different. It is, however, plausible to suppose that average labor productivity was much higher in the West. Two main reasons may be given: the man-land ratio was much more favorable throughout Europe, and, for the most part, agricultural revolutions had preceded industrial revolutions.

We can now summarize the conditions of Japanese agriculture during the initial stages of industrialization by underlining two distinctive features: a very unfavorable man-land ratio and a relatively low level of labor productivity, implying a low level of general economic performance. Japan shared these features with most Asian countries, which as a group stood in contrast to average European conditions.

A second point which can explain the differences between the tempo of sectoral change in Japan and in the West involves the speedy progress of Japanese agriculture before World War I. This has already been described in some detail, but a few comparative points may be raised now. We hesitated to label these events an "agricultural revolution" because technical innovations did not bring about a change in the structure of the producing unit. On the other hand, it is worth noticing that changes in agriculture took place at a speedy rate, comparable perhaps to the most speedy rates of Europe. It is not possible to produce the statistics which would allow us to raise these statements from the level of assertion to the level of fact. Nevertheless, consulting such data as are available, we believe that the fastest growth rates of agricultural output and productivity in Europe hardly ever exceeded 2 and 1.5 percent per year respectively.[32] If so, one may call the Japanese case revolutionary progress.

[31] See relevant years of *Nōshōmushō tōkeihyō*.

[32] We have made some rough calculations of the annual growth rates of real net product per man for several Western countries. Using data supplied by E. Ojala in *Agriculture and Economic Progress* (London: Oxford University Press, 1952), taking an average beginning and terminal period and assuming a compound growth between these two points, we get the following annual average growth rates: U.S.A. (1869–78-1909–18) 1.0; U.K. (1867–69-1904–10) 0.6; Sweden (1861–65-1906–10) 1.6. Colin Clark in *The Conditions of Economic Progress* (3d edition; London: Macmillan and Co., Ltd., 1957), chapter V, shows somewhat different results: U.S.A. (1870–1910) 1.6; U.K. (1860–1930) 0.7; Sweden (1860–1930) 2.4; France (1815–1870) 2.4. It should be understood, however, that Clark's annual growth rates must be higher than ours because of certain conceptual differences. We used net product per man throughout, while he used either gross product per man (France) or net product per man-hour (Sweden, U.K., and U.S.A.).

Thirdly, it has already been observed that revolutionary progress in Japanese agriculture occurred not before but side by side with industrialization. This was not the typical European sequence. The concurrent and rapid changes in Japanese agriculture and industry suggest to us the possibilities of a peculiar and interesting model of economic growth. It would have to emphasize several key relations observed in Japan: an increasing trend in the subsistence level of the peasantry, increasing real wages in the industrial sector, almost balanced growth of output in agriculture and industry, high rates of saving and investment, and low capital coefficients. In the model, agriculture would perform the crucial functions of supplying output, net increments of the labor force, and a large share of savings, all in an institutional framework of entrepreneurial landlordism and a paternal government. A model of this type could, when compared to Western experience, clarify the *role* of Japanese agriculture in economic development seen in an international setting. We must, however, postpone further development of these ideas for another time, except insofar as they relate directly to the topic of this paper, namely the changing position of agriculture before and after World War I.

The concurrence of rapid agricultural and economic development resulted in an unusual juxtaposition of sectoral growth rates. Just as industry was hitting its peak, agriculture went into a decline. In some sense the revolutionary developments in agriculture were short-lived, and this can be explained in terms of two major causes.

If we date the beginnings of Japanese economic growth in the 1870's —and for certain purposes this is perfectly legitimate—then the period of rapid agricultural expansion lasted less than fifty years. This view, however, fails to consider the fact that the groundwork for progress in agriculture, as distinguished from the other sectors, started at a much earlier date. The achievements of agriculture before World War I are part of a long chain of events beginning in the eighteenth century.[33] The unit of production, the system of tenure, and many other characteristics can all be traced back to the Tokugawa Era. A certain production potential existed at the time of the Restoration, and the introduction of some modern methods, the intensification of selected beneficial traditional methods, minimum fixed capital requirements, and a very dynamic economic climate, all help to account for the increases in output and productivity. But once this potential had been exploited within the inherited institutional framework and with almost unchanged factor proportions, further progress became much more difficult. By 1918, the traditional setting and rigid unit of production had become a limiting factor to further development.

Another reason for the rather short spurt of agricultural output and

[33] See Smith, *Agrarian Origins*

productivity is related to the general pattern of Japanese economic development. It must, however, be considered in conjunction with a few exogenous factors. The spurt of industrialization which started during World War I, efforts to cope with severe international competition abroad, enforced heavy industrialization in preparation for war in the 1930's—all these economic influences pressed the relative income share of agriculture into a less important place. These tendencies were reinforced by a factor which can only be called paradoxical. In spite of their very rapid expansion, the non-agricultural sectors grew barely sufficiently to absorb increases in the labor force produced by agriculture. This has meant that just before World War II an unfavorable man-land ratio of the Asian type, with which Japan originally started, still existed, and that rapid industrialization and urbanization had not succeeded in significantly decreasing the absolute agricultural population. In turn, this limited the possibilities of technical progress in agriculture.

There are signs that some of these conditions have changed in the postwar years, and one can already recognize a new wave of development in Japanese agriculture following the land reform. Once again, however, the much more rapid growth of the industrial sector poses difficult problems for the future.

3. Agriculture in Regional Economic Growth*

DOUGLASS C. NORTH

I

Despite the existence of a few dissenters there seems to be agreement amongst many economists that agriculture contributes little to economic growth. The argument has developed along two lines: The first equates economic growth with an industrial revolution and argues that a "take off" into industrialization "fails to occur mainly because the comparative advantage of exploiting productive land and other natural

* From the *Journal of Farm Economics*, vol. 51, pp. 943–951, December, 1959. Reprinted by permission of the American Farm Economic Association and the author. The theme of this article is discussed in more detail in the author's *The Economic Growth of the United States: 1790–1860*, Prentice Hall, Inc., Englewood Cliffs, N.J., 1961. The author is professor of economics at the University of Washington.

resources delays the time when self-reinforcing industrial growth can profitably get under way.[1] The argument stems from the classic view of diminishing returns in agriculture, the greater productivity of manufacturing and the difficulties associated with the shift of resources into secondary activities when diminishing returns obtain.[2]

The second argument is quite different and indeed stems from different theoretical underpinnings.[3] It has been most cogently stated by Professor Theodore Schultz as the following hypothesis: "(1) Economic development occurs in a specific locational matrix; there may be one or more such matrices in a particular economy. This means that the process of economic growth does not necessarily occur in the same way, at the same time, or at the same rate in different locations. (2) These locational matrices are primarily industrial-urban in composition; as centers in which economic development occurs, they are not mainly out in rural or farming areas although some farming areas are situated more favorably than are others in relation to such centers. (3) The existing economic organization works best at or near the center of a particular matrix of economic development and it also works best in those parts of agriculture which are situated favorably in relation to such a center; and it works less satisfactorily in those parts of agriculture which are situated at the periphery of such a matrix."[4] This hypothesis in effect states that it is industrial development which is the prime mover in economic growth and that agriculture is a dependent variable in the overall pattern of industrial urban growth.

I find parts of both hypotheses attractive and indeed there is abundant evidence to support particular illustrations that add weight to them.[5] Yet neither will stand generalization either in historical application or as policy guides in contemporary problems of economic growth. In this paper I shall argue that the successful production of agricultural (or indeed most extractive) commodities for sale without the region can be and under certain conditions has been the prime influence inducing

[1] W. W. Rostow, "The Takeoff into Self-sustained Economic Growth," *The Economic Journal,* Vol. LXVI, March, 1956, p. 28.

[2] The whole stage sequency of regional growth implicitly accepts this argument. See E. M. Hoover and J. Fisher, "Research in Regional Economic Growth" in *Problems in the Study of Economic Growth* (New York: National Bureau of Economic Research, 1949).

[3] The notion of diminishing returns is conspicuously absent. It is imperfections in the factor market rather than a relatively fixed factor supply which is strategic to the argument.

[4] Theodore Schultz, *The Economic Organization of Agriculture* (New York: McGraw-Hill, 1953) p. 147.

[5] See Rostow, *op. cit.* for supporting evidence. In connection with the United States, however, see my critical note, "A Note on Professor Rostow's 'Take-off' into Self-sustained Economic Growth," *The Manchester School,* January, 1958. In connection with Schultz's thesis see Anthony Tang, *Economic Development in the Southern Piedmont 1860–1950* (Chapel Hill: University of North Carolina Press, 1958).

economic growth, the development of external economies, urbanization, and eventually industrial development.

The argument baldly stated is as follows: (1) Specialization and division of labor have been the most important factor in the initial expansion of regions. (2) Production of goods for sale without the region has induced this specialization and (3) involvement in the developing international economy (or national in the case of some regions in the United States) of the past two centuries has been the way by which regions and nations have accomplished economic development. The argument is of course the classic one of Adam Smith as succinctly restated recently in the title of an article by George Stigler, "The Division of Labor is Limited by the Extent of the Market."[6] While I have no quarrel with Schultz that manufactured goods (and particularly fabricated as contrasted with processed goods) have enjoyed the most rapid expansion in demand in recent U.S. economic history, in contrast to the income inelasticity in demand for farm goods, the expanding demand for agricultural goods in the 19th century and the prospects for many primary commodities in world agriculture in the present century make the case of the United States (and some other industrial nations) in recent years atypical. Whether we look at Denmark between 1865–1900,[7] the Pacific Northwest between 1880–1920,[8] the Canadian economy between 1900–1913[9] or indeed any of a myriad of other possible illustrations, it has been the expansion from one or more agricultural commodities which has been the prime mover in initiating expansion. Since I have discussed the role of export industries in promoting regional economic growth in an earlier article in the *Journal of Political Economy*, an extended discussion here is unnecessary.[10] However, my original argument was incomplete. While the expansion of an export industry is a necessary condition for regional growth it is not a sufficient one. I should like to take this opportunity to elaborate the argument before returning to a specific rebuttal of the two hypotheses outlined above.

II

The first step in the analysis of regional economic growth consists of an exploration of the determinants of the export sector of the region.

[6] *Journal of Political Economy*, Vol. LIX, June 1951, pp. 185–193.

[7] A. J. Youngson, *The Possibilities of Economic Progress* (Cambridge, The University Press, 1959), pp. 191–230.

[8] See the brief description in my article "Location Theory and Regional Economic Growth," *Journal of Political Economy*, Vol. LXIII, June, 1955.

[9] G. M. Meier, "Economic Development and the Transfer Mechanism," *Canadian Journal of Economics and Political Science*, XIX, Feb., 1953.

[10] In addition to the original article, "Location Theory and Regional Economic Growth," *loc. cit.*, see the discussion with Charles Tiebout in the same *Journal*, Vol. LXIV, No. 2, April, 1955, pp. 160–69.

However, a necessary additional step is to examine the disposition of the income received from without the region. Certainly one of the perplexing problems in the study of economic growth has been the differential progress as amongst different regions resulting from an increment to income from the export sector. Why does one area remain tied to a single export staple while another diversifies its production and becomes an urbanized, industrialized region? Regions that remained tied to a single export commodity almost inevitably do not achieve sustained expansion. Not only will there be a slowing down in the rate of growth in the industry which will adversely affect the region, but the very fact that it remains tied to a single export industry will mean that specialization and diversion of labor are limited outside that industry. Historically it has meant that a larger share of the populace has remained outside the market economy. The answer lies (a) in the natural endowments of the region (at any given level of technology), (b) in the character of the export industry, and (c) in changes in technology and transfer costs. It is worthwhile to examine each of these in turn.

The natural endowments of the region dictate the initial export commodities of the area. If these endowments are such as to result in a tremendous comparative advantage in one commodity over any other, then the immediate consequence will be for resources to concentrate upon its production. If, on the other hand, the region has broad production possibilities such that the rate of return upon the production of a number of goods and services is not too much less than upon the initial export commodity, then with the growth of the region and accompanying change in factor proportions the production of other goods and services is likely to be a simple process.

The character of the export commodity in influencing regional growth is more complicated since there are several facets to it. A number of important consequences stem from the technological nature of the production function. If the export commodity is a "plantation" type commodity which is relatively labor intensive and in which there are significant increasing returns to scale, then the development will be in marked contrast to one in which the export commodity may be produced most efficiently on a family-size farm with relatively less absolute amounts of labor required.[11] In the first case there will tend to result an extremely unequal distribution of income with the bulk of the population devoting most of their income to foodstuff and simple necessities (much of which may be self-sufficient production). At the other end of the income scale, the plantation owners will tend to spend most of their income upon luxury

---

[11] This argument has been explored by R. E. Baldwin in some detail. See "Patterns of Development in Newly Settled Regions," *The Manchester School of Economic and Social Studies*, Vol. XXIV, No. 2, May 1956, pp. 161–79.

EDITOR'S NOTE: See Selection 16.

consumption goods which will be imported. In short, there will be little encouragement of residentiary types of economic activity. With the more equitable distribution of incomes, there is a demand for a broad range of goods and services, part of which will be residentiary, thus inducing investment in other types of economic activities. There will tend to develop trading centers to provide a wide variety of such goods and services, in contrast to the plantation economy which will merely develop a few urban areas devoted to the export of the staple commodity and the distribution of imports.

A natural consequence of the divergent patterns described in the previous paragraph will be the attitude towards investment in knowledge.[12] Under the plantation type with very unequal income distribution, the planter will be extremely reluctant to devote his tax monies to expenditures for education or research other than that related to the staple commodity. As a consequence skills and knowledge not directly related to the export commodity will be at a low level. In contrast, the region with more equitable income distribution will be well aware of the stake in improving its comparative position through education and research and will accordingly be willing to devote public expenditures in these directions. The result will be to relatively improve its comparative position in a variety of types of economic activity and therefore broaden the resultant economic base.

Equally important is the investment induced by the export commodity or service. If the export is such as to require substantial investment in transport, warehousing, port facilities and other types of social overhead investment, then the external economies are created which facilitate the development of other exports. Furthermore, if the export industry induces growth of subsidiary industries and if technology, transport costs and resource endowments permit these to be locally produced rather than imported, then this will induce further development. Both in the case of social overhead investment and investment in subsidiary industry the consequence is to promote urbanization and increased specialization and development of additional residentiary activity geared to the increasing local demand for consumption goods and services. At the other extreme is the export industry which requires only the immediate development of a few centers for the collection and export of the commodity and entails the development of little subsidiary industry or perhaps entails the development of such subsidiary industry and marketing facilities, but they are of a nature to be most efficiently imported.[13]

Changes in technology and transport may completely alter the region's

[12] I am in Professor Schultz's debt for focusing my attention on this problem in the course of a series of very stimulating discussions this past Spring.

[13] In part at least, therefore, the development of subsidiary industry depends upon the first point discussed above, the natural endowments of the region.

comparative advantage either favorably or unfavorably.[14] Technological change may increase the potential rate of return in the production of other goods and services and lead to the exploitation of new resources and a shift of resources away from the old export industry. The initial development of transportation facilities to implement the export industry tends to reinforce dependence upon it and inhibit more diversified economic activity in several ways. The early development of transport typically (under competitive conditions) leads to a rapid fall in the transport rate and therefore increases the comparative advantage of the export commodity.[15] Moreover, with newly settled regions the transportation is typically one way, the outward shipment of a bulky product having no counterpart in the inward shipment which must be made mostly empty or in ballast. In consequence, inward freights are very low and compete with locally produced goods. As a result a good deal of local industry which had been protected by high transport costs or might develop if high transport costs continued, faces effective competition from imports.[16] In summary the disposition of income earned from export industry plays a decisive role in the growth of the region. Related to this argument is the region's propensity to import. To the extent that a region's income directly flows out in the purchase of goods and services rather than having a regional multiplier-accelerator effect,[17] then it is inducing growth elsewhere, but reaping few of the benefits of increased income from the export sector itself.

Let me briefly illustrate the argument of the preceding pages by contrasting the economic structure of the South and the West in the years prior to the Civil War.[18]

Both regions enjoyed a thriving export trade in the years between the end of the second war with England and the Civil War. The cotton trade of the South accounted for more than half of total U.S. exports during the period, with rice, sugar and tobacco as subsidiary commodity exports. The value of cotton exports alone increased from $17.5 million in 1815 to $191.8 million in 1860. The West enjoyed an expanding trade in wheat and corn and derivatives thereof (pork, bacon, lard, flour, whisky) first

[14] A further discussion of this point is to be found in my article, "Location Theory and Regional Economic Growth," *loc. cit.*, pp. 254–56.

[15] See my article "Ocean Freight Rates and Economic Development 1750–1913," *The Journal of Economic History*, December, 1958, for a discussion on this point.

[16] The early sanguine hopes of Gallatin and Tench Coxe rested upon the burgeoning development of manufacturing during the Embargo, as reported in the 1810 census. This production, in good part for the local market, was completely unable to compete with imports following the end of the 2nd War with England.

[17] See J. S. Dusenberry, "Some Aspects of the Theory of Economic Development," *Explorations in Entrepreneurial History*, Vol. III, No. 2, December 1950.

[18] This very brief account is a summary from two chapters of my *The Economic Growth of the United States: 1790–1860* (Prentice-Hall, Inc., Englewood Cliffs, N.J., 1961).

with the South and then increasingly after the mid 1840's with the Northeast and Europe. However, at this point their similarity ends. Let me point up the contrasts.

1. The South was characterized by its concentrated production for the market of a single export staple with a comparative advantage so great that even in periods of low cotton prices, resources could not receive an equal return from alternative types of economic activity. The West had no overwhelming comparative advantage in a single commodity but rather branched out into mining (lead in Missouri, copper in Michigan and iron at Pittsburgh) and various kinds of processing.

2. Large scale organization typified the southern plantation and a resultant extremely unequal pattern of income distribution reinforced, of course, by the institution of slavery. Wheat and corn in the West could be produced most efficiently on the "family size farm" given early 19th century technology. In consequence the pattern of consumer demand was markedly different. The South was almost totally lacking in urban development during the period (with the exception of New Orleans which served as an entrepôt for western foodstuff for the southern planter and as a port for cotton exports), and its states were conspicuously at the bottom of the list of retail stores per thousand population in the 1840 census. A large percentage of the South's population remained outside the market economy. In contrast small community centers dotted the West to serve the local populace and served as nuclei for residentiary industry and trade and services. While these early developed to serve local consumer needs, with the gradual expansion of the market and the development of external economies many came to serve an increasingly large area and become export industries. With each surge of expansion in the West (1816–18, 1832–39, 1849–57), an increasing percentage of western farmers shifted out of self-sufficiency and became a part of the market economy.

A further consequence of these contrasting structures was the differential investment in education. The South had the highest illiteracy rate (as a percentage of the white population), the lowest ratio of pupils to (white) population, and the smallest number of libraries. Even western states that were just emerging from the pioneer stage were conspicuously higher than the South in educational investment.[19]

3. Little additional investment was necessary for the efficient export of southern cotton. Neither transportation development nor extensive subsidiary industry were required. The Factor with his ties with northern credit and shipping served as both the exporter of the planter's cotton, and importer of his foodstuff (from the West) and manufactures (from the Northeast and Europe). Large scale investment in the South was

[19] For interesting figures on investment in knowledge see H. R. Helper, *The Impending Crisis of the South* (New York: A. P. Burdick, 1860), pp. 144, 288–89.

devoted solely to the opening up of new cotton lands and the acquisition of slaves. Extensive investment in transportation (as well as other facilities to implement the export of goods) was essential to opening up the West. Moreover, there were important locational advantages to processing wheat and corn products into flour, corn meal, ham, bacon, salt pork, lard, and whisky within the region rather than without. In consequence a variety of such manufacturing grew up and promoted urban development in the West.

4. The unique characteristics of the ocean freight trade which resulted in one-way cargoes from the cotton ports resulted in back hauls of manufactured goods being imported into the cotton region at very low rates. As a result there was no protection for local consumer oriented industries from the cheap imports of the Northeast and Europe. In contrast manufactures had to come to the West either over land or via the long route back up the Mississippi, and the protection thereby assisted the early development of consumer oriented industries in the West.

Is this purely historical argument with little relevance for the contemporary scene? I think not. The special institution of slavery like the special characteristics of land tenure systems is capable of being examined in terms of economic analysis and we only beg analytical answers by retreating to the institution per se as an explanation.[20] The characteristics described above go far to explain the differential success of regional economies in the contemporary world. A positive restatement of the thesis elaborated above is that the development of a successful agricultural export industry will result in an increase in income to the region, and under the favorable conditions outlined above will lead to:

(1) Specialization and division of labor with a widening of the regional market;

(2) The growth of facilities and subsidiary industry to efficiently produce and market the export commodity;

(3) The development of residentiary industry to serve local consumers, some of which may, in consequence of expanding markets and external economies developed in association with the export industry, lead to a broadening in the export base;

(4) As a natural consequence of the above conditions, the growth of urban areas and facilities;

(5) An expanded investment in education and research to broaden the region's potential.

Under these circumstances, a good deal of industrial development will occur naturally as a consequence of the conditions described above. Indeed as the regional market increases in size, more and more manufacturing firms will find it feasible to establish branch plants there.

[20] See A. H. Conrad and J. A. Meyer, "The Economics of Slavery in the Ante-Bellum South," *The Journal of Political Economy*, Vol. LXVI, No. 2, April 1958.

Where the unfavorable conditions outlined above obtain, then there is room for effective governmental policy to modify them. The alteration of land tenure systems (which should not be done at the expense of productivity, however) and the redirection of public expenditure into research, technology, and education promise to yield very handsome returns.[21]

III

Let me point up the differences between the argument advanced in this paper and the two hypotheses of Professors Rostow and Schultz. My argument with Rostow is, I think, the more fundamental. Rostow's thesis is, in effect, the same as one presented at the annual meetings of this Association in 1951 by Professor J. K. Galbraith in a paper entitled "Conditions for Economic Change in Underdeveloped Countries."[22] Growth is associated with industrialization and stagnation with agriculture. It is my contention that this misses the whole problem of economic change and reflects a basic misreading of the economic history of the past two centuries.[23] Involvement in the larger market economies, despite the evident hazards entailed, has been the classic way by which regional economies have expanded. It has resulted in specialization, external economies, the development of residentiary industry, and the growth of vertical "dis-integration" as a result of the widening of the market to which Professor Stigler rightly attributes a good deal of the increase of manufacturing productivity.[24] I have made clear in the previous section the factors that can prevent successful regional expansion, but it should also be clear that these are not synonymous with agriculture per se.

My quarrel with Professor Schultz is not over the application of his "retardation hypothesis" to the contemporary American Scene, but rather with his contention that economic history strongly supports his argument that economic development has taken place in primarily industrial-urban matrices.[25] I don't think that the 19th century economic history of the Midwest from 1815–1860, the Pacific Northwest from 1880–1920, or even California from 1848–1900 (where it was first the impetus of mining and then agriculture) supports his argument. There is certainly not the space in this paper to explore the relative shifts in demand and supply, and the income elasticities, which make for the difference of opinion, and indeed

---

[21] See Arnold C. Harberger, "Using the Resources at Hand More Effectively," *Proceedings of the American Economic Association*, May 1959, pp. 134–46.

[22] *Journal of Farm Economics, Proceedings*, Nov. 1951, pp. 689–96.

[23] See A. J. Youngson, *Possibilities of Economic Progress* (Cambridge: The University Press, 1959), for evidence from the economic history of four regions to support this argument.

[24] Stigler, *op. cit.*, p. 190.

[25] Schultz, *op. cit.*, p. 147.

it is not necessary at this point since the facts of the matter are that these (and other U.S.) regions grew up, developed urban centers, external economies, and manufacturing in consequence of a successful agricultural export trade. I have no quarrel with Professor Schultz's argument with respect to imperfections in the factor market and the importance of investment in human capital, and indeed I believe that they fit in very well with the argument I made in the previous section of this paper. I would simply argue that a successful agricultural export trade can and has induced urbanization, improvements in the factor markets, and a more effective allocation of investment funds.

In conclusion I should like to restate the positive position that the relevant problems of regional economic development revolve around the issues raised in the main body of this paper. They are not issues of agriculture versus industrialization but rather revolve around a region's ability to become integrated into the larger markets of the world through exports, and of the resultant structure of the regional economy which will influence its ability to achieve sustained growth and a diversified pattern of economic activity.

4. The Share of Agriculture in a Growing Population*

FOLKE DOVRING

It has become almost axiomatic nowadays that a highly-developed economy should have only a small proportion of its population engaged in agriculture. The relatively low demand elasticity of most foodstuffs and the advantages of specialization are now common knowledge, to the extent that it is regarded as self-evident that expanding secondary and tertiary sectors of the economy are a condition for economic progress. The facts seem to underscore this, since practically all the economically less developed countries are predominantly agricultural and all the most highly developed ones have only a small sector of their population engaged in agriculture or depending upon it for their livelihood.

There seems to be no need at present to re-examine these assumptions. It is interesting, however, to discuss the circumstances under which a

* From *Monthly Bulletin of Agricultural Economics and Statistics,* vol. 8, pp. 1–11, FAO, Rome, August-September, 1959. Reprinted by permission of the author. The author is professor of agricultural economics at the University of Illinois.

speedy shift in the industrial structure of a country may take place. This issue is crucial for development economics; many of those working in this field seem to be convinced that one of the primary requisites for developing a less developed country is to reduce its agricultural population.

This proposition embodies two elements. Reducing the *relative* role of agriculture in the industrial or occupational structure of a country is a direct corollary of expanding other industries faster than population growth, which is an inevitable consequence of any increasing specialization within the economy. Such a process is therefore almost by definition a part of economic development, except in countries which have vast expanses of virgin land, a situation that was more common a hundred years ago than it is now. The second element of the proposition, and the more radical one, is to seek a reduction in the *absolute* numbers working in agriculture, as one condition for raising the productivity of those who stay in farming, as well as of the community at large. It is of some importance for our general thinking on economic development of the less developed countries to analyze these two propositions, and particularly the latter. What they imply in each country under the conditions the planner is confronted with, is of course of fundamental importance in any case of economic planning.

The two propositions would be identical if the population were stagnant. In this case, a change in the industrial structure would consist merely in transfer of people from one activity or livelihood to another. Such a situation is, however, exceptional nowadays. In almost all countries the population is growing; in most of the less developed ones it is growing rapidly. Expansion of nonagricultural activities does not therefore in itself imply any reduction of the agricultural population, either relatively or absolutely. How far it means a change in the proportions between the main sectors of the economy depends on the relation between the rate of expansion of nonagricultural activities and the rate of population growth.

DYNAMICS OF CHANGE

The conditions for such a change in the sector proportions can best be discussed if the nonagricultural sectors are regarded as the dynamic element which expands its employment at par with the build-up of productive capital. Agriculture is then assumed constantly to have a surplus of manpower, the size of which is residual. These assumptions are used in the present context for the purpose of elucidation, without overlooking existant examples to the contrary.

By simple arithmetic deduction, two rules of thumb can be established:

(*a*) When nonagricultural employment grows faster than total labor force, its percentage share in total labor force will increase at a rate which is the difference between the growth rates of nonagricultural and total labor force.[1] For instance, if total population grows by 1 percent per year, and nonagricultural population by 2 percent, then the percentage share of the latter will go up by 1 percent per year (for instance, from 20 to 20.2 or from 50 to 50.5 percent, and so on).

(*b*) If the agricultural population is assumed to remain stable (that is, without increase in absolute numbers), then the nonagricultural population should increase at a rate equal to the rate of population growth, multiplied by the denominator in the fractional number for nonagricultural over total population. This rate would be variable. For instance, if total population increases by 1.5 percent per year and the nonagricultural sectors employ one fourth of the total, they would have to increase by 6 percent per year to begin with, gradually declining to 3 percent when the 50 percent position were reached, and so on.

The former of these rules of thumb provides a convenient measure for the speed of sector changes. A given rate of growth of the nonagricultural sectors in excess of population growth thus releases change in the sector proportions at a constant rate, independently of the population growth to which it is added. This factor can therefore be termed the coefficient of *differential* growth and used for comparing the speed of change in sector proportions between countries at different stages of development.

The rule under (*b*) implies that, on the whole, a reduction in the absolute numbers working in and living from agriculture is most difficult to achieve when the agricultural population is a large majority, but it becomes increasingly easy to reach when the share of other industries has become larger. If, as is most probable, the growth of industries and tertiary activities takes the form of a more or less straight logarithmic series, then the changes in the agricultural population will form a curve, rising in the beginning and going down at later stages.

Data on such changes can preferably be presented in absolute numbers. In Figures 1 to 6 they are laid out on a semilogarithmic scale (time series on a natural scale and number series on a logarithmic scale).

Data of this nature, which cover a long period of time, are on the whole available from the now industrialized countries. The experience of these countries is of course not applicable, without further evidence, to the future of the less developed countries. Nor is a changed distribu-

---

[1] If the growth of labor force is different from that of total population, for instance because of changes in life expectancy and median age, or of the participation rate of women and children, etc., then it may be necessary to keep apart the rates of growth referring to manpower and total population. In the long run, of course, the result will be more or less the same, whichever definitions are used.

tion of people among industries or occupations in itself conducive to higher production, though it is a very important element in such a process. But the pattern of employment by industry or occupation is one of the chief elements and one which is relatively easy to analyze separately from other factors. A shift in the industrial structure toward smaller numbers in farming is, moreover, not only an element of change of production but also of demand, and therefore a stimulus to those who remain in farming. A comparative study of the process in a number of developed countries is therefore likely to facilitate the understanding of the process in general and its application in the less developed countries.

THE SPEED OF POPULATION INCREASE

Data from four groups of countries are presented in Figures 1 to 5.[2] Before discussing the graphs in some detail, it may be useful to recall that these countries have, on the whole, had a slower population in-

[2] When comparison is made only between the agricultural sector on the one hand and all other sectors on the other, the difference between industrial and occupational classification of workers is of small importance. The difference of structure between labor force and total population dependent on a certain activity is in some cases more significant, but data by both criteria cannot be always obtained. The data are borrowed from current national statistics, complemented from the following additional sources:

Great Britain: Ch. Booth. 1886. "Occupations of the people of the United Kingdom 1801–81," *Journal of the Royal Statistical Society;* Lord Eversley. 1907. "The decline in number of agricultural labourers in Great Britain." *Ibid.; Agricultural Tribunal of Investigation, Final Report,* London, 1924. Up to 1880, the chart shows only male workers aged 20 and over.

Belgium: G. Bublot. 1957. *La production agricole belge, Etude séculaire 1846–1955,* Louvain.

Denmark: H. Gad. 1956. *Befolknings—og Arbejdskraftproblemer i dansk Landbrug,* Copenhagen.

Italy: U. Giusti. 1943. *Caratteristiche ambientali italiane, argrarie, sociali, demografiche, 1815–1942,* Rome.

France: Mme. Cahen. "Evolution de la population active en France depuis cent ans d'après les dénombrements quinquennaux." *Etudes et conjoncture, Economie française,* No. 3, 1953; Lucchi. "Evolution de la population active entre 1906 et 1954." *Etudes statistiques, Supplément trimestriel du Bulletin mensuel de statistique,* No. 3, 1956.

Spain: "La población activa española de 1900 a 1957." 1958. *Estudios hispanicos de desarrollo económico,* Mongrafía No. 1 (Instituto de cultura hispanica), Madrid.

U.S.S.R.: A. G. Rashin. 1956. *Naselenie Rossii za 100 let (1811–1913),* Moscow; S. G. Strumilin. 1957. *Problemy ekonomiki truda,* Moscow.

Japan: S. Tōbata and S. Kawano. 1956. *Economics and Agriculture in Japan (in Japanese),* Vol. 2, Tokyo.

Data on labor force and industrial structure in several other countries are brought together in C. Clark, 1957, *The Conditions of Economic Progress,* 3 ed., pp. 510 sqq.

crease than that of the world today. This is true not only of Western Europe in recent decades but also of nineteenth century Europe. The following data refer to the compound rate annual growth of total population, generalized on 50-year periods. Further detail is reflected in Figures 1 to 5.

TABLE 1. LONG-TERM RATES OF ANNUAL POPULATION GROWTH, SELECTED COUNTRIES

Country	1800–1850	1850–1900	1900–1950
	Percentage		
Great Britain............	1.4	1.1	0.6
Belgium................	...	0.8	0.5
Netherlands.............	...	1.1	1.3
Switzerland.............	...	0.6	0.7
Denmark...............	0.9	1.1	1.0
Norway................	0.9	0.9	0.8
Sweden................	0.8	0.8	0.6
Finland................	1.3	1.0	0.8
France.................	0.5	0.2	0.2
Italy..................	0.6	0.6	0.6
Spain..................	0.6	0.5	0.8
Portugal...............	0.4	0.7	0.9
United States...........	3.0	2.4	1.4
U.S.S.R...............	1.2	1.4	0.8
Japan.................	...	...	1.3

SOURCE: National statistics and literature quoted in footnote 2.

The United States, as an immigration country, had of course exceptional possibilities. Apart from that, the now industrialized countries have only in their period of most vigorous population growth reached the present world average level of 1.5 percent per year. Even faster rates have occurred for shorter periods only, as in Russia during the first decade of the present century. The rates in Great Britain during much of the nineteenth century, or in the Netherlands, Japan and the United States at present, are only on a level with the lower rates occurring in less developed countries, several of which score between 2 and 3 percent per year.

NORTHWESTERN EUROPE

The data from early industrialized countries shown in Figure 1 evidence a relatively late phase in the process. In Great Britain, the abso-

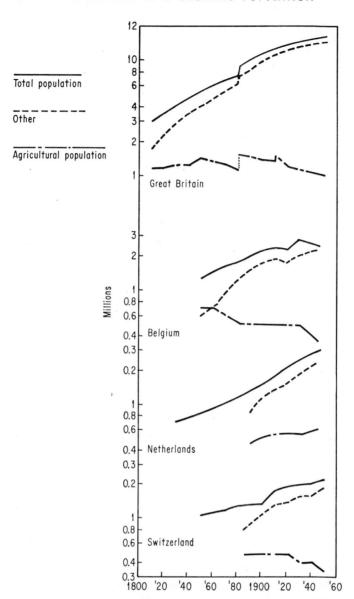

Fɪɢ. 1. Sector changes in early industrialized countries (semilogarithmic scale)
Note: Data refer to the active male population in Great Britain, Belgium, and the
Netherlands and to the active population in Switzerland.

lute numbers working in and living from agriculture have changed rather moderately. There was some increase in the numbers living on the land in the early part of the nineteenth century, partly due to immigration from Ireland. The decline during the sixties and seventies was genuine but moderate, and coincided with a period when farming prospered in Britain. The later decline is partly statistical; in terms of workers aged 20 and over (as in Figure 1, up to 1880) there was almost no decline at all during the decades around 1900. The number of people who live from agriculture in Great Britain was in the vicinity of 3 million at the last census (1951) and somewhere between 3 and 4 million at the beginning of the nineteenth century, while estimates from previous centuries are also of the same magnitude. Great Britain is thus not a case of large-scale depopulation of the countryside; the dwindling of agriculture to a small sector was mainly a process of relative change, when total population more than quintupled in the last century and a half.

Belgium showed a sharper decline in the number of agricultural workers, which now appears to be about half as many as a century ago. However, to some extent this decline is statistical. There was no appreciable change between the first two censuses, and the downward movement may thus have started after the second census (1856). In Switzerland, the decline came much later, after a prolonged period of stability, and has not yet reached the degree of Belgium. In the Netherlands, the agricultural population continued to rise until recently. By inference from the growth of total population, it is likely that this increase of people living from agriculture also went on for several decades prior to 1889. A gradual upward trend in the rate of population increase, and the acquisition of new land from the sea, are the counterpart to this development, which is unique among industrial countries in Europe.

Data from the Scandinavian countries are shown in Figure 2. In these countries, the whole process of industrial change can be followed from the stage of a large agricultural majority to that where the agricultural population is decidedly in a minority. All four countries have had increasing agricultural populations during the early phases of industrialization. In Sweden and Finland, this can be shown by inference from the growth of total population. For example, in Sweden, the agricultural population in 1870 equalled the total population in 1835. Since industries existed all the time, it follows that the agricultural population increased in absolute terms between the years quoted. In these two countries, the decline in absolute terms appears to have started slightly before the crossing of the curves. In the case of Finland, this may be related to the rapid changes following upon the war and the resettling of the population of Carelia. In Sweden, the last part of the nineteenth century was a period of large-scale emigration. There may also have

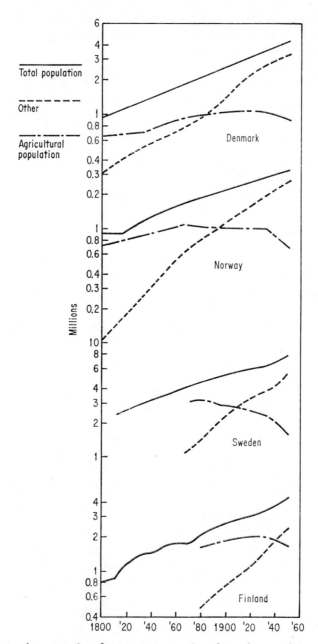

Fɪɢ. 2. Sector changes in Scandinavian countries (semilogarithmic scale)
Note: Data refer to the population as a whole.

been a change in the size of families; in data on male workers in agriculture (which are available only for a considerably shorter period) no decline is seen until after 1930.

It is interesting to note the different speed at which a structural change was achieved. In Denmark, the land reform of the nineteenth century may have contributed to the continued increase of the farming population over a long period. In Norway, with more limited resources for agriculture, and a long-established small family farm structure, the remarkable stability over a long period reflects, in fact, a slight decline in the farming population and a considerable increase of the small minority engaged in fishing. It would seem from these four countries that with a later shift in structure, the tempo has been more accelerated.

CENTRAL AND SOUTHERN EUROPE

France and Southern Europe (Figure 3) form a more heterogeneous group. In France, there was almost no population increase over nearly a century. For a long period this was reflected in slow expansion of industries, while decline in absolute numbers engaged in agriculture did not clearly come to light until after the First World War. According to the latest count, agriculture still appears to employ about half as many workers as a century ago. This decline, again, is partly the result of change in family size and not exclusively due to rural exodus.

Italy had a speedier population increase than France. Nevertheless, it was among the slowest in Europe, a fact which is often overlooked. This was partly due to emigration. Italy has also been a slow industrializer. Over most of the period illustrated in Table 1, the farming population has shown only moderate variations, which may be explained by differences in the statistical criteria. A small decline in recent decades can be localized entirely in Northern Italy, while the South still showed an increase at the latest census (see Figure 4). Spain and Portugal also showed a population increase below European average (partly due to emigration to Latin America), although until recently it had accelerated. The process, reflected in the accompanying graphs, was complex in both countries.

The case of Spain is both dramatic and unusual. Nonagricultural employment more than doubled between 1900 and 1930, at the same time as total population, and the labor force, increased slowly. This resulted in a distinct decline in the number of agricultural workers while the agricultural population was still in the majority. Moreover, this process was very unevenly distributed over the regions of Spain. After 1930, the trend was reversed, and only recently has lost ground been recovered. Portugal, with general and demographic conditions similar to those of Spain, appears to show a less pronounced variant of the same pattern. An early industrialization wave at the beginning of the century was fol-

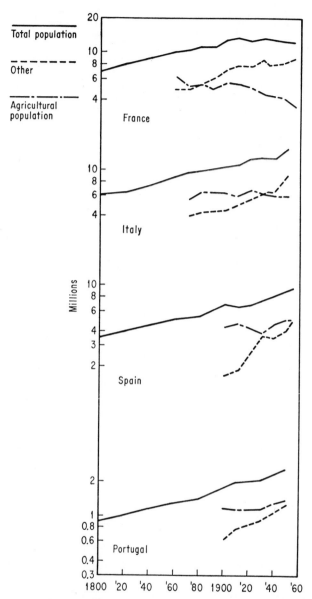

FIG. 3. Sector changes in France and Southern Europe (semilogarithmic scale)
Note: Data refer to the active male population.

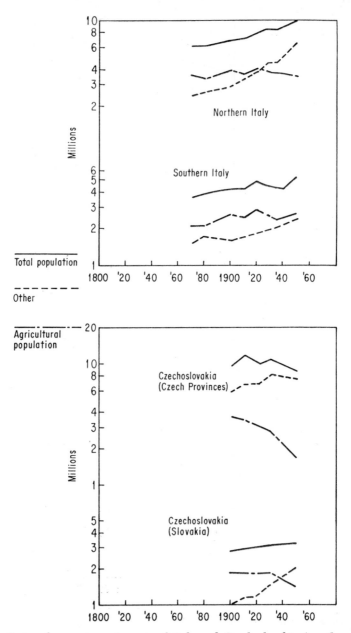

Fɪɢ. 4. Sector changes in main parts of Italy and Czechoslovakia (semilogarithmic scale)
Note: Data refer to the active male population in Italy, and to the population as a whole in Czechoslovakia.

lowed by a small decline in agricultural manpower (localized in the northern part of the country, i.e., the main emigration area). The following phase of slower expansion of nonagricultural employment was accompanied by an increase in the number of workers engaged in agriculture (up to the last census).

Figure 4 shows data for main regions in Italy and Czechoslovakia. The process of change in Northern Italy has been closer to certain countries of Western Europe. Already in the twenties, the North had a nonagricultural majority, and some decline in the agricultural population started not long after. In Southern Italy, of late, industries and services have also grown faster than total population but not fast enough to cause any decline in the absolute numbers of those working in agriculture. The same 80 years that brought about a radical change in the structure of Northern Italy only changed the share of agriculture in the South from 60 to 52 percent.

The regional contrast within Czechoslovakia is equally salient. In the Czech provinces, which were industrialized about as early as other parts of Central Europe, there has been little population increase in recent decades, even apart from the decline caused by the exodus of the German population. Continued industrial growth therefore could provoke a rapid decline in the agricultural sector. In Slovakia, which was a decidedly rural area at the beginning of the century, the nonagricultural sectors grew as fast, in relative terms, as in the Czech provinces. Industrialization had got a later start; hence, until recently, the agricultural population was still in the majority. The latter sector remained without any decline in absolute numbers until the dramatic changes in the last 10 or 12 years.

THE UNITED STATES, U.S.S.R., AND JAPAN

These data from Western and Central Europe may be supplemented by figures from the three big industrial countries outside these regions: the United States, the U.S.S.R. and Japan (see Figure 5).

The United States has probably had the speediest population increase of any large country throughout the nineteenth century. The agricultural population continued to increase as cultivation expanded over virgin land and long after agricultural pursuits had ceased to occupy the majority of the country's labor force, a shift which occurred around 1880. The recent reduction of the farm population, which is still going on, began only some time after 1910. The numbers living on farms are still about half compared to 1910, and it is only during the 1950s that the number of workers employed in agriculture fell below the 1880 figure. The rapid build-up of nonagricultural employment during the nineteenth

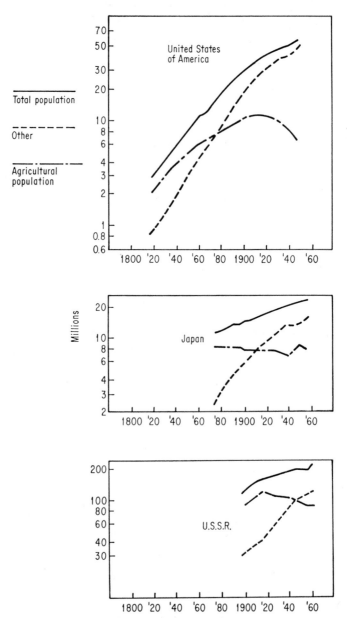

FIG. 5. Sector changes in the United States, the U.S.S.R., and Japan (semilogarithmic scale)
Note: Data refer to the civilian labor force in the United States, to the population as a whole in the U.S.S.R., and to the active male population in Japan.

century came largely from the immigration of urban people from Europe and is therefore only partly a reflection of change within the already settled population of the country.

The process in the U.S.S.R. differed in many respects. The long-term population increase, which had just reached 2 percent per year before the First World War, was radically slowed down as a result of all the events since 1914. Vital statistics indicate an average natural increase over the period since 1913 of not less than 1.5 percent per year. If this had been effective since 1913, the total population by 1956 would have been 300 rather than 200 million. It is of course futile to speculate how the industrialization movement would have developed in such a case. If it is recognized that the industrialization of a country has its main preconditions in the accumulation of capital equipment and skill, then it is perhaps of some significance that the long-term trend of increase in nonagricultural occupations from 1913 to 1956 appears to be very close to the trend between 1897 and 1913. The short-term trend, over the twenties and thirties, is difficult to compare, for several reasons (the chart interpolates straight between 1913 and 1940).

Of the two largest industrial countries today, the United States has had the exceptional advantage of speedy settlement through manpower arriving from the then most developed part of the world, and the U.S.S.R. has pursued the decisive phase of its industrial breakthrough in a period of virtually very slow population increase. The United States can well serve as a model when studying less developed countries of recent settlement, such as certain countries in Latin America, for example. Neither of the two comes very close to a model for discussion of the problems of already densely settled less developed countries faced with problems of rural congestion, such as in Southern Asia.

As regards the latter, the data from Japan (see Figure 5) are more conclusive. In the 1870s the country was as predominantly agricultural as the Scandinavian countries were in the early nineteenth century. By contrast, Japan was already very densely settled by any standards. In absolute terms, the population engaged in agriculture has only declined slightly. The present extreme density of labor on the land, with less than 1 hectare of cropland per male worker in agriculture, thus gives an idea of the population pressure in Japan at that time, when techniques were less developed and yields lower than now. The rate of population increase was not as rapid as it is at present in Southern Asia, the Near East, Africa and Latin America, but the initial density on the land was even higher. The spurt of industrialization was, in relative terms, fastest in the initial phase and has successively slowed down somewhat. The total picture is as vigorous as in the fastest changing countries in Europe. The impact of postwar difficulties, now overcome, is given overdue significance in the figure, owing to a change in the statistical definition of employment in agriculture. As of now, the pull from urban occupations may prove strong enough to cause a decisive reduction in the still extremely high density of people on the land.

THE TEMPO OF CHANGE

Some common features may be deducted from these figures. As would be expected from the arithmetic observations made above, there has normally been increase in absolute numbers living from agriculture in the early phases of industrialization, and a decline only in late periods. Spain appears to be the only country in which there was a decisive decline in the agricultural population while the latter was still the majority in the country. In most of the countries shown, the agricultural population has remained relatively stable over a long period of time and has shown considerable decline in absolute numbers only recently, long after the countries were definitely industrialized.

The reasons for this relative stability of the agricultural populations are complex. They include not only the degree to which urban occupations exercise a "pull" on rural workers in each given situation but also, apart from sociological and psychological factors, include the internal transformation of agriculture as an industry—a transformation which is also closely connected with the changes in the urban sectors. The speed at which workers are absorbed in nonagricultural employment may be discussed by applying the arithmetical rules of thumb given above to the data used for the figures. Table 2 lists data analyzed from those presented in Figures 1, 2, 3 and 5. Medium-term trends are shown for periods of about two to three decades, as data are available. The length of the periods is partly due to the availability of census data, and the periods are so chosen as to represent the phases of most vigorous growth of nonagricultural employment in each country, to the extent that data are available.

With the exception of the United States, none of the countries shown in Table 2 has had a medium-term growth of nonagricultural employment exceeding 3 percent per year. Another exception would have been the U.S.S.R., if the 1928–56 trend could have been shown separately. "Differential" growth rates, as shown in the last column, appear never to have reached 2 percent per year during the periods shown in the table. Moreover, wherever the last column shows high differential rates, about 1.5 percent or more, they have been associated with a slow increase in total population, except in the United States and in Japan (in the early phase).

Doubling the percentage share of nonagricultural employment took a century or more in the early industrialized countries but only about 50–60 years in some of the more recently industrialized ones, such as the

United States, Sweden, Finland and Japan. Another feature which can be illustrated from the above data is the point at which an agricultural population can be expected to start declining, in absolute numbers. For this to take place while this sector is still in the majority, as occurred in Spain and, to a minor extent, in Sweden, Finland, the U.S.S.R. and Japan,

TABLE 2. GROWTH RATES DERIVED FROM DATA IN FIGURES 1, 2, 3 AND 5

Country	Year	Compound-rate annual growth of:		Difference
		Total population	Nonagricultural population and/or employment	
		Percentage		
Great Britain.........	1801–31	1.5	2.1	0.6
Belgium..............	1846–80	0.7	2.1	1.4
Netherlands..........	1899–1930	1.5	2.6	1.1
Switzerland..........	1888–1910	1.1	2.2	1.1
Denmark.............	1855–80	1.0	1.3	0.3
	1880–1911	1.1	2.2	1.1
Norway..............	1865–90	0.7	1.9	1.2
	1890–1920	0.9	1.7	0.8
Sweden..............	1880–1910	0.7	2.2	1.5
	1910–40	0.5	1.3	0.8
Finland..............	1910–40	0.8	2.4	1.6
France..............	1861–91	0.1	0.7	0.6
Italy................	1911–31	0.6	1.3	0.7
	1931–51	0.6	1.6	1.0
Spain...............	1900–30	0.8	2.7	1.9
Portugal............	1900–30	0.8	1.3	0.5
United States........	1850–80	2.6	4.2	1.6
	1880–1910	2.1	3.6	1.5
Japan...............	1890–1915	1.1	2.6	1.5
	1915–40	1.2	1.8	0.6
U.S.S.R.............	1913–56	0.5	2.2	1.7

nonagricultural employment would need to increase more than twice as rapidly as total population, as was also the case in these countries during their early phases of industrialization. The same was true in Norway, where some early decline in agricultural population is concealed by the simultaneous increase in fishermen. The rates in the last column are shown to be higher than those in the first, also in France and Italy, but only in the late phases. The decline would take place close to the 50:50 ratio if the nonagricultural population consistently increased twice as fast as the total population.

EFFECT OF URBANIZATION

There is no particular correlation between the rates shown in columns 1 and 2. Industrial growth is thus neither the effect nor the cause of population increase. As can easily be shown from less developed countries, population increase is, within wide limits, independent of economic growth. Rapid population growth may be a burden or a stimulus to an economy but to what extent it is one or the other can only be concluded by analyzing the economic situation.

The data in Figures 1 to 5 also reflect a certain resistance on the part of the agricultural population to reduction in absolute numbers. Even in phases of advanced industrialization, decline in absolute numbers has on the whole remained moderate up to the present. The reason is not only in the structure of family farms prevalent in several of the countries shown, a structure which has a tendency to retain people beyond the limit of relative advantage against other industries. Such an explanation would have no relevance to Great Britain and would have limited significance in other countries. Apart from other social factors, as well as the protective policies which have aimed at counteracting rural exodus in several industrial countries, there is also increased demand for agricultural products. Growing industries and services mean expanding markets for agricultural products, and particularly those of labor intensive animal husbandry, and of market gardening. Expanding cities have thus tended to create more employment in farming.

In this respect, the experience of Europe is likely to be instructive for the future of many less developed countries. In many of them, more agricultural work will be needed in the future. In certain situations, rural underemployment will therefore become less serious than it is at present, even though there is no reduction in the number of people living on the land. As a result of the relative dwindling of the agricultural sector, which received less than its share of the population increase, the industrialized countries are now—and in most cases only recently—in a situation where agriculture need not retain a large surplus of manpower simply because many people were born into farming. The possibility exists of adjusting the numbers working in agriculture to the technical need for labor. This is one of the conditions for accelerated technical progress in agriculture and a gradual adjustment of rural levels of living to rising urban standards. Though experience seems to show that there is a constant backlog of about a generation in this adjustment of numbers, which preserves a margin of underemployment in agriculture responsible for a continued disparity of incomes, nevertheless the farming industry does catch up, if with some degree of delay. The circumstances of early industrialization, when the gap between town and country tended to widen, have been basically overcome.

THE LESS DEVELOPED COUNTRIES

In many of the present less developed countries, on the contrary, there is still a large agricultural majority. As a consequence, it would take very rapid rates of industrialization to absorb all the annual population increment into other industries, and even more so to reduce the existing surplus in agriculture. This is not only the situation in a large number of individual countries but is also typical of much of the world today. As yet, the majority of all the world's people live in less developed countries, and the majority of all the world's population depends on agriculture for a livelihood. Rapid population increase in these countries raises the problem of how quickly they will be able to catch up economically with their own numerical growth and build an industrial structure where food production is the task of a minority.

The rates of growth possible cannot of course be answered exclusively from past experience. Modern technique and modern planned economy should be able to do better than the immature industrialization of the nineteenth century. On the other hand, as has already been pointed out, the rates of population increase were also lower at that time and there was more leeway for emigration than there is now.

Recent data on industrial structure in less developed countries indicate that certain among them have achieved high rates of change in their industrial structure as well as in urbanization.[3] In most cases, however, such data refer to a short period only and may be misleading without further analysis, because a short period (a decade or less) may include progress which is temporary rather than sustained. There is also in certain countries the tendency for rural surplus population to be squeezed out of farming because of lack of sufficient employment under prevailing conditions. Migration to towns and inclusion in other (and to a large extent tertiary) occupations is not necessarily a sign of change in the production structure to the extent the data might suggest. Differences in statistical criteria and coverage also become more misleading in short-term than in medium- or long-term data series.

Discussion of the future of the less developed countries will therefore have to include theoretical considerations. The consequences of alternative rates of growth of total population and of nonagricultural employment are shown in Figure 6, which refers to a 50-year period. Rates of

[3] See *The State of Food and Agriculture 1959,* Chapter III, Table III–17.

population increase of 1, 1.5, 2 and 2.5 percent per year are combined with rates of increase in nonagricultural population exceeding them by 0.8, 1.4 and 2.2 percent respectively. As anticipated in the arithmetic rules of thumb indicated above, most of the alternatives shown imply

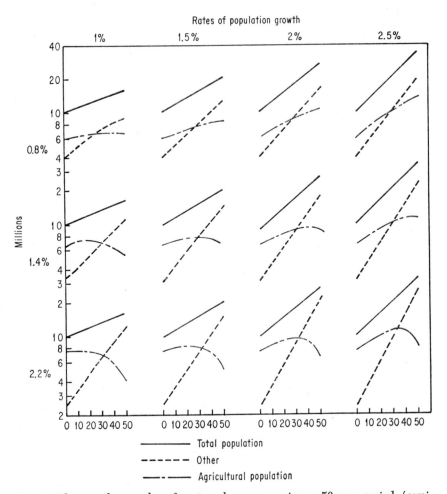

FIG. 6. Theoretical examples of sector changes covering a 50-year period (semilogarithmic scale)
Note: The percentage figures along the vertical scale represent the differential growth of the nonagricultural population over the total population.

continued increase of agricultural population in the early part of the period indicated. In some of them, this growth continues through all or most of the period. Decline in the agricultural population from the beginning of the period shown requires the combination of a low rate of population increase with a high rate of industrialization.

In somewhat more concrete terms, the example of a less developed country may be illustrated, in which 70 percent of the population live from agriculture and 30 percent from other industries. Population increase is, for example, 1.5 percent per year. If this 70:30 position were to be changed to 40:60, which does not seem overambitious for a period of 50 years, then effective employment in industries and services will have to grow by nearly 3 percent per year, a rather high rate, as experience has shown. With 2.5 percent it would take 70 years to reach the same target; with 3.5 percent it can be achieved in 35 years. If the rate of total population increase is 2 instead of 1.5 percent per year, the growth rates required for nonagricultural employment will be 3.5, 3, and 4 percent respectively. It is noteworthy that a narrow margin in the differential growth rate results in considerable differences in performance of economic development, when the compound-interest factor is at work. Even when the nonagricultural percentage is doubled over 50 years, as in the first assumption, agricultural population will at first rise and then decline and regain the starting level at the end of the period indicated, and so on.

If the urban sector in the country includes an under-employed slum population working at low productivity with very little equipment and a low level of skill, then the differential growth rates would apply not to the whole nonagricultural sector but to its reasonably productive part, which is an even smaller fraction of the country. The growth rate to apply to this sector may then climb to staggering levels. In such circumstances, the capacity for savings within these industries themselves may be entirely inadequate to meet their need for investment funds. The low capital-output ratio applying to agriculture in many less developed countries may then be indicative that agriculture is the first industry to develop, in order to generate the starting capital for the growth of the whole economy. The possible pace in building up skilled staff, and particularly a stratum of able foremen, is a further brake on the rapid transformation of a country.

A RURAL WORLD

The conclusion that emerges from the above is that in most of the less developed countries today, there is no reason to expect reduction of absolute numbers in the agricultural population within the near future. In several of them, continued increase of the agricultural population must be expected for quite a long time to come. The latter conclusion extends to the world of today, taken as a whole. It will take decades before agriculture ceases to employ and support the majority of the world's population.

For the FAO and others working on international development this implies that economic studies of the agricultural sector of the economy must not be made in isolation. Similarly, the general economist should not regard the agricultural sector as the exclusive realm of certain specialists or as inherently passive or backward. Where the agricultural population is at present in the majority and can be expected to be so for some time to come, a dynamic approach to the problems of interrelationship between the main sectors of the economy is essential.

part *2*

MEASUREMENT PROBLEMS
IN THE AGRICULTURAL SECTOR

In Part 1, we noted that the new school of quantitative economic historians are trying to improve measurement techniques in order better to explain the development process. The articles by Ohkawa and Rosovsky and North are examples of this concern for improved measures and measurements. We turn from specific country studies to papers by Simon Kuznets and Glenn Johnson in this section which present some of the *current* problems confronting the profession in this area. First, however, let us review some of the literature to assist the reader in gaining a long-run perspective. Clark's intercountry income estimates[1] and Bennett's intercountry consumption estimates[2] are well known. Bellerby's *Agriculture and Industry: Relative Incomes*[3] presents valuable estimates of farm and nonfarm incomes in different countries. Since changes in consumption that are likely to occur as a result of a development program must be taken account of in planning, studies are frequently undertaken to generate income elasticity coefficients. Houthakker recently surveyed the published income and expenditure surveys in a wide range of countries and stated that "if no data on the expenditure patterns of a country are available at all, one would not be very far astray by putting the partial elasticity with respect to total expenditure at 0.6 for food."[4]

[1] Colin Clark, *Conditions of Economic Progress*, London, 1940.
[2] M. K. Bennett, "International Disparities in Consumption Levels," *American Economic Review*, vol. 41, pp. 632–649, September, 1951.
[3] London, 1956.
[4] H. S. Houthakker, "An International Comparison of Household Expenditure Patterns, Commemorating the Centenary of Engel's Law," *Econometrica*, vol. 25, p. 550, October, 1957.

The important point is, however, that the assumptions underlying income elasticity estimates (such as the distribution of income) are often not carefully considered and as a result the income elasticity coefficients are of limited value. The FAO's recent agricultural projection study for 1970 is valuable as a reference for techniques of computing income elasticity coefficients and as a guide to the use of these coefficients in a commodity projection study.[5]

USDA and FAO agricultural economists have undertaken frequent studies of national food consumption estimates since World War II. These estimates are known as food balance sheets. Food balance studies are aggregative relations between production, trade, and population growth and thus focus on national deficits in actual food supplies. They of course do not consider the distribution of food within the country, among areas and income groups. Some of the problems encountered in these studies and the shortcomings of the usual results are discussed in a comprehensive review by Farnsworth.[6]

The accumulation of data to determine the size and extent of a problem, to evaluate the results of current programs, and for many other purposes is a difficult task in most underdeveloped countries. Field surveys are one way in which economists in these countries are attempting to improve the empirical basis for interpretation and action. For methodology in making such studies, the reader is directed to Wharton's study in Brazil,[7] Mukherjee's in India,[8] and Edwards's in Jamaica.[9]

In Selection 5, Kuznets points out that structural interdependence and structural shifts are at the heart of economic development. Therefore, the frequent enumeration of the contributions of agriculture to economic development sometimes fails to emphasize that the contribution of a sector to development is contingent upon what happens in the other sectors and in some cases, what happens outside the country. Kuznets suggests that agriculture makes product, market, and factor contributions to economic development; Kahan in Selection 16 utilizes these concepts to analyze the collective farm system in Soviet development.

Nonconventional inputs have been frequently cited as a major source

[5] FAO Commodity Review 1962, "Agricultural Commodities Projections for 1970," Special Supplement, 1962. See "Annex on Methods."

[6] Helen C. Farnsworth, "Defects, Uses and Abuses of National Food Supply and Consumption Data," *Food Research Institute Studies*, vol. 2, pp. 179–201, November, 1961.

[7] Clifton Wharton, Jr., "Processing Underdeveloped Data from an Underdeveloped Area," *Journal of the American Statistical Association*, vol. 55, pp. 23–37, March, 1960.

[8] P. K. Mukherjee, *Economic Surveys in Under-developed Countries: A Study in Methodology*, Asia Publishing House, Bombay, 1960.

[9] David Edwards, *An Economic Study of Small Farming in Jamaica*, University College of the West Indies, Kingston, Jamaica, 1961.

of economic growth in the United States.[10] The reader will note that some of the papers in Part 4 imply that nonconventional inputs are the obvious solution to many problems in underdeveloped countries. In Selection 6, Glenn Johnson argues that no miraculous or "ghost" input enters the production process through nonconventional inputs such as technological advance and education, but rather that the conventional inputs—land, labor, and capital—are modified as a result of technological advance, better management, and improvement in the human agent. Therefore, he contends that these three "nonconventional inputs" should be viewed as entering the production process by creating new conventional inputs or new combinations of conventional inputs.

[10] E. F. Denison, *The Sources of Economic Growth in the United States and The Alternatives Before Us,* Committee for Economic Development, New York, 1962.

5. Economic Growth and the Contribution of Agriculture: Notes on Measurements*

SIMON KUZNETS

I

We deal here with the economic growth of nations since the late eighteenth or early nineteenth century. This limitation allows us to specify most clearly the distinctive aspects of modern economic growth that should be measured.

The aspect most easily perceived and most commonly measured is the aggregative. In fact, the usual definition of economic growth—a sustained increase in a nation's total and *per caput* product, most often accompanied by a sustained and significant rise in population—stresses this aspect. "Sustained" means persisting over a long period and not in the nature of a cyclical or otherwise short-term expansion. "Increase" means more than a formal mathematical requirement, in that it could not be satisfied by a rate of one-millionth of 1 per cent per century. In the eighteen to twenty-four nations that may be said to have experienced modern economic growth, product *per caput* grew at rates ranging from well above 10 to close to 30 per cent per decade and total product at rates ranging from 15 to over 40 per cent per decade; and, with some striking exceptions, population grew at rates ranging from 8 to 20 per cent per decade.[1] A rate of 10 per cent per decade means doubling in somewhat over 70 years; of 20 per cent in less than 40 years; of 30 per cent in less than 30 years; of 40 per cent in about 20 years. With modern economic growth extending over a century in many

* From the *International Journal of Agrarian Affairs*, vol. 3, pp. 59–75, April, 1961. Reprinted by permission of the *International Journal of Agrarian Affairs* and the author. The author is professor of economics at Harvard University.

[1] See my *Six Lectures on Economic Growth*, The Free Press of Glencoe, Ill., 1959, pp. 19–28.

of the developed nations, the rise sustained in total and *per caput* product was of a magnitude rarely if ever reached in the past.

The second interesting aspect is the structural. The significant characteristics of the rises associated with modern growth are the large and rapid shifts that occur in the structure of an economy—in the relative importance of various industries, regions, classes of economic units distinguished by form of organization, economic classes, commodity groups in final output and so on. The frequent references to modern economic growth as "industrialization" and to its important constituent elements in terms such as "urbanization" and "mechanization," clearly indicate these structural aspects; while even slight acquaintance with the literature on economic growth reveals that the main burden of the analysis is not on the aggregative but on the structural characteristics. The measures usually provided are the familiar distributions of product, capital and labour among industrial sectors; among regions; between the private and the public sectors, and by further divisions within each; and among various socio-economic groups.

The third aspect is the international. We distinguish this aspect in order to stress the facts that, except for the single pioneer nation, all nations participating in modern economic growth view the prospects initially as the task of adopting (and adapting) potentials already demonstrated elsewhere in the world; that no nation can grow in an international vacuum; and that the process of a nation's growth involves a pattern of sequential interrelations with others—more developed and less developed. In a sense, then, the modern economic growth of any one nation is a process of shifting from the underdeveloped to the developed group, utilizing the appropriate channels of international trade, finance and communications in general. Although this whole process of borrowing the knowledge and resources that are indispensable in a nation's modern economic growth cannot be measured, a wide variety of statistical data on foreign trade, foreign capital movements and international migrations have been assembled. Hence the view of the changing *domestic* structure of a nation's economy in its process of growth can be supplemented by a view of the sequential pattern of the economic flows between it and the rest of the world.[2]

The three aspects are clearly interrelated. The rise in *per caput* product, essential to the aggregative view of economic growth, in and of itself means a shift in consumption and savings patterns and thus contributes

[2] The importance of this aspect is not denied by the experience of the Communist countries. Initially they also borrowed extensively and imported considerably from abroad—which is natural, since they were follower nations. That these ties with other nations have not continued to grow as they did with the more freely organized societies is but another case of changes in the pattern of economic growth as we move from the pioneer nation, to the first and then the more removed (in time and in character of historical antecedents) follower nations.

to the shift in the industrial and other structures of the economy. On the other hand, it is the utilization of the technological potential of modern times through the development of new industries and new methods of production—which means structural shifts—that permits a rise in product *per caput*. And the aggressive growth and certain structural shifts provide the surpluses for international trade and capital movements; while the latter, bringing the benefits of international division of labour, are in turn conducive to the greater aggregative growth of the participating nations and thus to greater structural shifts within them. This close association is hardly surprising, since a nation's modern economic growth may be described as the utilization of domestic and international division of labour, under conditions of changing technology, to increase *per caput* product of a growing population.

Given this interrelation, it is often impossible to specify the contribution of a single industrial sector, say agriculture, to each aspect of economic growth. Nor is it particularly illuminating to do so. For if a sector contributes directly to the growth of product per worker, it indirectly contributes to structural shifts and greater international division of labour; if a sector contributes directly to foreign trade, it indirectly contributes to growth of product *per caput* and to structural shifts within the country. It would seem preferable to consider the contribution of agriculture to economic growth jointly in all three aspects of the process, and then examine the various ways in which such a contribution may be rendered. Some of these ways bear more directly on aggregative aspects of growth than on the structural; others bear more directly upon the structural or international than upon the aggregative. But each has some bearing on all three related aspects of economic growth.

II

In considering the contribution of agriculture, or for that matter of any sector, to the economic growth of a country, we must first recognize an element of ambiguity. Since any sector is part of an interdependent system represented by the country's economy, what a sector does is not fully attributable or credited to it but is contingent upon what happens in the other sectors (and perhaps also outside the country). Thus, even if we deal with net product originating in, or contributed by, a sector, deducting the purchases or contributions from others and limiting the total to the product of the factors attached to that sector, the magnitude and movement of the net product so measured still depend upon the rest of the economy; and its product may perhaps be more correctly described as the result of the activities of the economy whose particular *locus* is the given sector—rather than as a contribution of the given sector fully creditable to it as if it were outside the economy and offering something to the latter. But so long as we keep the semantic caution in mind, and remember that the capacity of a sector to "contribute" depends not upon the sector alone, no harm is done by retaining this familiar expression.

The first type of contribution of agriculture to the economic growth of a nation is that constituted by growth of product within the sector itself. An increase in the net output of agriculture, in and of itself, represents a rise in the product of the country—since the latter is the sum of the increases in the net products of the several sectors. This type, which we may call the product contribution, can be briefly examined—as a contribution first to the growth of *total* net or gross product, and second to the growth of product *per caput*.

We begin with a simple algebraic notation and refer to "product," since the formal conclusions are the same for product gross of capital consumption (gross national product, and corresponding gross product originating in the sector) or net of it (net national product, and corresponding net product originating in the sector).

Designate:

P_a = product of agriculture (A sector).
P_b = product of all other sectors (non-A sector).
P = total product = $P_a + P_b$.
δP = increment in total product–aggregate growth.
r_a = rate of growth of P_a so that $P_a^1 = P_a^0(1 + r_a)$, the superscripts referring to time.
r_b = rate of growth of P_b so that $P_b^1 = P_b^0(1 + r_b)$.

Then,
$$\delta P = P_a r_a + P_b r_b. \tag{1}$$

And the equation for the share of the growth of agricultural product in the growth of total product is:

$$\frac{P_a r_a}{\delta P} = \frac{1}{1 + \left(\dfrac{P_b}{P_a} \times \dfrac{r_b}{r_a}\right)}. \tag{2}$$

Thus, if at the initial point of time, the share of agriculture in country-wide product is 60 per cent—which is about the highest for an underdeveloped country[3]—and if over the next decade the rate of growth of the non-A sector (r_b) is four times as high as that of the A sector (r_a), the product contribution of agriculture to the growth of total product will be 1 divided by $(1 + 0.67 \times 4)$, or about a quarter. At the end of that decade the initial share of agriculture in total product will be less than 60 per

[3] See my paper on "Industrial Distribution on National Product and Labor Force," *Economic Development and Cultural Change*, vol. v, no. 4, supplement, July 1957, table 3, p. 10.

cent, and if r_b/r_a remains four, the following decade will witness a product contribution of agriculture to growth of total product smaller than a quarter.[4]

Several conclusions can be derived from equation (2). Firstly, so long as the rate of growth of the non-A sector is higher than that of agriculture, all other conditions being equal, the proportional contribution of agriculture to the growth of total product will decline. The only component in equation (2) that might prevent such a decline is the ratio r_b/r_a: a decline in *it* might counteract the effect of the rise in P_b/P_a. Secondly, if r_b/r_a rises, i.e. if the rate of growth of the non-agricultural sector is increasingly higher than that of agriculture, the decline in the share of agriculture in the growth of total product would be even greater. Thirdly, if we assume that the rate of growth of countryside product is *constant* over time (only a few countries showed acceleration in the long-term movement), and if r_b/r_a is over 1, i.e. if the rate of growth of the non-agricultural sector is higher than the rate of growth of agriculture, then either r_b, or r_a, or both, must decline over time. For if they remain constant, the increasing weight of P_b (enjoying a higher rate of growth) will make for an *acceleration* in the rate of growth of total product.

Let us turn now from the product contribution of agriculture to the growth of countrywide product *per caput*, or rather per worker—a more meaningful unit for sectoral analysis.

---

[4] There is a direct relation between the ratio of rates of growth of product in the non-A and A sectors (r_b/r_a) and the movement of the ratio of the product of the A sector to the total. This can be expressed by the following equation:

$$\frac{(1 + r_b)}{(1 + r_a)} = \frac{P_a{}^0}{P_b{}^0}\left(\frac{P^1}{P_a{}^1} - 1\right). \tag{3}$$

Thus, if at time point 0, the first ratio in the right-hand side of equation (3) is 1.5, meaning that the shares of the A sector and the non-A sector in total product are 60 and 40 per cent respectively; and if over the next decade the share of the A sector drops to 55 per cent, the value on the right-hand side becomes 1.5 (1/0.55 − 1) or 1.23. Then, if the rate of growth for agriculture is 10 per cent per decade, $(1 + r_a)$ becomes 1.10; and $(1 + r_b)$ becomes 1.35; and the rate of growth for the non-A sector 35 per cent per decade, or 3.5 times as high as that for the A sector. When the share of agriculture drops from 30 to 25 per cent, the right-hand side of equation (3) becomes:

$$\frac{0.30(4 - 1)}{0.70} \text{ or } 1.29;$$

and if $(1 + r_a)$ is still 1.10, $(1 + r_b)$ becomes 1.42, yielding a rate of growth 4.2 times as high as that for agriculture. Likewise, if we lower the rate of growth in agriculture, and set $(1 + r_a)$, at, say, 1.05, under the conditions illustrated above, $(1 + r_b)$ becomes 1.29 and 1.35 respectively, yielding rates of growth for the non-A sector six or seven times as high as those for the A sector.

Designate (in addition to the notation above):

L_a = workers in the A sector.
L_b = workers in all other sectors.
L = all workers = $L_a + L_b$.
R = rate of growth of product per worker (same in both the A and non-A sectors).

Then, we have the following expression for the change in total product per worker:

$$\frac{P^1}{L^1} - \frac{P^0}{L^0} = \left(\frac{P_a^1}{L_a} - \frac{P_a^0}{L_a^0}\right)\left(\frac{L_a^1}{L_1}\right) + \left(\frac{P_b^1}{L_b^1} - \frac{P_b^0}{L_b^0}\right)\left(\frac{L_b^1}{L^1}\right)$$
$$+ \left(\frac{P_b^0}{L_b^0} - \frac{P_a^0}{L_a^0}\right)\left(\frac{L_b^1}{L^1} - \frac{L_b^0}{L^0}\right). \quad (4)$$

Equation (4) tells us that the increment in a country's aggregate product per worker is the sum of: (a) the increment in product per worker in the A sector, weighted by the share of the A sector in labour force *at the end* of the period; (b) the increment in product per worker in the non-A sector, weighted by the share of the non-A sector in labour force *at the end* of the period; (c) the *change* in the share of the non-A sector in the labour force (usually a rise) during the period, weighted by the difference between product per worker in the non-A and A sectors at the beginning of the period.

If we assume that P_b/L_b is larger than P_a/L_a, which is usually the case, and set the ratio for time 0 at 2; and if we assume further that products per worker in the A sector and in the non-A sector grow at about the same rate—not an unreasonable assumption in the light of records for the developed countries—equation (4) can be simplified to:

$$\frac{P^1}{L^1} - \frac{P^0}{L^0} = \frac{P_a^0}{L_a^0}[(L_a^1/L^1)R + (L_b^1/L^1)2R + (L_b^1/L^1 - L_b^0/L^0)]. \quad (5)$$

Thus, if the initial share of the labour force in agriculture is as high as 75 per cent, product per worker in agriculture only half of that in the non-agricultural sectors, the rate of growth in product per worker per decade (for both sectors) 20 per cent, and the share of labour force in the non-agricultural sector increases 5 percentage points per decade—a not unreasonable figure—the right-hand side of equation (5) for the first decade becomes

$$\frac{P_a^0}{L_a^0}[(0.70)0.20 + (0.30)0.40 + 0.50].$$

The first component (a) of the right-hand side of both equations (4) and (5) is clearly a measure of the contribution of agriculture to the

growth of country-wide product per worker; while the second component (*b*) is clearly a measure of the contribution of the non-*A* sector.
But what about the third component (*c*), the effect of the shift in the percentage distribution of the labour force from the *A* to the non-*A* sector?
It is in this connexion that the ambiguity of the term "contribution"
emerges. In one sense it is a contribution of the *A* sector, since the latter
provides additional labour force to the non-*A* sector; and as will be seen
below, the internal migration involved in this shift must be quite large
in the process of modern economic growth. In another sense the shift
is a contribution of the non-*A* sector, since the latter provides the essential employment opportunities to the labour moving from the *A* sector.
The allocation of this joint contribution to the *A* and non-*A* sectors is
clearly a matter of judgement. If we divide it equally between the two,
the proportional contribution of agriculture to the countrywide growth
of *per caput* product becomes in the example above $(0.14 + 0.025)/0.31$,
or somewhat over one-half.

On the assumptions underlying equation (5), and however we allocate the third component, some general statements can be made as
to the level and movements of the proportional contribution of agriculture to additions to countrywide product per worker. Firstly, this proportional contribution will be larger, the larger the terminal share of
agriculture in the country's labour force, and the higher the ratio of
product per worker in agriculture to that in the non-*A* sector. And,
if we permit the rate of growth of product per worker in the *A* and
non-*A* sectors to differ, the proportional contribution of the *A* sector will
be larger, the higher the ratio of the rate of growth of product per worker
in the *A* sector to that in the non-*A* sector. Secondly, in so far as in the
course of economic growth the share of agriculture in the labour force
declines, there will be a continuous decline in the proportional contribution of agriculture to the growth in countrywide product per worker—
unless the rate of growth of product per worker in the non-*A* sector falls
behind the rate of growth of product in the *A* sector—which is unlikely.
Thirdly, if we assume that the countrywide product per worker grows at
a constant percentage rate, the continuous shift of the labour force from
the *A* sector with its lower product per worker to the non-*A* sector with
its higher product per worker *must* be accompanied by a decline in the
rate of growth of product per worker in the *A* sector, or in the non-*A*
sector, or in both. The slight damping influence of the third component
—the absolute rise in the share of the non-*A* sector in the labour force—
may be disregarded, since its weight is likely to be small. The parallelism
of these conclusions to those derived for the proportional contribution
of agriculture to growth of total product is obvious.

These rather simple schemes could be applied to the empirical long-
term records on product, labour force and product per worker—in total
and for the two sectors separately—for a number of countries, and with

the product valued at constant prices to eliminate the effect of price changes. Such statistical analysis would probably show in countries with a high rate of economic growth, with respect to overall aggregates and consequent structural shifts, a rapid decline in the proportional contribution of agriculture—from a quarter or more of the growth of total product and a half or more of the growth of *per caput* product, to a few percentage points. It must be remembered that currently the share of agriculture in both product and labour force in many developed countries is well below 20 per cent. The analysis of the statistical evidence might also reveal more about the time pattern of the movements. But to present such an analysis in adequate detail would transcend the limits of the paper; and we prefer to devote the rest of the discussion to other somewhat less obvious and perhaps less familiar types of contribution of agriculture to a country's modern economic growth.

III

A given sector makes a contribution to an economy when it provides opportunities for other sectors to emerge, or for the economy as a whole to participate in international trade and other international economic flows. We designate this contribution the market type because the given sector provides such opportunities by offering part of its product on either domestic or foreign markets in exchange for goods produced by the other sectors, at home or abroad.

Thus in the case of agriculture, we can envisage two contrasting situations. In one, agriculture engages 100 units of labour force to turn out 1,000 units of product without any purchases from other sectors, and thus in complete independence of the country's production processes. In another, agriculture engages 80 units of labour force and still turns out 1,000 units of product—but does so by purchasing 200 units of fertilizers, &c., provided by 20 units of the country's labour force. In both cases, the net output of the economy, with the same labour force, is the same—1,000 units of final goods. But in the second case we have market transaction and diversification of the structure of production.

The example is unrealistic, for the division of labour in the second case would, usually, result in an appreciably higher product per worker. Indeed, this rise is the very reason for the reduction in the economic independence of a sector and its engagement in trade with other sectors at home or abroad. But the illustration does emphasize the contribution of changes in a sector to the significant element in economic growth of diversification of structure—the intensification of the internal and international division of labour. These changes are important in and of themselves—apart from the contribution that they make to growth in total or *per caput* product.

Thus agriculture makes a market contribution to economic growth by

(a) purchasing some production items from other sectors at home or abroad; (b) selling some of its product, not only to pay for the purchases listed under (a) but also to purchase consumer goods from other sectors or from abroad, or to dispose of the product in any way other than consumption within the sector. In all these ways, agriculture makes it feasible for other sectors in the economy to emerge and grow and for international flows to develop; just as these other sectors and the international flows make it feasible for the agricultural sector to operate more efficiently as a producing unit and use its product more effectively as a consuming unit.

In this connexion, some familiar trends in agriculture in countries that have experienced modern economic growth come easily to mind. There is first the spread of modern technology to agriculture proper: chemical fertilizers, machinery and mechanical power replaced extensively means of production originating within agriculture itself (such as natural fertilizers, draught animals and hand-made tools). The need to purchase these new production goods from other sectors meant an increasing "marketization" of the production process within agriculture; and it is reflected in the increasing proportion that purchases from other sectors constitute of the product of agriculture—gross of all production expenses. To cite an easily available statistical example: in the United States of America the *net* farm income in 1910 amounted to slightly less than 80 per cent of *gross* farm income; whereas in 1950 it was less than 70 per cent (both totals are in constant prices, and are five-year averages centred on the years cited).[5] Thus the proportion of outside purchases (including capital consumption) rose over the forty years from about 20 to about 30 per cent of the gross product.

The proportion of gross income accounted for by purchases from other sectors is clearly a crude and incomplete measure of the marketization of the production process in agriculture. We treat all agriculture here as one sector, disregarding the network of market transactions within agriculture—transactions which presumably grow in absolute and *proportional* volume as agriculture becomes more specialized and diversified in the course of economic growth. A more complete measure would be based on records of outside purchases at each farm—making it independent of arbitrary definitions of a sector. But so long as we understand what is involved in the marketization of the production process in agriculture, we need not dwell upon its measurement.

There is another question, however, viz. how to measure the "contribution" to economic growth. The measure just discussed is a gauge of relative importance of purchases from outside to the gross product of a sector—not of their proportional contribution to a country's economic

[5] See Alvin Tostlebe, *Capital in Agriculture: its formation and financing since 1870,* National Bureau of Economic Research, New York, 1957, table 20, p. 101.

growth. We need here to define the aspect of the latter to which we think marketization contributes—over and above its indirect contribution to total and *per caput* product.

The aspect is clearly development of sectors other than agriculture; and this could be measured by comparing the non-agricultural sectors in the country providing production goods to agriculture with all the non-agricultural sectors. In other words, the percentage of the growth in output of all non-agricultural sectors (including the transportation and other facilities involved), accounted for by the fertilizer, agricultural machinery and other plants that provide the production goods to agriculture, would measure the proportional contribution which marketization of the production process in agriculture made to the industrialization aspects of economic growth within the country. What the facts in the situation are I am in no position to state, but a realistic illustration may suggest the order of magnitude. Assume that the proportion of purchases from other sectors to *gross* product of agriculture increased in the process of growth from 10 to 30 per cent; which, in percentages of *net* product, meant a shift from 11 to 43 per cent. Assume further that at the initial point of time the proportion of net income from agriculture to net national product was 60 per cent, and declined to 15 per cent at the end. Purchases by agriculture from other sectors (gross) were therefore 6.6 per cent of net national product at the initial point of time and less than 6.5 per cent at the end point; and if we reduce this proportion by a fifth to allow for the difference between gross and net content ("net" representing returns to factors), we have roughly 5.3 per cent of net national product represented by industries whose only function is to supply producers' goods to agriculture. The percentage works out at 13 and 6 per cent respectively (5.3/40 and 5.3/85) of the net product of all non-agricultural industries. Marketization of the agricultural production process thus accounted for a significant but declining fraction of the "industrialized" sectors and of the structural aspect of economic growth.

We turn now to the increase in the proportion of agricultural *net* product which is not consumed within the producing farm or agriculture proper but is sold on the markets in which agriculture trades with other sectors of the economy or abroad. This trend is largely due to a rise in net product per worker within agriculture combined with the low secular income elasticity of the demand for agricultural consumer goods, but it may also reflect technical progress that reduces cost and facilitates transportation and trade over wide areas. The contribution to economic growth here is the release of a larger proportion of the *net* product of agriculture as a basis for demand for consumer goods (or, to a more limited extent, of producer goods) from other sectors in the economy and from foreign countries.

Some suggestion of the magnitude of such marketization of the net product of agriculture can be made on two alternative assumptions, both disregarding the minor fraction of the net product that may be saved (rather than consumed). On the first assumption, the per worker (or *per caput*) consumption of agricultural net product is the same in both the A and non-A sectors, despite the large difference in their total income *per caput*. On this assumption, if we begin with a share of the A sector in net national product of 60 per cent and in the labour force of 75 per cent, per worker or *per caput* consumption of agricultural net product throughout the economy will be 0.6 (in percentages of net national product); the consumption by the agricultural population of its own product will be 75 per cent multiplied by 0.6, or 45 per cent of national product; and their consumption of other goods will be 15 per cent (i.e. 60 per cent of total net product minus 45 per cent represented by agricultural product). If we also assume that all the non-agricultural final product goes through the market, the total marketed net product is 55 per cent of net national product, of which 15 per cent is agricultural final product. The contribution of agriculture to total marketed net product is then slightly over a quarter; and it is clear that as the shares of agriculture in national product and in labour force decline, its proportional contribution to the growing marketed net product will decline. Thus when the share of agriculture in the national product is down to 15 per cent, and in the labour force correspondingly down to 26.1 per cent (to preserve a ratio of product per worker in the non-A sector to that in the A sector of 2 to 1), the marketed portion of agricultural net product will, on the assumptions stated, be 11.1 per cent of national product; the total marketed portion will be 96.1 per cent (i.e. 85 per cent non-agricultural output plus 11.1 per cent agricultural); and the proportional contribution of agricultural marketings to total will be about a ninth rather than over a quarter.

An alternative assumption would be that the distribution of final consumption (which, disregarding savings or capital formation, we equate to net national product) between agricultural and non-agricultural products—for both agricultural and non-agricultural populations—is the same and in fact is shown by the shares of agriculture and of other sectors in the countrywide total of net product. Thus, at the initial point of time, with the share of agriculture in the net national product of 60 per cent, the agricultural population would consume only 60 per cent of its net income in the form of agricultural products; and trade the remainder, i.e. 24 per cent of net national product, to the people dependent upon the non-agricultural sectors. The total marketed product would be 64 per cent of net national product (40 per cent represented by non-agricultural output, all marketed; and 24 per cent by the marketed, agricultural output); and agriculture's contribution to it will be 24 out of 64, or close to four-tenths. On this assumption, when the share of agriculture in national product drops to 50 per cent, half of the agricultural output would be traded, i.e. 25 per cent of total product—a slightly higher percentage than in the first instance, but a lower share of the total marketed output (which will be 75 per cent).

Which assumption is the more realistic would have to be determined by empirical study; and the actual behaviour of agricultural and non-agricultural producers and consumers may fall within the range suggested by the two assumptions. However, the main points to be noted are suggested under either assumption. Firstly, at the initial point of time, when agriculture accounts for a large share of the net output of the economy, the extent to which such product is traded with the other sectors has a major bearing upon the width of the economic base which these other sectors may enjoy. If, for simplicity's sake, we think of a closed economy, any difficulty in increasing the marketable surplus of agricultural product will restrict the growth base of the other sectors. Secondly, once growth occurs and is accompanied by a decline in the shares of agriculture in both product and labour force, the increased productivity per worker in agriculture reflected in these trends assures an increasing proportion of marketed agricultural net product and at the same time a decreasing proportional contribution of such marketings to the total product of the economy. In short, the market contribution of agriculture to a country's economic growth, strategic in the early periods of growth, must, in the nature of the case, diminish in relative weight once growth has proceeded apace.

The same conclusion is suggested by the third aspect of the market contribution of agriculture: that bearing upon the type of trading partner with whom market relations are established. The market contribution to economic growth will be the greater the higher the growth-inducing power of the trading partners whose co-operation via the market is being secured. The same volume of purchases by agriculture from a host of village carpenters, blacksmiths, &c., and from a factory that produces agricultural machinery by advanced methods, will have different impacts on the growth not only of the non-agricultural sectors of the economy but also of agriculture itself.

It is in this connexion that the contribution of agriculture to exports assumes strategic importance, since in most countries modern economic growth is a matter of following the pattern set by the nations that have already experienced this process; and it is exceedingly important for a follower nation to trade with the more advanced countries which can provide it with the tools of modern technology. Even with allowance for capital imports a country in the early stages of economic growth that cannot itself produce, even at high cost, the tools of modern technology, must be able to offer the more advanced countries a *quid pro quo*. It can do this only with products in which it has a comparative advantage; and in the nature of the case this advantage is likely to lie in natural resources rather than in skills. Since agriculture, after mining, is the sector in which natural endowments have greatest weight, it is hardly a surprise that in the initial stages of growth of many presently developed countries, agriculture was a major source of exports and that the resulting command over the resources of the more developed countries played a strategic role in facilitating modern economic growth. It is also apparent that, as economic growth continued, the advantage with respect to products affected by natural resource endowments might recede relative to that resulting from economies of scale and accumulation of skills in other sectors. Consequently, in addition to the reduction in the weight of agriculture in the total output of a country, there may be an even greater reduction in its share of exports. Thus the market contribution of agriculture, this time in specific connexion with the capacity of a country through international trade to tap the resources of the more advanced units, is likely to be large in the initial stages of growth (unless the mineral resources are sufficiently great to make agricultural exports less strategic) and bound to decline as economic growth takes hold in a country. While any detailed analysis of the relations touched upon here would raise difficult questions concerning the phasing of this process of building economic growth on trade with the more advanced countries, the substance of the contribution is clear and the measures, in terms of shares of exports and feasible imports of capital goods, are obvious without further discussion.

IV

The third type of contribution by a sector to economic growth occurs when there is a transfer or loan of resources from the given sector to others. Thus if agriculture itself grows, it makes a product contribution; if it trades with others, it renders a market contribution; if it transfers resources to other sectors, these resources being productive factors, it makes a *factor* contribution.

The resources being transferred are either capital, or rather funds for financing acquisition of material capital, or labour. In the case of the former, two different types of transfer may occur. In the first there is a compulsory transfer from agriculture for the benefit of other sectors; and this is ordinarily done through taxation of a kind in which the burden on agriculture is far greater than the services rendered by government to agriculture (including an adequate share of overhead government expenses), the residue being spent by government for the benefit of other sectors. To illustrate, the government may use a tax on agriculture as its only revenue, and expend it all either on a subsidy to some manufacturing industry (thus in fact providing capital funds for the latter), or use it all in the construction of some public utility. To be sure, both the factory and the public utility contribute to growth within agriculture proper; but the direct contribution to economic growth is to the non-agricultural sectors, and this flow, originating in the agricultural sector, is not covered in its product or market contribution.

The measurement of such forced contributions of agriculture to economic growth is not easy; the incidence of some indirect taxes is difficult to ascertain and the allocation of government expenditures in terms of benefits to agriculture and to economic growth elsewhere is far from simple. But this factor contribution by agriculture was clearly quite large in the early phases of economic growth in some countries. Thus in Japan in the last two decades of the nineteenth century the land tax was over 80 per cent of central government taxation, and the direct tax ratio to income produced was between 12 and 22 per cent in agriculture, compared with from 2 to 3 per cent in the non-agricultural sectors.[6] Forced extraction of surplus from agriculture by taxation, confiscation and other measures also probably financed a considerable part of industrialization in the Soviet Union. Indeed, one of the crucial problems of modern economic growth is how to extract from the product of agriculture a surplus for the financing of capital formation necessary for industrial growth without at the same time blighting the growth of agriculture, under conditions where no easy *quid pro quo* for such surplus is available within the country. It is only the open economy, with access to the markets of the more highly developed countries, both for goods and for capital loans, that can minimize this painful task of initial capital accumulation.

The other form of capital transfer is, of course, lending, or the utilization of savings originating in the agricultural sector in financing the growth of the non-agricultural sectors. Provided that we have data both on savings and capital formation, both in agriculture and in other sectors of the economy, there is no problem in measuring the extent to which savings originating in agriculture contribute to the financing of capital formation elsewhere in the economy. But no such data are at hand for my purposes, and we are forced to speculate on the magnitudes involved.

In such speculation the following general points must be taken into account. In the initial phases of growth the share of agriculture in total national product is large, but the *per caput* income in the A sector is distinctly lower than that in the non-A sector. Hence the share of do-

[6] See *Kazushi Okhawa and Henry Rosovsky*, "The Role of Agriculture in Modern Japanese Economic Development," in City and Village in Japan, *Economic Development and Cultural Change*, vol. ix, no. 1, part ii, October 1960, tables 14 and 15, pp. 61 and 62. [EDITOR'S NOTE: Selection 2.]

mestic savings originating in agriculture is a function of the share of agriculture in total income, the lower level of real income in agriculture than in the other sectors, and the relative propensity to save of the agricultural population and of other groups in the economy. To assay these three variables would necessitate much empirical study. But to make the discussion more meaningful let us begin with a share of the A sector in income of 60 per cent, in labour force of 75 per cent; and assume that savings amount to 5 per cent of the A sector income, which on a *per caput* basis is only half of the income in the non-A sector, compared with a 10 per cent savings rate for the non-A sector. Total domestic savings would then amount to 7 per cent of national income, 4 per cent originating in the non-A sector and 3 per cent in the A sector.

The flow of savings out of the A sector to finance capital formation elsewhere would depend largely upon the relative needs of these sectors for capital, which needs are reflected in differential rates of return (all other conditions being abstracted from). Perhaps the incremental capital-output ratios might suggest how much capital is needed to secure additional output. The data for recent years indicate that in all but the most fully developed countries the incremental capital-output ratios for the A sector, while higher than those for manufacturing, are not too different from the countrywide ratios and hence from those for the non-A sector as a whole.[7] If this situation can be assumed to hold for the early phases of economic growth, the allocation of savings depends largely upon the relative rates of growth of the A and non-A sectors, reflecting differences in long-term demand for additions to their product. Hence, whether or not there will be a flow of savings from the A sector to finance capital formation in the non-A sector will be revealed by a comparison of two fractions: the first is the ratio of additions to product of the A sector to additions to the total product of the economy—already discussed under the product contribution of agriculture, and expressible as $P_a r_a / (P_a r_a + P_b r_b)$; the other fraction is the ratio of savings originating in agriculture to all savings originating in the economy, which can be written as $s_a / (s_a + s_b)$. Now if we assume, in addition, that the net savings rate is 7 per cent, that national product grows at a rate of 3 per cent per year (or 34.4 per cent per decade), implying an incremental capital-output ratio of 2.3 to 1; and that the rate of growth of the product of the non-A sector is four times that of the product of the A sector, the *needed* capital formation in the A sector will be only 27 per cent of total capital formation needed;[8] whereas savings

[7] See my paper "Capital Formation Proportions: International Comparisons for Recent Years," *Economic Development and Cultural Change*, vol. viii, no. 4, part ii, July 1960, table 15, p. 64.

[8] This can be calculated from the equation: $(0.60)r + (0.40)4r = 3.0$. r, the rate of growth for the A sector, is then 1.364 per cent, that for the non-A sector four

originating in agriculture are 43 per cent of total savings. There will therefore be a flow of savings originating in the A sector into capital formation in the non-A sector, accounting for 16 out of 73, or somewhat less than a quarter of the latter.

The example is purely illustrative; and the discussion is designed only to bring out the variables that would have to be measured in empirical study. The rate of growth of the product of the non-A sector might well be more than four times that of the A sector. The incremental capital-output ratio for the A sector might well be distinctly lower than, rather than equal to, the capital-output ratio for the non-A sector— in some countries in some periods agricultural output could be increased significantly with little or no capital investment. If these two contingencies were to materialize, the flow of savings from agriculture to finance capital formation elsewhere would be relatively larger than is suggested in the illustration. On the other hand, we are dealing with domestic savings alone, disregarding financing from abroad—capital imports that were quite important in the early phases of growth of several countries, such as Canada, Australia and Scandinavia.

We may now turn to the third type of factor contribution made by agriculture to the economic growth of a country—the provision of labour. While this shift of labour from the A to the non-A sectors in the process of modern economic growth has become quite familiar, the magnitude of the migration and of the factor contribution involved may not have been given the attention that it deserves.

To begin with, we must stress the fact that through the periods under discussion and in almost all the countries, the crude (and refined) birth-rates of the agricultural populations were distinctly higher than those of the non-agricultural; whereas the death-rates were at least equal, if not lower, for the agricultural.[9] This means that the rate of natural increase was very much higher for the agricultural than

---

times as high, or 5.456 per cent. Multiplying the former by 0.60 yields the increment of the product of the A sector, or 0.818; multiplying the latter by 0.40 yields the increment of the product of the non-A sector, or 2.182; and the ratio of the increment in the A sector to increment in total product, and, on the assumption used, of the capital needs of the A sector to total capital needs, is then 0.818/3, or 27 per cent.

[9] See a summary discussion in United Nations, *The Determinants and Consequences of Population Trends,* New York, 1953, p. 62, on urban-rural differentials in mortality, and pp. 85–86 on urban-rural differentials in fertility. For more recent discussion of these differentials in fertility see the papers by Gwendolyn Johnson (pp. 36–72) and by Clyde Kiser (pp. 77–113), in Universities-National Bureau Committee on Economic Research, *Demographic and Economic Change in Developed Countries,* Princeton University Press, 1960; and the paper by T. Lynn Smith, "The Reproduction Rate in Latin America: Levels, Differentials and Trends," *Population Studies,* vol. xii, no. 1, July 1958, pp. 1–17.

for the non-agricultural population; and consequently for the agricultural than for the non-agricultural labour force.

The orders of magnitude can now be suggested. At the initial point of time, when the share of the A sector in the labour force was 75 per cent, we may set the crude birth-rate for the agricultural population at about 40 per 1,000, with that for the non-agricultural at about 27 (the ratio of the former to the latter being roughly 1.5). If we set the crude death-rates at 20 per 1,000 for both groups, the rate of natural increase for the two sectors, for population and hence for the labour force (with some lag), will be 20 and 7 per 1,000, respectively. Thus the rate of growth of the agricultural labour force, owing to its rate of natural increase, is almost three times that of the non-agricultural. Incidentally, on these assumptions the rate of natural increase for total population, i.e. the countrywide rate, works out at 16.75 per thousand.

Consider now the internal migration of the labour force that would be required over a decade for the share of the A sector in the labour force to decline from 75 to 70 per cent, under the assumption of a closed population (i.e. no international migration). Over that decade, total labour force would rise from 100 to 118.23, labour force in the A sector would rise from 75 to 91.425, and that in the non-A sector from 25 to 26.805. To secure a 70–30 apportionment, the 91.425 in the A sector would have to be reduced by internal migration to 82.761—a migration out of the A sector of roughly 8.7 per cent of the countrywide initial labour force, or over 9 per cent of the labour force that would have been in the A sector at the end of the decade if not for internal migration.

This transfer of workers from the A to the non-A sector means a sizeable capital contribution because each migrant is of working age and represents some investment in past rearing and training to maturity. What is the magnitude of this investment in human beings? Let us assume that every worker migrating from the A sector embodies outlays on rearing, education and training equal to ten times the current product per worker in the A sector (this is a rough ratio, based on an average prior year's outlay of about six-tenths of the current *per caput* income multiplied by 17, the age assumed at transfer). If, then, in each year of the decade something like 1.01 per cent of the labour force in the A sector moves to the non-A sector (the difference between a rate of natural increase of 2 per cent and 0.89 per cent required by the conditions of the illustrative example), we have a transfer embodying outlays equal to 10.1 per cent of the total income of the A sector. This, in the first interval, would be 10.1 per cent of 60, or over 6 per cent of total national product; but the addition to the factor endowment of the non-A sector is over 25 per cent of its current product (10.1 as per cent of 40).

The figures in the illustration could be modified in the light of empirical data, but they are realistic enough for us to draw some plausible conclusions. Firstly, if we accept the interpretation of internal migration as a transfer of capital invested in human beings, this factor contribution of the A sector to the growth of the non-A sectors must have been quite large in the early and even later phases of modern economic growth—since internal migration of the labour force was from the A to the non-A sectors and sizeable. In the illustration, the value of the transfer was estimated at over 6 per cent of total current income; and it would have been easier, without violating the rules of plausibility, to raise this percentage significantly than to lower it. Yet under the assumptions of the illustration, total net savings in the economy were not more than 7 per cent of national income. And, granting that the "contribution" in question depends upon the employment capacity of the non-A sector, we could still argue that the internal migration of labour from agriculture represents a large transfer of valuable resources to the non-A sectors and a large contribution to the country's economic growth. This conclusion has several implications, not the least of which is that the kind of investment in human beings that is, and can be, made in the A sector determines the quality of an important part of the labour force in, and hence of its contribution to the growth of, the non-A sector.

Secondly, if the share of the A sector in the labour force and the relative magnitude of labour transfers from it decline, there is bound to be a decline even in the absolute value of the factor transfers thus made; and most certainly in its proportion to the stock of labour already available in the non-A sector. After a while, although it may be fairly late in the course of modern economic development, the absolute numbers of workers in the A sector decline; and transfers that may be a large fraction of the current labour force in agriculture would mean only minor fractional additions to the labour force outside the agriculture, and for the country as a whole.

Finally, it need hardly be pointed out that what is true of internal migration applies to the international movement of labour which through the nineteenth and early twentieth centuries assisted a number of rapidly developing countries. This migration was most often from the agricultural sector in one country to the non-A sector in another, and in that sense was similar to what we have been discussing—except that the factor contribution was to the economic growth of another country. At some time this may have had a curious effect on internal migration within the recipient country, impeding internal migration from at least some parts of the domestic A sector. But these aspects of the factor contribution of the A sector, while of great interest, would take us into an analysis of the growth process for different groups of countries that would be too detailed for treatment here.

6. A Note on Nonconventional Inputs and Conventional Production Functions*

GLENN L. JOHNSON

Three "nonconventional" inputs have been giving students of economic development serious trouble for some time. They include technological advance, management, and improvements in the human agent. The productivity of economies depends upon inventions, organizational innovations, managerial skill, managerial capacity, and various other skills possessed by productive inhabitants. From easy observations of this relationship, it has been but a short *non sequitur* to (1) attempted quantification of technological advance, managerial capacity, and improvements in the human agent, and (2) attempted use of such variables in conventional production functions as inputs. It does not follow that because output is related to technological advance, improvements in the human agent, and increases in managerial skills, these changes should be quantified and treated as factors of production. Though, for instance, a decision to use more fertilizer does change output indirectly, it is the fertilizer, not the decision, which is a factor of production.

It will be the thesis of this short note that such "unconventional" inputs, if they can be regarded as inputs at all, should not be treated as factors of production in any sense and that attempts to do so are not likely to be helpful in understanding the roles that technological advance, improvements in managerial capacity, and improvements in the human agent play in production and in economic development. Quite to the contrary, it will be argued that such attempts reduce the effectiveness with which production function analyses can be carried out and reduce our ability to understand (1) the creation of technological advance, (2) the performance of the managerial processes, and (3) the processes of investing in and of improving the human agent.

PRODUCTION FUNCTION CONCEPTS

The usual concept of a production function treats output as dependent on a long list of factors of production. At any point in time, man knows

* An original contribution. The author is professor of agricultural economics, Michigan State University, and director, Economic Development Institute, University of Nigeria.

some of the possible factors of production which might contribute to the production of a particular product. Thus, in some sense, there are always two production functions: (1) that using factors known by man, and (2) that still to be discovered in its entirety.

Typically, it is assumed and observed that a production function displays constant returns to scale when all factors of production being used are controllable. However, there are natural, sociological, and economic restrictions on the ability of man to control all factors of production. When some of the factors are fixed by natural, social, and economic conditions, an increase in the quantity of the variable inputs is not expected to yield a proportionate increase in output. In fact, after a certain level of input use is reached, each succeeding unit of variable input will add less to total output than did the preceding unit of that input. This phenomenon is known as the *law of diminishing returns*.

Economists recognize that empirical production relationships are ordinarily subject to random variations generated by variations in uncontrolled factors of production. Aside from this recognition of unexplained residuals, conventional production economic analysis assumes *the stability of nature*. By this assumption, exactly the same amounts and combinations of factors of production used under exactly the same physical conditions are expected to produce the same physical product. If this assumption is not true, it is much more difficult to predict or understand the results of the production process, and present prediction methods are largely inapplicable. Stability in nature precludes the "miraculous presence" of "ghost" inputs which cause nature to produce one result at one time and another result at another time, *ceteris paribus*. This view insists that production functions do not shift upward or downward from a given set of rigorously defined input axes;[1] instead, production changes with movements along one or more of the input axes.

TECHNOLOGICAL ADVANCE

When technological advance involves a new factor of production or previously unknown way of combining old factors of production, the so-called upward shift in the production function from the horizontal axis is not an upward shift from the same set of rigorously defined input axes; instead, it is the product associated with a new input axis in the function, or the result of using a previously excluded combination of inputs. In such cases, there is no mysterious upward shift of the production function, as a result of using some mysterious nonconventional input called new technology. In this case, the "scientific" procedure

---

[1] Rigorously defined input axes represent a factor of production of unchanging composition with each unit of exactly the same size.

requires finding out what new factor or combination of factors of production has been discovered. Once the new factor or combination is known, its productivity can be measured and the production function relationship involving that factor or combination can be determined in a straightforward conventional manner with the new input or new combination treated as a conventional input or combination. No miraculous or mysterious presence of a ghost input called new technology is required to explain changes in output. New technology does not even enter the production function as a factor of production, conventional or otherwise; instead, a new but *conventional* type of input or a new but *conventional* combination of inputs enters into a very, very conventional kind of production function. Though hybrid seed corn is different from open pollinated seed corn, the relationships between these two inputs and with output are entirely conventional. When conventional steel and wood are combined in a new way to form a new tool such as a long-handled hoe instead of a short-handled one, a new set of production relationships of an entirely conventional nature results, while the process of inventing the new hoe does not enter into the production process.

If the relationship of a technological advance to production is viewed as in the last section, then the study of how new inputs and/or combinations of inputs are discovered or created is easily separated from the mechanistic study of production functions. So separated, the tools of historical analysis; the insights of sociology; biographical studies of inventors, industrialists, and scientists; educational studies; and case studies of institutes and research laboratories can all contribute to our understanding of technological advance without being forced through "production functions" in an over-simplified, unrealistic manner.

INCREASES IN MANAGERIAL SKILL

In the case of management, a similar pattern of reasoning applies. Some analysts write about increases in managerial skill as capable of shifting production functions upward from a rigorously defined set of input axes. This mysterious upward shift of a production function denies the stability assumption. It implies that exactly the same combination and amounts of inputs used under exactly the same conditions somehow or other acquire the ability to produce more than they would previously have produced. Something miraculous is assumed to happen as the result of the presence of a ghost input. A more scientific alternative to this questionable procedure is to regard the managerial unit of a business as a decision making unit which controls the amounts and combinations of *conventional* factors of production entering into a *conventional* production process. Superior managers, under this procedure, may be regarded as making superior decisions about the amounts and combinations of conventional factors of production which will be employed. These superior decisions may result in a more profitable or more advantageous position on a production function but cannot be regarded as miraculous or mysterious, or as factors of production.

So viewed, the problem is to estimate the productivity of the factors of production which the managerial unit decides to employ. The production function and the factor of production concepts are preserved in their conventional workability and scientific integrity. This spares the economist the embarrassing task of informing himself and his colleagues about just how management becomes a factor of production. He does not have to answer questions about just how a cow, for instance, absorbs managerial capacity into its production processes, yielding a marginal physical product of management in the production of milk which, in turn, appears in the bulk tank for delivery to the consumers of a given milk consumption area. Also, the production economist does not have to understand the physiology of how a growing corn plant absorbs managerial inputs and eventually delivers a marginal physical product of management in the production of corn to the combine as it comes through the field. Instead, the production economist needs only to estimate the consequences of managerial decisions to employ so much of such and such conventional inputs in the conventional production of ordinary milk and corn. Though this attitude on the part of an economist would not contribute to the understanding of the managerial process itself, it does have the advantage of freeing the researcher's time for attention to the managerial process itself instead of wasting it on some imaginary factor of production. This managerial unit makes decisions about the use of *conventional* inputs in *conventional* production processes. The processes of the managerial unit involve the definition of problems. They also involve both the acquisition and analysis of normative information leading to decisions as to what inputs to use in attaining what objectives. Also involved is ability to execute or put decisions into action. As such, managerial processes are conditioned by the bearing of responsibility for attaining certain goods and avoiding certain ills inherent in the total environment in which the managerial activity takes place. This view of management has the advantage of not cluttering up perfect good *conventional* production function concepts with slipshod mystical thinking, while concentrating the attention of students of management on the hard core of the managerial process itself.

IMPROVEMENT IN THE HUMAN AGENT

Improvement in the human agent is likely to take place with respect to its capacity to manage, including the ability to acquire and originate technological advance. Such improvements have been handled in the above two sections. Other improvements are likely to involve acquisitions of skills such as those of a machinist, tractor driver, or dairy husbandryman. Here, again, it seems advantageous to treat each *kind* of skilled labor as a separate input. This permits them to be treated as conventional inputs for conventional production functions, thereby preserving the integrity of production analysis while avoiding "mystical presences" which contradict the stability assumption. It also has the advantage of drawing a sharp distinction between production processes and the processes of improving the human agent.

SUMMARY

This very brief note has argued that technological advance, improvements in managerial capacity, and improvements in the human agent involve the use of conventional kinds of inputs in conventional kinds of production processes and that the production economic analyst's task is to estimate the productivity of various amounts and combinations of such inputs as are involved. At the same time, it is contended that regarding technological advance, improvements in managerial capacity, and improvements in the human agent in this way would free investigators to examine the processes of developing new technologies, managerial processes, and improvements in the human agent without the restrictions imposed by the rather mechanistic production function concept. This separation of the mechanistic estimation of the relationships between use of inputs and output from the much less mechanistic processes of creating technological advance, improving managerial capacity, and improving the human agent, it seems, should preserve both the power of production function analysis and the breadth and flexibility of other approaches more appropriate to understanding the technological creativity of mankind, the spontaneity of the managerial process, and the very complex procedures of training and developing this skill of human beings, as humans, rather than as factors of production such as fertilizer, gasoline, chicken feed, and irrigation water.

part 3

THEORETICAL ASPECTS OF AGRICULTURE
IN ECONOMIC DEVELOPMENT

The post-World War II period brought forth a series of discussions on how growth could be sustained in advanced nations. The Harrod-Domar model was foremost among the growth models in these discussions. Other models which followed were those by Smithies, Dusenberry, Tobin, Solow, and Kaldor. Typically one input such as capital held the center of the stage in these models. These models, of course, were of little interest to those concerned with agricultural development—especially in less developed nations.[1]

The postwar theoretical work on how development could be initiated and accelerated in the less developed nations typically has been couched in partial equilibrium analysis and has reflected the important policy issues of the day. Economists generally assumed that there were some particular barriers or obstacles to overcome and that the problem at hand was one of breaking down the particular economic barrier. Hagen[2] and Hirschman (Selection 25) have been critical of this approach to development strategy.

Gutman in a 1957 paper challenged the view that agricultural development would facilitate industrial expansion;[3] he contended that since

---

[1] For a discussion of these and earlier theories of growth see Bert F. Hoselitz (ed.), *Theories of Economic Growth*, The Free Press of Glencoe, New York, 1960.

[2] Everett E. Hagen, "On the Theory of Social Change: How Economic Growth Begins," Chap. 3 in *Inadequacy of Economic Theories of Growth*, The Dorsey Press, Inc., Homewood, Ill., 1962.

[3] G. O. Gutman, "A Note on Economic Development with Subsistence Agriculture," *Oxford Economic Papers*, vol. 9, pp. 323–329, November, 1957.

agricultural workers in many less developed nations are rewarded with the average rather than the marginal product, a rise in agricultural output per worker may pull nonagricultural workers back into agriculture. Enke[4] criticized Gutman and demonstrated that, given certain realistic assumptions about income and price elasticities of demand among peasant workers, a comparative increase in agricultural productivity will expand the industrial sector in a closed economy. Therefore, Enke shows that industrialization tends to be a consequence rather than a cause of development in a closed economy. In an open economy, however, Enke shows that other national and international variables may dictate a different chain of events.

Disguised unemployment is one of the recurring concepts in the postwar development literature—especially in the agricultural development literature. The authors of Selection 7 survey the disguised unemployment literature, examine its theoretical underpinnings, and appraise recent studies of disguised unemployment in Thailand, India, Italy, and Greece. Disguised unemployment gained attention in the development literature through Ragnar Nurkse's *Problems of Capital Formation in Underdeveloped Nations*[5] in 1953. Nurkse argued that development could be accelerated through measures which mobilized the concealed saving in the surplus agricultural labor through using this labor in social overhead construction. Disguised unemployment came under strong attack later in the 1950s. Some writers shifted their position on disguised unemployment; nevertheless, the theory still has a strong body of followers. An Indian economist wrote in 1961, for example, "By far the most serious problem in underdeveloped countries is that of disguised unemployment."[6] In addition, Georgescu-Roegen argues in Selection 8 that "To regard the notion of overpopulation (disguised unemployment) as a myth is undoubtedly a Marxist residual." Georgescu-Roegen believes overpopulation to exist in many countries today; he presents a theoretical rationale for an institutional structure which will employ the residual population until an increasing portion can be absorbed into the nonagricultural sector. He argues that socialism and capitalism are inefficient forms for such organization of agriculture in overpopulated lands. He points out that under feudalism, however, total agricultural output may be maximized along with high labor-utilization, since the governing principle of peasant employment is total family output, not marginal productivity. This feature of the feudal structure is present today in individual peasant holdings. Therefore, Georgescu-

---

[4] Stephen Enke, "Industrialization through Greater Productivity in Agriculture," *Review of Economics and Statistics*, vol. 44, pp. 88–91, February, 1962.

[5] Oxford University Press, New York, 1953.

[6] Nasir Ahmad Khan, "Problems of Growth of an Underdeveloped Economy—India," Asia Publishing House, New York, 1961, p. 155.

Roegen cautions planners against adopting the marginal principle prematurely in overpopulated countries because this will increase leisure and reduce total agricultural output.

In Selection 9, Dandekar rejects Georgescu-Roegen's institutional organization for agriculture in an overpopulated country, advocating an agricultural organization based upon "large units of land, and population, feudal in theory, modern in technology and oriented to a socialistic purpose."

Among the important contributions in the theoretical aspects of underdevelopment is Leibenstein's article, in which he attempts to rationalize the existence of a positive wage in areas of surplus rural labor through the introduction of a wage-productivity relationship.[7] He shows that under conditions where the level of wages affects the amount of effort a worker puts forth, it is rational for an employer to employ workers beyond the point where their marginal productivity equals the wages paid.

Dualism has been another recurring concept in the development literature. J. H. Boeke in 1942 advanced the concept of dualism which suggested that an economy had a modern or advanced sector and a traditional sector.[8] Boeke's theory was based on cultural contrasts and sociological underpinnings; his thesis and policy prescriptions have been sharply criticized by Higgins.[9]

With the notions of dualism and disguised unemployment in agriculture in mind, we turn to Lewis's celebrated two-sector growth model[10] in which the economy is divided into a capitalist or advanced sector and a subsistence sector. The capitalist sector expands by drawing the cheap agricultural labor into its employment. The Lewis model has been widely reprinted and needs no further elaboration. One word of caution, however, is called for. It appears that economists sometimes collect data on an aspect of agricultural change and then attempt to enhance their findings by hitching them to the Lewis growth model. Models are designed to facilitate our thinking by helping to formulate some of the important variables for consideration. It is an understatement to note that the Lewis growth model has frequently been taken out of context and used quite superficially in field studies and in policy formation.

[7] Harvey Leibenstein, "The Theory of Underemployment in Backward Economies," *The Journal of Political Economy,* vol. 65, pp. 91–103, April, 1957.

[8] J. H. Boeke, *Economics and Economic Policy of Dual Societies,* Tjeenk Willnik, Haarlem, The Netherlands, 1953. (Earlier edition in two volumes, 1942, 1946.)

[9] Benjamin Higgins, "The 'Dualistic Theory' of Underdeveloped Areas," *Economic Development and Cultural Change,* vol. 4, pp. 99–115, January, 1956.

[10] W. Arthur Lewis, "Economic Development with Unlimited Supplies of Labour," *The Manchester School,* May, 1954. Reprinted in A. N. Agarwala and S. P. Singh, *The Economics of Underdevelopment,* Oxford University Press, New York, 1958 and 1963.

While the Lewis model ignores the agricultural sector, except as a reservoir of labor, the agricultural sector was rediscovered and the structural interdependence of the agricultural and nonagricultural sectors was emphasized in two-sector models by Jorgenson[11] and Ranis and Fei (Selection 10) in 1961. Whereas Jorgenson assumes a positive productivity for the agricultural labor force, Ranis and Fei assume a marginal product of zero or close to zero. The main contribution of the Ranis-Fei model—showing the interaction between the agricultural and nonfarm sectors in initiating and accelerating development—is contained in the first portion of their article. Therefore, only the first fourteen pages are reprinted in Selection 10.

The Ranis-Fei model of development, like most other models, has many shortcomings. In Selection 11, Oshima comments on these shortcomings, and Ranis and Fei offer their reply.

[11] Dale W. Jorgenson, "The Development of a Dual Economy," *Economic Journal,* vol. 71, pp. 309–334, June, 1961.

7. Disguised Unemployment in Agriculture: A Survey[*]

CHARLES H. C. KAO, KURT R. ANSCHEL, AND CARL K. EICHER

INTRODUCTION

One of the recurring concepts in the postwar economic development literature is that of disguised unemployment—that is, the case in which the marginal product of labor is zero or negative. Although much has been written about this topic, the literature is widely scattered and often inaccessible. Moreover, the articles and papers reprinted in this Part assume an implicit knowledge about the evolution of the concept of disguised unemployment, the theoretical underpinnings of the concept, and the present status of empirical studies of the issue. Therefore, the modest objective of this survey paper is to review the literature on disguised unemployment as background for understanding the articles reprinted as Selections 8, 9, 10, and 11.

This paper is divided into three sections. In the first, disguised unemployment is discussed in historical perspective. The second examines the theoretical foundation of disguised unemployment with special references to contributions by Nurkse,[33] Lewis,[24] Eckaus,[7] Leibenstein,[21,22] and Mellor.[29] Since the presence or absence of disguised unemployment is an empirical issue, the final section examines recent empirical studies to appraise methodological advances in measuring disguised unemployment in less developed countries.

DISGUISED UNEMPLOYMENT IN HISTORICAL PERSPECTIVE

Joan Robinson coined the words "disguised unemployment" in 1936 to describe workers in developed countries who accepted inferior occupations as a result of being laid off from industries suffering from a lack

[*] The authors are research assistants and assistant professor of agricultural economics at Michigan State University.

of effective demand.[43,44] She was referring to workers having a low rather than a zero marginal product of labor.

Studies by Buck,[2] Warriner,[55] and Rosenstein-Rodan[45] in the 1930s and 1940s in less developed countries presented statistical data for China and Southeastern Europe to suggest that a large percentage of agricultural labor was idle for substantial periods of the year. In fact, Buck collected data on over 15,000 farms in China during the years 1929–1933 which revealed that only 35 per cent of the men between fifteen and sixty years of age had full-time jobs. Buck's labor utilization approach,[2] of course, did not reveal anything about the marginal product of labor. Doreen Warriner followed in 1939 with a widely quoted study[55] which revealed that before World War II in "Eastern Europe as a whole, one-quarter to one-third of the farm population is surplus . . ." (p. 68). Next, in 1943, Rosenstein-Rodan[45] wrote that twenty to twenty-five million of the 100 to 110 million people in Eastern and Southeastern Europe were either wholly or partially unemployed (p. 202). In 1945, Mandelbaum[26] estimated that from 20 to 27 per cent of the active rural workers in Greece, Yugoslavia, Poland, Hungary, Rumania, and Bulgaria were redundant; he presented a "mechanical" model of planned industrialization to absorb the surplus labor within one generation. The studies cited so far all measured labor utilization in agriculture in many countries in the 1930s and 1940s and are widely cited as support for the existence of disguised unemployment in agriculture. In fact, the widely quoted 1951 United Nations report[53] by a group of experts including W. Arthur Lewis, T. W. Schultz, and D. R. Gadgil cited these studies and added that it seems "safe to assume that for many regions of India and Pakistan, and for certain parts of the Philippines and Indonesia, the surplus [rural population] cannot be less than the pre-war average for the East European Region" (p. 9). The experts advanced this definition of disguised unemployment: zero marginal product of agricultural labor and the condition of *ceteris paribus,* which has been adopted by Leibenstein,[21,22] Viner,[54] Rosenstein-Rodan,[46] and many others.

The presence or absence of disguised unemployment is partly an issue of definition. While the writers mentioned above accept a zero marginal product of labor and the condition of *ceteris paribus,* Navarrete and Navarrete in a 1951 article[32] relaxed the *ceteris paribus* assumption and included the introduction of some capital into the production function in their definition of underemployment. Obviously the greater the reorganization of agriculture and the greater the introduction of capital, the larger the volume of workers who can be transferred out of agriculture without affecting agricultural output.

In 1953, Nurkse[33] introduced a theory of economic development on the assumption that disguised unemployment was present over a wide portion of Asia. Nurkse stated that development could be initiated and accelerated in these countries, by forming capital through the employment of redundant rural labor. Farm output does not fall, in the Nurkse schema, when workers are shifted to nonfarm tasks, because he relaxes the static assumptions slightly to permit better organization through "consolidation of scattered strips and plots of land" (p. 33). The Egyptian economist Koestner was among the first to criticize the disguised unemployment doctrine when, in an article written in 1953,[20] he strongly criticized Nurkse's position.

Lewis presented another version of disguised unemployment in 1954, when he introduced a model of capital formation and development in which the capitalist sector grew by drawing on cheap rural labor without any significant reduction in agricultural output.[24,25] This is discussed in more detail in the next section of this paper. Next, Eckaus explained the existence of disguised unemployment by limited technical substitutability of factors of production in agriculture.[7]

Concentrated opposition to disguised unemployment came from Warriner in 1955[57] and Schultz in 1955 and 1956.[47,48] Warriner reversed her earlier position in Land and Poverty in the Middle East[56] in which she showed that 50 per cent of the Egyptian rural population was surplus by noting that she had omitted the labor requirement for capital maintenance in agriculture (p. 26). Schultz[47] wrote that "all too much attention is being directed to taking up the existing slack in countries that now have a poor collection of resources on the assumption that there are many underemployed resources readily available for economic growth" (p. 373). While Schultz cited examples in Latin American countries where the removal of agricultural labor resulted in a decline in agricultural output,[47] he argued on a broader scale and wrote, "I know of no evidence for any poor country anywhere that would even suggest that a transfer of some small fraction, say, 5 per cent, of the existing labor force out of agriculture, with other things equal, could be made without reducing its [agricultural] production" (p. 375). Viner was the next strong opponent of disguised unemployment.[54] Writing in 1957, he criticized writers such as Eckaus[7] who contended that disguised unemployment could exist in agriculture because of limited technical substitutability of factors of production, by noting:[54]

> I find it impossible to conceive a farm of any kind on which, other factors of production being held constant in quantity, and even in form as well, it would not be possible, by known methods, to obtain some addition to the crop by using additional labor in more careful selection and planting of the seed, more intensive weeding, cultivation, thinning, and mulching, more painstaking harvesting, gleaning and cleaning of the crop (p. 347).

In an unpublished dissertation in 1957, Kenadjian reviewed a wide range of studies of disguised unemployment and concluded:[18]

> . . . that almost invariably the estimates of surplus labor have been inflated and the opinions about the extent of redundance in a particular country have contained elements of gross exaggeration in all the countries about which quantitative information can be found to any significant extent. In particular, assertions that disguised unemployment exists in proportions as high as 25 to 30 percent of the labor force in any sector of the economy of even the most overpopulated countries of the world appear to be entirely without foundation (p. 259).

Haberler joined the attack in 1957[12] and 1959[13] and criticized disguised unemployment, basing his reasoning on the propositions earlier advanced by Schultz and Viner.

Our discussion so far has summarized the important literature in the disguised unemployment debate, with the exception of theoretical developments by Eckaus, Leibenstein, Lewis, Nurkse, Georgescu-Roegen and Mellor, which are inspected more fully in the next section. Five empirical studies will be discussed in detail in the final section.

THE THEORETICAL FOUNDATION OF DISGUISED UNEMPLOYMENT

This section will examine the assumptions and theoretical foundation underlying the concept of disguised unemployment. Almost all economists define disguised unemployment as the existence of a portion of the labor force which can be removed without reducing output. Most also assume that no other changes occur (*ceteris paribus*). The theoreticians must suggest answers to the following questions if they are to explain why disguised unemployment exists contrary to the expectations of orthodox theory. First, if labor is unemployed or otherwise wasted, why are techniques not introduced which use less land and capital relative to labor? Second, with given technology (fixed capital-land-labor ratios), why is labor used to the point where no returns are forthcoming? Employers of hired labor lose money when they pay a wage to labor whose product is zero or negligible. The self-employed who produce nothing would do better to hire out their surplus labor for a wage. Third, why are wages higher than the marginal product? If large numbers of people produce nothing or very little, wages normally would be bid down to the marginal product of labor.

We will attempt to outline how several economists deal with one or more of the above questions. Eckaus[7] discusses only the first; Lewis,[24] Georgescu-Roegen,[11] Leibenstein,[21,22] and Nurkse[33] propose solutions to the second and third. Mellor,[29] on the other hand, pursues a different path by arguing that unemployment may be related to a deficiency of demand.

Eckaus, writing in 1955,[7] is the only one who systematically analyzes the technological restraints which might lead to disguised unemployment. He says that disguised unemployment exists when "with agricultural techniques remaining unchanged, withdrawal of farm labor would not reduce output" (p. 545). He then asks why, if labor is in surplus, more labor-intensive techniques are not in use. He believes that even the most labor-intensive agricultural process requires some minimum amount of capital per unit of labor; there is some minimum ratio of capital to labor, but many underdeveloped nations have less capital than is required to utilize their whole labor force. Hence, a portion of the available labor supply is unused. Eckaus left it to others to explain why labor is used until its marginal product is zero, but continues to be paid a positive wage.

Lewis, in his well-known article[24] "Economic Development with Un-limited Supplies of Labor," analyzes the relationship between the subsistence and capitalist sectors of an underdeveloped country.* In his model, surplus labor is available in both rural and urban areas. The rural labor surplus is disguised in the sense that everyone is working, but if some portion is withdrawn output will not fall; the remaining workers will just work harder. The urban surplus labor is openly unemployed; porters waiting for the next ship to come in, retail traders waiting for a customer, messengers sitting in the courtyard. Workers, rural and urban, do not receive their marginal product, but a higher traditional wage. Lewis suggests that the average product per worker in agriculture determines the traditional wage. Labor employed in the capitalist sector will also be paid the traditional wage as long as there is a surplus of labor in the subsistence sector. The low and constant wages permit large profits for potential reinvestment in the capitalist sector. The economy grows at a faster rate, because profits grow relative to the size of the capitalist sector and an increasing proportion of national income is reinvested.

In this article, Lewis's chief contribution to the concept of disguised unemployment is his explanation of the existence of a greater than zero wage when the marginal product of labor is zero. He explains by tradition and lack of alternatives the existence of self-employed labor which receives a positive wage, but whose marginal product is negligible. In peasant agriculture, each family member receives the family's average product regardless of contribution. Since there are no opportunities for receiving a wage higher than the average product on the family's

* For amendments to the Lewis model, see the articles by Ranis and Fei (Selection 10), Barber, and Enke, References 41, 1, and 6.

farm, there is no motivation to leave the farm and the average product will be greater than the marginal product.

Georgescu-Roegen, in Selection 8 of this book, provides an alternative explanation of zero marginal product of agricultural labor.[11] Georgescu-Roegen contends that neither capitalism nor socialism is an efficient form of organizing agriculture in an overpopulated country. Under capitalism, labor will not be employed beyond the point where its marginal product equals the wage rate and, as a result, a portion of the labor force will remain idle and the total agricultural output will not be maximized. Feudalism, as Georgescu points out, provided such an institutional framework because the family maximized employment beyond the point where its marginal product equaled wages. Today feudalism has been replaced by individual peasant holdings and the total agricultural output is still maximized because the employment of the peasant family is governed by maximizing total family output rather than by the principle of marginal productivity. Hence, marginal product is zero when the total output of the family farm is maximized.*

Leibenstein provides another explanation of a greater than zero wage rate. When labor is unemployed and the labor market is competitive, wages would be bid down to very low levels. He explains the phenomenon of greater than zero wages through an interaction between labor productivity and wage rates. Since output per man increases due to improved nutrition when wage rates increase, landlords find it profitable to hire all available labor to prevent wage rates being bid down, poor nutrition, and the resulting small output per man. Although net revenue would be higher if only a portion of the labor force were utilized, wages would fall, causing productivity to decline.†

Nurkse defines disguised unemployment as zero marginal product of labor when some organizational changes are introduced. If minor changes such as consolidation of landholdings are permitted, then a substantial amount of agricultural labor can be used in other pursuits, such as building dams and rural roads, without reducing agricultural output. Nurkse explains that labor is used until no more output is forthcoming, because family labor is not paid. He assumes a freeholding peasant agriculture in which food is shared among all family members. Nurkse does not believe that significant savings of labor can be made through the reduction of leisure time or through the exertion of greater effort by the remaining workers, but must be obtained through better use of labor time. Owing to poor organization, much time is spent on essentially inefficient tasks, such as walking from place to place, transporting materials and products, and organizing and supervising

---

* Dandekar (Selection 9) disagrees with Georgescu-Roegen's analysis.

† Criticisms and amendments to Leibenstein's propositions are found in References 36, 9, 27, and 58.

other workers. He suggests that through reorganization enough labor time can be saved to make feasible the utilization of labor in other capacities.

Nurkse's early optimism for releasing surplus labor through changes in agricultural organization was qualified somewhat in 1958[35] when he wrote that such changes in agricultural organization "are a major undertaking and cannot be lightly taken for granted" (p. 262).

The last approach to disguised unemployment to be discussed assumes a deficiency of demand. Mellor[29] is the chief proponent of this position. He argues that the peasant in the underdeveloped country works hard to achieve some traditionally determined minimum standard of living, but has no motivation for increasing his income above that level because of tradition-bound consumption patterns.

Mellor's deficient demand approach is similar to the concept of unemployment advanced by Joan Robinson in her demand deficiency theory. There are few empirical data to support Mellor's position. For a survey of literature rejecting the notion of tradition-bound peasant consumption patterns in Africa, for example, see the recent article by Jones.[17]

EMPIRICAL STUDIES OF DISGUISED UNEMPLOYMENT

Five empirical studies of disguised unemployment in Thailand, India, Italy, and Greece are examined in this section (References 30, 31, 40, 46, and 49).* Three are on the micro level. Two are on the macro level. Discussion will center on two aspects: the methodology adopted in these studies and their empirical results.

Generally speaking, two methods are available to measure disguised unemployment. The first is the direct method, which is based upon a sample survey. This method uses the labor utilization and the labor productivity approaches. The labor utilization approach presents an inventory of what labor is used in the field or in other farm tasks as a percentage of the available supply. The labor productivity approach goes a step further and examines the relationship between the quantity of labor used and/or available and the level of production.[29]

The indirect method, which relies on secondary data, is the second method of measuring disguised unemployment. The three variants of this method measure (1) the difference between the number of labor hours required to produce a given output and the number of labor hours available from the active agrarian population, (2) the difference between the density of population deemed adequate for a given type of cultivation and the actual density of population, and (3) the difference between the number of acres or hectares required under a given type of

---

* Other empirical studies of disguised unemployment are in References 4, 18, 38, and 39. Oshima also mentions some additional empirical studies in Reference 36.

cultivation to provide one person with a "standard income," in contrast
to the number of available acres or hectares and available agrarian
population. (See Reference 46, p. 2.)

Mellor and Stevens's Study in Thailand

Mellor and Stevens undertook a study of the average and marginal
product of farm labor in Thailand, which was based on labor income
records obtained by personal interviews in 104 rice farms at Bang Chan,
Thailand, and published in 1956.[30] All farms were assumed to have
a similar rice production function. The total output of rice was estimated
with a high degree of accuracy because most of the rice was taken to the
local miller for polishing. Labor inputs were measured in terms of man
equivalents on the basis of interviews concerning the number of persons available for farm work on each farm. In their analysis, Mellor and
Stevens[30] said: " . . . labor that is available for farm work but is doing
no work is counted as part of labor input. Labor that is actually on the
field but contributing no increment in output through its efforts is not
treated differently from labor that is not working but is available for
such work" (p. 785). To estimate the productivity of labor they used
a least-square linear regression equation. The equation is $Y = 30.4 +$
$13.5X$ (Y = total product, X = man equivalent). The b (slope) value in
the equation of 13.5 tang (which is equal to approximately 24 pounds
or 0.54 bushel) is not significantly different from zero at the 5 per cent
level of significance. They write,[30] "This is consistent with the hypothesis that in this type of area, the marginal product of labor will be
zero or close to zero" (p. 987). Thus, disguised unemployment existed in
this area. More recently, Mellor[29] commented on this village study and
stated that the data were inadequate for more than a rough approximation of disguised unemployment (p. 3). Given the assumptions of labor
homogeneity and a uniform production function, this study represents a
valid method of measuring marginal labor productivity.

Harry T. Oshima, commenting recently on the Mellor and Stevens's
study, stated:[37] [EDITOR'S NOTE: See Selection 11.]

> There is one empirical study, . . . of 104 farms in one Thai village.
> In this pioneer study, the conclusion is reached that there is substantial
> zero MPP farm workers. I feel it is hazardous to regard this study as
> conclusive for either theoretical or policy use. The spread of the data
> in the scatter diagram relating rice yields to labor input for each of the
> 104 farms suggests to me, not a linear regression line as it does to the
> authors, but inadequate data and/or dubious assumptions. For example,
> they assume that rice production functions for each of the 104 farms were
> the same. In estimating labor input, the authors exclude working children
> under 15 years old and include all persons 15 years and above, whether
> working or not (p. 450).

Mujumdar's Study in India

In a recent book, Mujumdar studies two facets of underemployment in agriculture, namely, disguised and seasonal unemployment.[31] Attention here is given to the empirical results of disguised unemployment.

Field investigation covering three months in 1954–1955 was conducted in nine selected villages of the Bombay Karnatak region to measure the degree of disguised unemployment. The author interviewed village officers and studied village records to determine the population, occupations, land use, number of livestock, labor movements, work schedule, and standard cultivated holdings in each village. Also, twenty-five families in each village were intensively interviewed to determine family size, occupation, sources of income, size of holdings, and annual work schedule.

The author uses the standard cultivated holding as his most important tool in estimating underemployment. He defines it as "the area of land which is sufficient to absorb, in given conditions of techniques and type of farming, the labour of an average farm family working with a pair of bullocks" (pp. 83–84). Unfortunately, Mujumdar does not tell us how he determined the standard holding. He simply states: "When once the standard holding is defined for a village or area, the intensity of employment can be measured against the standard so determined. The ideal case being that of full employment when the cultivated holding is of the size of the standard unit or above. All other cases come under disguised unemployment . . ." (p. 202).

Mujumdar finds in his nine-village study of small farmers that "roughly about 71 per cent of the farmers are affected by disguised unemployment" (p. 208). Thus, this figure, "in spite of all the limitation, present[s] in concrete terms the alarming proportions which the phenomenon of disguised unemployment has assumed" (p. 208).

There are at least three shortcomings of Mujumdar's methodology. First, the standard holding is essentially an arbitrary unit. It assumes that bullocks are used in producing all crops and allows no alternative production techniques. Nor does it recognize the possibility that bullocks may be labor-replacing, and hence uneconomical, on farms with large amounts of available family labor relative to land. In addition, Mujumdar makes no adjustments for differences in capital, land fertility, and irrigation on each farm. Second, Mujumdar makes no special attempt to quantify the labor input and include it in his analysis. He assumes that all farms are using the most labor-intensive techniques available. Yet, this, he admits, is not true of India. Third, Mujumdar, like many other economists, fails to relate his empirical definition to his theoretical definition of disguised unemployment which is defined as "taking the size of labour force as given, disguised unemployment may be described as a situation in which the withdrawal of a certain quantity of the factor labour to other uses, will not diminish the total output of the sector from which it is withdrawn, *given* a measure of reorganization in the sector" (p. 39).

Mujumdar's empirical definition classifies any worker on a farm of less than the standard holding as underemployed; he sees no need to estimate his productivity or the productivity of the group. Using the standard holding rather than the marginal productivity technique, Mujumdar arrives at the dubious conclusion that more than 70 per cent of the agricultural population could be removed from the region without lowering production.

Rosenstein-Rodan's Study in Southern Italy

In 1957, Rosenstein-Rodan[46] wrote that it was his firm belief that disguised unemployment of more than 5 per cent exists in many—though not all—underdeveloped countries; he supported this belief by measuring disguised unemployment in southern Italy (p. 1). He used the static concept of disguised unemployment.*

The following major assumptions and criteria were used:† (1) Only agricultural small holdings of peasant owners and tenants were included. (2) The active population was assumed to be between fourteen and sixty-five years of age. Coefficients of labor efficiency of men, women, and children were used for each type of cultivation. (3) Surplus workers were assumed to be involuntarily unemployed. (4) Labor hours required for each type of cultivation over the whole year, month by month, were counted and compared with available labor hours. An average of 270 available workdays per year was assumed. (5) A distinction was made between (*a*) removable disguised underemployment or disguised unemployment, (*b*) disguised fractional underemployment, that is, labor hours not used throughout the whole year which do not add up to an entire labor unit (persons in this category cannot be moved out of agriculture), and (*c*) seasonal underemployment due to climatic factors. These distinctions were taken into account in calculating the number of laborers, affected by disguised unemployment. (6) A slight deviation from the static concept was allowed in the analysis. The author used the direct method of questionnaires to distinguish different types of cultivation, different sizes and forms of property, the composition of the labor force, and the number of labor hours required and supplied.

* The static concept refers to the amount of population in agriculture which can be removed without any change in the method of cultivation and without leading to any reduction in output. Hence, the marginal product of labor is zero. See Reference 46, p. 1.

† Only the six most relevant considerations are listed here.

Rosenstein-Rodan[46] found that "more than 10 per cent of the active labor force in southern Italian agriculture is surplus . . ." (p. 4). Later, however, Kenadjian[18] discussed this matter with Rosenstein-Rodan and reported: "When Rosenstein-Rodan observes that in southern Italy around 10 to 12 per cent of the actual population in agriculture are removable, he is including among the removable surplus the individuals who are needed for 50 days or less. If the more rigid definition, which is also the more sensible one, is adopted, the removable surplus is reduced to 5 per cent" (p. 250).

This clearly illustrates that a careful appraisal of the definition is necessary before one so blindly accepts an author's statement that 10, 20, or 70 per cent of the labor is redundant in agriculture.

Schultz's Study in India

As was pointed out earlier, T. W. Schultz supported the validity of the disguised unemployment concept in the United Nations report[53] in 1951 (p. 9) and later rejected the existence of disguised unemployment in publications in 1956.[47,48] In his recently published book, he reinforced this position by turning to the influenza epidemic of 1918–1919 in India to test the hypothesis that the marginal product of a part of the labor force in agriculture was zero.[49] This incident was used because the epidemic struck suddenly; the death rate reached a peak within weeks and then diminished rapidly. Those who survived were not debilitated for very long. Schultz estimated the existence of disguised unemployment by comparing the reduction in acreage sown with the reduction in the labor force. Such a comparison assumes that if any disguised unemployment exists, the acreage sown will not be reduced as a result of a sudden reduction in the labor force. The rationale for such a comparison is[49] "where there are many people relative to land and much land is cultivated intensively, the expectation would be that acreage sown would be less sensitive to a decrease in the labor force than total yield" (p. 11). Therefore, the acreage sown "would be a more decisive test than . . . a reduction of the same percentage in agricultural production" (p. 11). Schultz found that the agricultural labor force in India was reduced by about 9 per cent, while:[49]

> The area sown in 1919–20 was, however, 10 million acres below, or 3.8 percent less than that of the base year 1916–17. In general, the provinces of India that had the highest death rates attributed to the epidemic also had the largest percentage decline in acreage sown to crops. It would be hard to find any support in these data for the doctrine that a part of the labor force in agriculture in India at the time of the epidemic had a marginal product of zero (p. 67).

The influenza epidemic test was a unique laboratory technique to use in measuring disguised unemployment. An advantage of this approach was that the influenza epidemic did not directly affect animals, and therefore the only change in the factors of production was in the number of workers. Since India's population grew 44 per cent from 1921 to 1951 as compared with 5 per cent from 1894 to 1921,* the population pressures in India today are much different from those of the period studied by Schultz. Therefore, one wonders whether Schultz needs more observations from India in the post-1920 period and from other countries in the 1960s before he can conclude "a part of the labor working in agriculture in poor countries [today] has a marginal productivity of zero . . . is a false doctrine" (p. 13).

Pepelasis and Yotopoulos' Study in Greece

Pepelasis and Yotopoulos[40] recently published a macro level study which was designed to measure the volume of removable surplus labor as well as that seasonal surplus labor in Greek agriculture for the period from 1953 to 1960. Removable (chronic) surplus labor was defined as the amount of labor which could be removed for at least one year without any change in the quantities of other factors of production and without leading to any reduction in output (p. 86). The authors measured surplus labor by comparing the labor available with the labor required for a given volume of output within the agriculture sector. The indirect method, using secondary data, was employed to derive estimates of labor availability and labor requirements.

The labor available was calculated from the total size of the agricultural population from fifteen to sixty-nine years old, as measured by the Census. This estimate was converted into a labor potential and into homogeneous Man Productive Units on the basis of conversion coefficients measuring the workday of an adult male farm worker. Finally the Man Productive Units were converted into Man Productive Days available during the period from 1953 to 1960 (Chapter Four).

Separate estimates of the annual agricultural labor requirements for farming, husbandry, forestry, fishing, and agricultural transport were computed. Given each year's agricultural activities, Pepelasis and Yotopoulos derived annual labor requirements by product by applying a "labor-intensity coefficient," that is, a labor/land and/or a capital output ratio. The labor coefficients were "expressed in terms of man and supplementary . . . nine-hour workdays estimated to be used per *stremma* of animal or unit of output to produce the given volume of agricultural output of the year" (p. 108). The authors found that "chronic

---

* See A. Coale and E. Hoover, *Population Growth and Economic Development in Low-income Countries: A Case Study of India's Prospects*, Princeton University Press, Princeton, N.J., 1958.

surplus labor in Greek agriculture is virtually nonexistent. From the eight years of our series, it existed only in 1953 and 1954 to a degree of 3.5 and 2.3 respectively. The other years of the period are marked by a seasonal shortage of labor" (p. 136). The authors commented on the feasibility of removing the chronically unemployed by noting "if in one village of 100 working agricultural population the surplus labor is 2 percent, this does not imply that we can remove for a whole year two workers without decreasing the total output of the village" (p. 138). This is so because that labor is not divisible, for both physical and institutional reasons. The 2 per cent, for example, may consist of fractions of labor in surplus spread among a number of families; therefore, "we cannot exactly determine how much chronic surplus labor it is feasible to remove . . . . Its size can only be determined through a *disaggregative microeconomic investigation based on the direct method of studying a sample of farm households*" (p. 138). The important point of this study is the nonexistence of disguised unemployment in Greek agriculture since 1954.

SUMMARY

We have pointed out that the existence of disguised unemployment is largely a matter of definition and the assumptions about the institutional forces involved. Nevertheless, some writers agreed upon the zero product of labor definition in the early 1950s, and it is an understatement to say that the development literature in this period was optimistic about development through the transfer of redundant agricultural labor to other occupations. We have shown that the empirical studies supporting this optimism were often poorly conceived. In addition, we have noted that by considering temporary rather than permanent labor transfers and by allowing some reorganization of production, various writers have arrived at a high percentage of disguised unemployment. To date, there is little reliable empirical evidence to support the existence of more than token—5 per cent—disguised unemployment in underdeveloped countries as defined by a zero marginal product of labor and the condition of *ceteris paribus*.

REFERENCES

1. Barber, William J.: "Disguised Unemployment in Underdeveloped Economies," *Oxford Economic Papers*, vol. 13, pp. 103–115.
2. Buck, John Lossings: *Chinese Farm Economy*, The University of Chicago Press, Chicago, 1930.
3. ———: *Land Utilization in China*, The University of Chicago Press, Chicago, 1937.

4. Cho, Yong Sam: *Disguised Unemployment in South Korean Agriculture,* University of California Press, Berkeley, 1963.
5. Dandekar, V. N.: "Economic Theory and Agrarian Reform," *Oxford Economic Papers,* vol. 14, pp. 69–80, February, 1962.
6. Enke, S.: "Economic Development with Unlimited and Limited Supplies of Labor," *Oxford Economic Papers,* vol. 14, pp. 158–172, June, 1962.
7. Eckaus, R. S.: "Factor Proportions in Underdeveloped Countries," *American Economic Review,* vol. 45, pp. 539–565, September, 1955.
8. Ezekiel, Hannan: "An Application of Leibenstein's Theory of Underemployment," *Journal of Political Economy,* vol. 68, pp. 511–517, October, 1960.
9. Fei, J. C. H. and Gustav Ranis: "Capital Accumulation and Economic Development," *American Economic Review,* vol. 53, pp. 283–313, June, 1963.
10. Frankel, S. Herbert: *The Economic Impact on Under-developed Societies,* Basil Blackwell, E. Mott, Ltd., Oxford, 1953.
11. Georgescu-Roegen, N.: "Economic Theory and Agrarian Economics," *Oxford Economic Papers,* vol. 12, pp. 1–40, February, 1963.
12. Haberler, Gottfried: "Critical Observations on Some Current Notions in the Theory of Economic Development," *L'Industria,* no. 2, pp. 3–13, 1957.
13. ———: "International Trade and Economic Development," Fiftieth Anniversary Commemoration Lectures, Lecture III, National Bank of Egypt, Cairo, 1959.
14. Hsieh, Chiang: "Underemployment in Asia: Nature and Extent," *International Labor Review,* vol. 55, pp. 703–725, January-June, 1952.
15. ———: "Underemployment in Asia: Its Relation to Investment Policy," *International Labor Review,* vol. 56, pp. 30–39, July-December, 1952.
16. International Labor Office: *Measurement of Underemployment,* Geneva, 1957.
17. Jones, William O.: "Economic Man in Africa," *Food Research Institute Studies,* vol. 1, pp. 107–134, May, 1960.
18. Kenadjian, Berdj: "Disguised Unemployment in Underdeveloped Countries," unpublished doctoral dissertation, Harvard University, 1957.
19. Khan, Nasir Ahmad: *Problems of Growth of an Underdeveloped Economy—India,* Asia Publishing House, New York, 1961, Chap. VII.
20. Koestner, N.: "Comments on Professor Nurkse's Capital Accumulation in Underdeveloped Countries," *L'Egypte Contemporaine,* vol. 44, pp. 1–8, Cairo, April, 1953.
21. Leibenstein, Harvey: "The Theory of Underemployment in Backward Economies," *Journal of Political Economy,* vol. 65, pp. 91–103, April, 1957.
22. ———: *Economic Backwardness and Economic Growth,* John Wiley and Sons, Inc., New York, 1957.
23. ———: "Underemployment in Backward Economies: Some Additional Notes," *Journal of Political Economy,* vol. 66, pp. 256–258, June, 1958.
24. Lewis, W. Arthur: "Economic Development with Unlimited Supplies of Labour," *Manchester School of Economic and Social Studies,* pp. 139–192, May, 1954.
25. ———: *The Theory of Economic Growth,* George Allen & Unwin, Ltd., London, 1955.
26. Mandelbaum, K.: *The Industrialization of Backward Areas,* Basil Blackwell & Mott, Ltd., Oxford, 1945.
27. Mazumdar, Dipak: "The Marginal Productivity Theory of Wages and

Disguised Unemployment," *Review of Economic Studies,* vol. 26, pp. 190–197, June, 1959.

28. ——: "Underemployment in Agriculture and the Industrial Wage Rate," *Economica,* vol. 26, pp. 328–340, November, 1959.

29. Mellor, John W.: "The Use and Productivity of Farm Family Labor in Early Stages of Agricultural Development," *Journal of Farm Economics,* vol. 45, pp. 517–534, August, 1963.

30. Mellor, John W. and Robert D. Stevens: "The Average and Marginal Product of Farm Labor in Underdeveloped Economies," *Journal of Farm Economics,* vol. 38, pp. 780–791, August, 1956.

31. Mujumdar, N. A.: *Some Problems of Underemployment,* Popular Book Depot, Bombay, 1961.

32. Navarrete, Alfredo, Jr. and Ifigenia M. Navarrete: "Underemployment in Underdeveloped Economies," *International Economic Papers,* no. 3, pp. 235–239, London, 1953, translated from *El Trimestre Economico,* vol. 17, no. 4, October-December, 1951.

33. Nurkse, Ragnar: *Problems of Capital Formation in Underdeveloped Countries,* Oxford University Press, Fair Lawn, N.J., 1953.

34. ——: "Excess Population and Capital Construction," *Malayan Economic Review,* vol. 2, pp. 1–11, October, 1957.

35. ——: "Epilogue: The Quest for a Stabilization Policy in Primary Producing Countries," *KYKLOS,* vol. 11, fasc. 2, pp. 261–262, 1958.

36. Oshima, Harry T.: "Underemployment in Backward Economies: An Empirical Comment," *Journal of Political Economy,* vol. 66, pp. 259–264, June, 1958.

37. ——: "The Ranis-Fei Model of Economic Development: Comment," *American Economic Review,* vol. 53, pp. 448–452, June, 1963.

38. Parthasaratry, Gogula: "Underemployment and Indian Agriculture," unpublished doctoral dissertation, University of Wisconsin, 1957.

39. Patel, K. R.: "The Nature and Extent of Under-Employment of the Self-Employed Cultivators," unpublished doctoral dissertation, University of Bombay, India, 1962.

40. Pepelasis, Adam A. and Pan A. Yotopoulos: *Surplus Labor in Greek Agriculture, 1953–1960,* Center of Economic Research, Research Monograph Series 2, Athens, Greece, 1962.

41. Ranis, Gustav and John C. H. Fei: "A Theory of Economic Development," *American Economic Review,* vol. 51, pp. 553–558, September, 1961.

42. ——: "The Ranis-Fei Model of Economic Development: Reply," *American Economic Review,* vol. 53, pp. 452–454, June, 1963.

43. Robinson, Joan: "Disguised Unemployment," *Economic Journal,* vol. 46, pp. 225–237, June, 1936.

44. ——: *Essays in the Theory of Employment,* Oxford University Press, London, 1947.

45. Rosenstein-Rodan, P. N.: "Problems of Industrialization of Eastern and South-Eastern Europe," *Economic Journal,* vol. 53, pp. 202–211, June-September, 1943.

46. ——: "Disguised Unemployment and Underemployment in Agriculture," *Monthly Bulletin of Agricultural Economics and Statistics,* vol. 6, pp. 1–7, FAO, Rome, July–August, 1957.

47. Schultz, Theodore W.: "The Role of Government in Promoting Economic Growth," in Leonard D. White (ed.), *The State of the Social Sciences,* University of Chicago Press, Chicago, 1956, pp. 372–383.

48. ——: *The Economic Test in Latin America*, New York State School of Industrial and Labor Relations Bulletin 35, Cornell University, Ithaca, pp. 14–15, August, 1956.

49. ——: "The Doctrine of Agricultural Labor of Zero Value," *Transforming Traditional Agriculture*, Yale University Press, New Haven, Conn., 1964.

50. Sen, A. K.: *Choice of Techniques*, Basil Blackwell & Mott, Ltd., Oxford, 1960.

51. Singh, Tarlok: *Poverty and Social Change*, Longmans, Green & Co., Ltd., London, 1945.

52. Sovani, N. V.: "Underemployment, Micro and Macro, and Development Planning," *Indian Economic Journal*, vol. 2, no. 4, pp. 301–310, April, 1955.

53. United Nations, *Measures for the Economic Development of Underdeveloped Countries*, Department of Economic and Social Affairs, New York, 1951.

54. Viner, Jacob: "Some Reflections on the Concept of Disguised Unemployment," *Contribuções a Analise do Desenvolvimento Economico*, Livraria Ager Editora, Rio de Janeiro, 1957. Reprinted under the same title in *Indian Journal of Economics*, vol. 38, pp. 17–23, July, 1957.

55. Warriner, Doreen: *Economics of Peasant Farming*, Oxford University Press, London, 1939.

56. ——: *Land and Poverty in the Middle East*, Royal Institute of International Affairs, London, 1948.

57. ——: "Land Reform and Economic Development," Fiftieth Anniversary Commemoration Lectures, National Bank of Egypt, Cairo, 1955.

58. Wonnacott, Paul: "Disguised and Overt Unemployment in Underdeveloped Economies," *Quarterly Journal of Economics*, vol. 76, pp. 279–297, May, 1962.

8. Economic Theory and Agrarian Economics*

N. GEORGESCU-ROEGEN

According to some recent studies, more than 1.3 billion people still live in a self-subsistence economy, that is, as peasants. Most of these also live on the verge of starvation. Asia and Africa, which together represent more than 60 per cent of the world's population, produce only a little more than 30 per cent of the world's agricultural output. Conservative estimates show that if basic nutritional needs for the entire population

* From *Oxford Economic Papers*, vol. 12, pp. 1–40, February, 1960, with omissions. Reprinted by permission of the Clarendon Press, Oxford, and the author. The author is professor of economics at Vanderbilt University.

of the world are to be met, it is necessary that the food production be increased by at least 30 per cent.[1] Neither the overwhelming numerical importance of peasant economy nor the scarcity of food is a new economic development peculiar to our own time.

In spite of all this, agrarian economics—by which I mean the economics of an overpopulated agricultural economy and not merely agricultural economics—has had a very unfortunate history. Non-capitalist economies simply presented no interest for Classical economists. Marxists, on the other side, tackled the problem with their characteristic impetuosity, but proceeded from preconceived ideas about the laws of a peasant economy. A less known school of thought—Agrarianism—aimed at studying a peasant economy and only this. An overt scorn for quantitative theoretical analysis prevented the Agrarians from constructing a proper theory of their particular object of study, and consequently from making themselves understood outside their own circle. There remain the Standard economists (as a recent practice calls the members of the modern economic school for which neither neo-Classical nor General Equilibrium suffices as a single label). Of late, as economic development has become tied up with precarious international politics, Standard economists have been almost compelled to come to grips with the problem of underdeveloped economies, and hence with non-capitalist economics. But in their approach they have generally committed the same type of error as Marxists.

Thus, the agrarian economy has to this day remained a reality without a theory. And the topical interest of a sound economic policy in countries with a peasant overpopulation calls for such a theory as at no other time in history. But one cannot aspire to present a theory of a reality as complex as the peasant economy within the space of an article. My far more modest aim is to point out the basic features that differentiate an overpopulated agricultural economy from an advanced economy. I have endeavoured to present the argument in terms of the familiar analytical tools of Standard theory or others akin to these. The brief historical critique which prefaces the theoretical analysis is intended to place the latter in a better perspective, particularly as concerns policy implications.

THEORY, REALITY, AND POLICY

Theory and reality. Theory is in the first and last place a logical file of our factual knowledge pertaining to a certain phenomenological domain.[2] Only mathematics is concerned with the properties of "any ob-

[1] The above data are found in W. S. and E. S. Woytinsky, *World Population and Production,* New York, 1953, pp. 307, 435 *passim.*

[2] That is not to deny that theory may serve other purposes, but these are by-products of its essential nature.

ject whatever," for which reason since Aristotle's time it has been generally placed in a special category by itself. To each theory, therefore, there must correspond a specific domain of the reality. In any science, the problem of precisely circumscribing this domain faces well-known difficulties. Where physics ends and chemistry begins, and where economics ends and ethics begins, are certainly thorny questions, although not equally so. Here, however, I want to discuss a quite pedestrian query pertaining to the problem of the proper domain of a theory. And this query is: Can an economic theory which successfully, describes the capitalistic system, for instance, be used to analyse successfully another economic system, say feudalism?

Let us observe that a similar question hardly ever comes up in the physical sciences, for no evidence exists to make physicists believe that matter behaves differently today than yesterday. In contrast, we find that human societies vary with both time and locality. To be sure, one school of thought still argues that these variations are only different instances of a unique archetype and that consequently all social phenomena can be encompassed by a single theory. This is not the place to show precisely where the weakness of the various attempts in this direction lies. Suffice it to mention here that when the theories constructed by these attempts do not fail in other respects, they are nothing but a collection of generalities of no operational value whatever. As Kautsky once judiciously remarked, "Marx designed to investigate in his 'Capital' the capitalistic mode of production [and not] the forms of production which are common to all people, as such an investigation could, for the most part, only result in commonplaces."[3] For an economic theory to be operational at all, i.e. to be capable of serving as a guide for policy, it must concern itself with a specific type of economy, not with several types at the same time.

What particular reality is described by a given theory can be ascertained only from the latter's axiomatic foundation. Thus, Standard theory describes the economic process of a society in which the individual behaves *strictly* hedonistically, where the entrepreneur seeks to maximize his cash-profit, and where any commodity can be exchanged on the market at uniform prices and none exchanged otherwise. On the other hand Marxist theory refers to an economy characterized by class monopoly of the means of production, money-making entrepreneurs, markets with uniform prices for all commodities, and complete independence of economic from demographic factors.[4] Taken as abstractions of varying degree, both

---

[3] Karl Kautsky, *The Economic Doctrines of Karl Marx*, New York, 1936, p. 1.

[4] I refer to the fact that the assumption of a permanent reserve army simply means that at the subsistence wage-rate the supply of labour is "unlimited" both in the short and in the long run, while Classical economics held that this was true only in the long run. *Infra*, p. 18 n.

these axiomatic bases undoubtedly represent the most characteristic traits of the capitalist system.[5] Moreover, far from being absolutely contradictory, they are complementary, in the sense of Bohr's Principle of Complementarity.[6] This is precisely why one may speak of Marx as "the flower of Classical economics."[7]

A far more important observation is that the theoretical foundations of both Standard and Marxist theories consist of cultural or, if you wish, institutional traits. Actually, the same must be true of any economic theory. For what characterizes an economic system is its institutions, not the technology it uses. Were this not so, we would have no basis for distinguishing between Communism and Capitalism, while, on the other hand, we should regard Capitalism of today and Capitalism of, say, 50 years ago as essentially different systems.

As soon as we realize that for economic theory an economic system is characterized exclusively by institutional traits, it becomes obvious that neither Marxist nor Standard theory is valid as a whole for the analysis of a non-capitalistic economy, i.e. of the economy of a society in which part or all of the capitalist institutions are absent. A proposition of either theory may eventually be valid for a non-capitalistic economy, but its validity must be established *de novo* in each case, either by factual evidence or by logical derivation from the corresponding axiomatic foundation. Even the analytical concepts developed by these theories cannot be used indiscriminately in the description of other economies. Among the few that are of general applicability there is the concept of a production function together with all its derived notions. But this is due to the purely physical nature of that concept. Most economic concepts, on the contrary, are hard to transplant. "Social class" seems the only exception, obviously because it is inseparable from "society" itself (save the society of Robinson Crusoe and probably that of the dawn of the human species). This is not to say that Marxist and Standard theories do not provide us with useful patterns for asking the right kind of questions and for seeking the relevant constituents of any economic reality. They are, after all, the only elaborate economic theories ever developed.

All this may seem exceedingly elementary. Yet this is not what Standard and (especially) Marxist theorists have generally done when confronted with the problem of formulating policies for the agrarian over-

[5] We have left out the surplus value proposition from the Marxist axioms because this proposition—as we shall argue later—belongs to feudalism, not to capitalism.

[6] This principle by which Bohr overcame the impasse created by the modern discoveries in physics states that reality "cannot be comprehended in a single picture" and that "only the totality of the phenomena exhausts the possible information about objects." Niels Bohr, *Atomic Physics and Human Knowledge,* New York, 1958, pp. 40 *passim.*

[7] Terence McCarthy in the Preface to the English translation of K. Marx, *A History of Economic Theories,* New York, 1952, p. xi.

populated countries. And, as the saying goes, "economics is what economists do."

A *reality without theory.* As has often been remarked, economists
of all epochs have been compelled by the social environment to be far
more opportunistic than their colleagues in other scientific fields, with
the result that their attention has been concentrated upon the economic
problems of their own time.[8] And as the transition of economic science
from the purely descriptive (i.e. taxonomic) to the theoretical stage coincided with the period during which in Western Europe feudalism was
rapidly yielding to capitalism, it was only natural that the latter should
become the objective of the first theoretical economists. That may explain
only why most Western economists have been interested in developing
the theory of the capitalist system, but not why none attempted a theory
of a non-capitalist economy. The only explanation of this omission is the
insuperable difficulty in getting at the cultural roots of a society other
than that to which one actually belongs. And, as we have seen, an
intuitive knowledge of the basic cultural traits of a community is indispensable for laying out the basis of its economic theory.

By its very nature, a peasant village is the milieu least fit for modern
scientific activity. The modern scientist had therefore to make the town
his headquarters. But, from there, he could not possibly observe the life
of a peasant community. London, for instance, offers indeed "a favorable
view . . . for the observation of bourgeois society"—a circumstance im-
mensely appreciated by Marx[9]—but not even a pinhole through which to
look at a peasant economy. Even if, unlike Marx, an economist was born
in a village, he had to come to town for his education. He thus became
a true townee himself, in the process losing most, if not all, *verstehen* of
the peasant society. It was natural, therefore, that to Marx as well as to
other Western economists (to those coming from a peasantless country,
especially) the peasant should seem "a mysterious, strange, often even
disquieting creature."[10] Yet none showed Marx's unlimited contempt for
the peasantry. For him, the peasantry was just a bag of potatoes, not
a social class. In the *Communist Manifesto* he denounced "the idiocy of
rural life" to the four corners of the world. But these Marxist hyperboles
apart, there is, as we shall presently see, a spotless rationale behind
Marx's attitude towards the peasant.

The difference between the philosophy of the industrial town and of
the agricultural countryside has often attracted the attention of sociolo-

[8] The point finds an eloquent illustration in the vogue that the problem of economic
development has recently acquired among Western economists: we have reached the
point where the development of underdeveloped nations is as much an economic
problem of the West as of these other nations.

[9] K. Marx, *A Contribution to the Critique of Political Economy*, Chicago, 1904,
Preface, p. 14.

[10] Karl Kautsky, *La Question agraire*, Paris, 1900, p. 3.

gists and poets alike.[11] But few have realized that this difference is not like going to another church, and that it involves every concrete act concerning production and distribution as well as social justice. Undoubtedly the basis of this difference is the fact that the living Nature imposes a different type of restriction upon *homo agricola* than the inert matter upon *homo faber.*

To begin with, no parallelism exists between the law of the scale of production in agriculture and in industry. One may grow wheat in a pot or raise chickens in a tiny backyard, but no hobbyist can build an automobile with only the tools of his workshop. Why then should the optimum scale for agriculture be that of a giant open-air factory? In the second place, the role of the time-factor is entirely different in the two activities. By mechanical devices we can shorten the time for weaving an ell of cloth, but we have as yet been unable to shorten the gestation period in animal husbandry or (to any significant degree) the period for maturity in plants. Moreover, agricultural activity is bound to an unflinching rhythm, while in manufacture we can well do tomorrow what we have chosen not to do today. Finally, there is a difference between the two sectors which touches the root of the much discussed law of decreasing returns (in the evolutionary sense). For industrial uses man has been able to harness one source of energy after another, from the wind to the atom, but for the type of energy that is needed by life itself he is still wholly dependent on the most "primitive" source, the animals and plants around him. These brief observations are sufficient to pinpoint not only why the philosophy of the man engaged in agriculture differs from that of the townee but also why agriculture and industry still cannot be subsumed under the same law. Whether future scientific discoveries may bring life to the denominator of inert matter is, for the time being, a highly controversial—and no less speculative—topic.

Probably the greatest error of Marx was his failure to recognize the simple fact that agriculture and industry obey different laws; as a result he proclaimed that the law of concentration applies equally well to industry and agriculture.[12] To repeat, Marx had no opportunity to observe a peasant economy. Nor is there anything in his vast literary activity to indicate that he ever studied a non-capitalist agriculture.[13] The analysis of rent in *Capital* is based entirely on capitalist production even during Marx's brief excursion into peasant agriculture.[14]

Probably no other theoretical aberration has been refuted by historical

[11] In the Western literature, Oswald Spengler is probably the best known author for placing a great historical value upon this difference. See especially his *The Decline of the West*, New York, 1928, vol. ii, ch. iv.

[12] K. Marx, *Capital*, Chicago, 1906, i, ch. xiv, sec. 10.

[13] Kautsky, *La Question agraire*, p. xii. Also F. Engels in the Preface to the third volume of *Capital* (Chicago, 1909, p. 16).

[14] Marx, *Capital*, iii, ch. xlvii, sec. 5.

developments as promptly and as categorically as the Marxist law of concentration in agriculture. During the second half of the nineteenth century one census after another revealed that in agriculture concentration was continuously decreasing while the peasants instead of being proletarianized became landowners in increasing numbers. In Kautsky's own words, "the capitalists were on the increase, not the proletarians." The indictment was all the more unappealable since this phenomenon was taking place in capitalist countries without any planned intervention. That convinced everyone save the ultra-orthodox Marxists that the concentration law is false.

Policy and factitious theory. The aftermath of "the sorest experience of Marxist doctrine"—as Veblen labelled the refutation of the concentration law[15]—can be best appraised in the light of the Hegelian tenet which is the cornerstone of the Marxist doctrine. To recall, according to that tenet it is beyond man's power to change the course of history. This is why Marx argued that socialism is to come as the natural product of the evolution of the relations of production, not because the interests of the working class would in any sense be superior to or more important than those of capitalists. Marx even scoffed at those who wanted to base a socialist platform on such "unscientific" arguments as greater social justice. But, always according to the Marxist Hegelianism, man can speed up the historical process so as to shorten the periods of growing-pains. A right policy must be based on the acceptance of the inexorable outcome. Because of the belief in the concentration law in agriculture, Socialists were advised to more than welcome any measure that would tend to proletarianize the peasants so that the advent of socialism would be hastened. But since the peasant did not want to hear of proletarianization, Socialist parties found themselves rejected everywhere by the peasant masses. Failures on the electoral front, combined with the mounting evidence against the Marxist theory, brought about the internal crisis known as the Agrarian Question. At the Frankfurt (1894) and Breslau (1895) congresses, the Question almost wrecked the unity of the party.[16] Even if officially this unity was then saved, the Question continued to make life difficult for Marxism. In the end Marx himself was obviously disturbed by the overwhelming evidence and the mounting criticism, for in the last two years of his life he pain-

[15] Thorstein Veblen, *The Place of Science in Modern Civilization,* New York, 1919, pp. 450 ff.

[16] For the Agrarian Question one may consult Kautsky, *La Question agraire,* and G. Gatti, *Le Socialisme et l'agriculture,* Paris, 1902. The first work is important because it appeared only a few years after the Breslau Congress (German edition, *Die Agrarfrage,* Stuttgart, 1899), where Kautsky had a decisive role in defeating the "deviationist" motion. Gatti, on the other hand, was a prominent Socialist who ultimately embraced the non-Marxist view on agriculture.

fully sought to amend his theory, but not so as to jeopardize the political movement which he had set in motion and to which he was attached from first to last.[17] But his desire was unrealizable, because contradictory. After Marx's death the party made great efforts to cover up the Agrarian Question. They vacillated between Leninist opportunism, by proclaiming loudly that no one intends to destroy the peasant, and various dialectic circumvolutions aimed at proving that there *is* concentration although in an entirely new sense.[18] The Agrarian Question was thus kept on a low flame until Stalin decided to solve it by proclaiming a holy war against the peasants, a war with which neo-Marxism has since become almost synonymous.

It is hard not to see in this momentous decision the ultimate product of Marx's scorn for the peasant. Indeed, this scorn constituted a lasting ferment for the thinking of Marxist leaders. Quite early, none other than Engels spoke of the necessity for the proletariat "to crush a general peasant uprising."[19]

Be this as it may, the Stalinist war, which by its number of victims surpasses all other wars known to history, could not have found sufficient momentum in the cultural opposition between the urban and the rural sectors. Nor could this war feed on "sacking the rich," for precisely in the regions where Stalinism has till now spread the capitalist-bourgeois class was paper-thin, and the rich peasant quite a rarity. The war must have had other springs.

That the interests of the town conflict with those of the countryside is by now a well-established fact. However, it is not always realized that

---

[17] Marx's public concession, though somewhat veiled, is found in the preface to the 1882 Russian edition of the *Communist Manifesto* (K. Marx and F. Engels, *Correspondence, 1845–1895*, New York, 1935, p. 355). A clearer expression of the deviation from "the Marxist line" came in a letter Marx wrote in 1881 to Vera Zasulich in answer to a definite question regarding the necessity of speeding up the proletarianization of the Russian peasant. The letter, however, was published by the Marx-Engels Institute only in 1924, when the struggle between Russian Marxists and their adversaries was long since over. (D. Mitrany, *Marx Against the Peasant*, The University of North Carolina Press, 1951, pp. 31–33, was the first to draw the attention of the English-speaking reader to this letter.)

We know also that in his last years Marx decided to learn Russian (and apparently even Turkish) to have access to the original sources concerning the agrarian problems of Eastern Europe (*Correspondence*, p. 353). For more than one reason, it was too late.

[18] An epitome of these endeavours is offered by Kautsky, *La Question agraire*. He argued that, although the concentration law is not true as to the size of the holdings, it is true as to the global ownership, with more landowners having important outside sources of income. Then he threw everything overboard by arguing that peasant agriculture must disappear in any case because the optimum scale of production is that of latifundia.

[19] Quoted in Mitrany, op. cit., p. 219.

the price-scissors do not tell the whole story. For this story, we must observe that food is indispensable, while the need for industrial products is secondary, if not superfluous. To obtain its foodstuff from the agricultural sector, and moreover to obtain it *cheaply*, constitutes a real problem for the industrial community. In the ultimate analysis, "cheap bread" is a cry directed against the tiller of the soil rather than against the capitalist partner of the industrial worker. In some circumstances this conflict may become very spiny. And it is permanently spiny in the overpopulated countries where the income of the masses allows only the satisfaction of the most elementary needs and where the population of the town is unduly swollen by a rural exodus. That has been the situation in all countries—with one or two exceptions—where Stalinism has come to power. And it is in this situation that the war against the peasant found its needed spring.[20]

Clearly, the Stalinist formula constitutes a solution (at least a temporary one) of the conflict between the industrial and agricultural sectors. But the solution is based on the primacy of the interests of the industrial and bureaucratic sections of the society, not on some evolutionary law regarding the inexorable proletarianization of the peasants.[21] Consequently according to the very essence of Marxism the Stalinist formula cannot claim to be "scientific."[22]

Marx was, however, aware of the conflict between the industrial and agricultural divisions of society. He once remarked quite *en passant* that "the whole economic history of society is summed up in the movement of this antithesis [the division between the city and the countryside]."[23] This remark is extremely important. It shows that Marx, for once, recognized the existence of an antithesis which—as we argued in the preceding sec-

[20] The conflict between the interests of the agricultural and industrial sectors exists also in the advanced economies, including the United States. Cf. J. D. Black, Discussion, *Proceedings of the Fifth International Conference of Agricultural Economists*, London, 1939, pp. 86 f. The only difference is that in these economies the conflict is attenuated by the high income, and therefore it can be resolved by such methods as the Agricultural Price Support Programme. Overpopulation is the necessary condition for the conflict to become a social *vis viva*.

[21] A London tailor, J. G. Eccarius, *Eines Arbeiters Widerlegung der nationalökonomischen Lehren John Stuart Mills*, Zurich, 1868, was the first to argue that to guarantee "cheap bread" to the industrial worker the peasant must be placed under the dictatorship of the proletariat. The book, it is said, enjoyed great prestige among the Marxists during the 1870's (see Mitrany, op. cit., p. 15). That Eccarius's view has become the basis of Communist agrarian policy is beyond question: "general collectivization of the peasants is indeed a means of . . . securing the supply of food [for the towns]" (V. Lenin, *Selected Works*, Moscow, 1934–9, vol. xii, p. 13).

[22] As we shall see, neither can it be justified on positive welfare grounds, *infra*, p. 37 n. 2, p. 38 n. 1.

[23] Marx, *Capital*, i, ch. xiv, sec. 4, p. 387.

tion—seems rooted in the permanent conditions of the human species, and which should therefore outweigh any antithesis peculiar to a particular economic system. Unfortunately, Marx did not explore this point further to explain how he would have envisaged the *scientific* (in the Hegelian sense) solution of that antithesis.

Policy without theory. In the first half of the nineteenth century, while the West grew intensively preoccupied with the lot of the industrial masses, Russia witnessed the rise of a social movement concerned solely with the peasant. Time and again, essentially different economic conditions imposed entirely different preoccupations. It was not, therefore, because of the much discussed intellectual isolation of Russia that the founders of this new ideology borrowed nothing from Western economic theories. They simply drew the logical consequences from the fact that these theories were moulded on a different economic reality. But as their intellectual inheritance contained nothing regarding the economics of a peasant community, the new social reformers had to start from scratch. They soon discovered that their personal social background could not help them in grasping the problems in which they were interested, and as a consequence decided to go "to the people." This slogan earned them the Russian name of *Narodniki*, but outside Russia they became generally known as Populists.[24]

As Marxism began to acquire a basis of its own in Russia, the incompatibility between Marxist theory and the Russian reality gave rise to a fierce and more lasting conflict between *Narodniki* and Marxists than that between the orthodox Marxists and the Agrarian Socialists in the West. Some *Narodniki* did become attracted by Marxism, primarily because its programmatic implications and social dialectics appealed to their revolutionary spirit. But as it was impossible to fit the peculiarities of an agrarian economy into the Marxist frame, most of these succumbed as hetero-Marxists. The great majority of the *Narodniki*, however, refused to be lured into denying the specific traits of that economy. And thus the Agrarian ideology came to be identified with a double negation: not Capitalism, not Socialism. It is precisely this double negation that has been called into question by Western economists, whether Marxist or not.

Mitrany observes that Marx's view on peasant agriculture combines "the townsman's contempt for all things rural and the economist's disapproval of small scale production."[25] But this is true for most Western social scientists. Add to this, especially, their usual disdain for any idea

[24] Alexander Herzen, who in 1847 went into exile because of his political activity, is generally regarded as "the founder of Russian 'Socialism,' or 'Narodnikism,'" as Lenin put it. Quoted *Correspondence*, p. 285.

[25] Mitrany, op. cit., p. 6.

that is not prescribed through a mathematical model, and you have the explanation for the misunderstanding of the Agrarians by the West.[26] Indeed the *Narodniki,* like the Agrarians of latter days, have not only failed to construct a theory of the peasant economy—as the others have done for capitalism—but they have distinguished themselves by a lack of interest in, almost a spurn for, analytical preoccupations. They relied exclusively on the intuitive approach, on the *verstehen* of the peasant's *Weltanschauung,* much like the German historical school advocated (although there was hardly any direct contact between the two schools). Populism, like Marxism, represented not only an economic doctrine but a faith as well. And this faith "fed on a strong sentimental undercurrent, on the emotional piety and rustic ties" of its believers.[27] All this laid Populism open to the accusation of romanticism.

The particular circumstances in which *Narodnikism* began its career may account for much of its peculiar spirit. But the lack of any true theorizing in the Populist doctrine was due more to the unusual difficulty of casting the peasant's economic conduct into a schema than to anything else. For this we have the testimony of one of the most praiseworthy Russian Agrarians, Alexander Tschajanov, who gave to one of his works the symptomatic title: *Die Lehre von der bäuerlichen Wirtschaft: Versuch einer Theorie der Familienwirtschaft im Landbau* (Berlin, 1932). In the concluding remarks of this book, in which he submits only the various activities of agricultural production to quantitative analysis, Tschajanov confesses his dissatisfaction over the fact that we still do not possess a theory of the economic behaviour of the peasant. He significantly observes that the relation between Classical economics and an economic theory of a peasant community seems to be similar to that between Euclidian and non-Euclidian geometry. Yet he ends with the admission that an abstract theory of agrarian economics cannot easily be constructed.[28]

Whatever the explanation for the outlook of the Agrarian, there is no more dramatic example of the disaster that awaits him who in formulat-

---

[26] In this respect, it is highly instructive to compare, for instance, the analysis of Populism by L. H. Roberts, *Rumania,* New Haven, 1951, pp. 142 ff., with that by Rosa Luxemburg, *The Accumulation of Capital,* London, 1959, pp. 271–91. Although Rosa Luxemburg was "a more genuine Marxist than any other member of the German movement" (Paul M. Sweezy, *The Theory of Capitalist Development,* New York, 1942, p. 207), her analysis is far more objective than Roberts's.

On the *Narodniki,* one may fruitfully consult also J. Delewski, "Les Idées des 'narodniki' russes," *Revue d'économie politique,* xxxv (1921), pp. 432–62, and above all Mitrany, op. cit., ch. iv. The memoirs of the "grandmother" of the Russian revolution, Katerina Breshkovskaia, *Hidden Springs of the Russian Revolution,* Stanford, 1931, are interesting as personal history.

[27] Mitrany, op. cit., p. 40.

[28] Op. cit., p. 130.

ing an economic policy disregards theoretical analysis, than the well-known fate of the Agrarian parties of Eastern Europe.

OVERPOPULATION: A RE-EXAMINATION

The facts analysed. The Agrarians have at all times sensed that the plague of most underdeveloped agrarian economies is overpopulation and that consequently the problem of a peasant economy is to a large extent a population problem.[29] It is natural, therefore, for us to see whether an analysis of overpopulation would not offer a lead in the solution of the Agrarian riddle.

Whoever speaks of "excess" is naturally expected to define it in terms of a point of reference which in some way must represent a normal if not an optimum situation. But to define "normal" or "optimum" is not easy, especially if one faces a quibbling relativist. Such a relativist may argue, for instance, that the excess capacity of a monopolistic industry is a fiction because all capacity could be used if monopoly were removed and a new system of distribution were introduced. A wholly analogous position is adopted by Marx in arguing that overpopulation exists only relative to "the average needs of the self-expansion of capital."[30] Be this as it may, we must recognize that the concept of overpopulation presents unusual difficulties. Normal (or optimum) population implies the concept of normal (or optimum) life. And even if the latter were not such an elusive concept, we would still find it impossible to choose a "normal" valid for all times and localities. To avoid the trivial conclusion that every population is normal for the time and place in which it lives, it is necessary to adopt some criterion of normality. This criterion may be dynamic or static, depending on the problem at hand.[31]

Ever since statistical data have been used for comparative purposes, it has become obvious that some agricultural countries presented symptoms suggesting the existence of some sort of overpopulation. It has been remarked that given the following data for two prominently agricultural economies, as for instance

	Denmark	Yugoslavia
Inhabitants per km.² of arable land.........	36.6	157.4
Wheat yield in quintals per ha.............	22.9	11.0

[29] Cf. Tschajanov, op. cit., p. 131, for instance.
[30] *Capital,* i, ch. xxv, sec. 3, p. 695.
[31] Marx, for instance, argued that the developed means of communication in the United States at the middle of the last century made that country more densely populated than India. Ibid. i, ch. xiv, sec. 4, p. 387.

even if Yugoslavia could raise her agricultural yield to the Danish level, the average Yugoslav would still have only one-quarter as much food as the average Dane. This observation has supplied the basis for a crude concept of relative overpopulation upon which are based the measures of overpopulation in terms of some crop basket as a standard.[32] As has generally been admitted, the concept of relative overpopulation thus defined is ambiguous and the procedure for its measure debatable.[33] The chief drawback of this approach, however, is that it sidetracked the analysis from the right direction. Indeed, a difference in the *per capita* national product (or a sector of it) may be a *symptom* of the difference between two economic systems, but by no means an *intrinsic co-ordinate* of that difference. Otherwise we should regard the economic system of Belgium as different from that of the United States. But the belief that the difference between an agrarian and a capitalist economy is a matter of degree only, not of essence, is still very frequent.

And yet, the elements for the solution of the problem were not out of reach. In the 1930's, studies originating in several countries with large peasantries revealed the astounding fact that a substantial proportion of the population could disappear without the slightest decrease in the national product.[34] The closeness of the independent estimates of the *superfluous* population for each case shows that we are confronted with a real quantitative phenomenon.[35] If additional proof of this is needed, one may invoke some relevant "experiments" history carried out *in vivo*. For two years after the beginning of hostilities in 1914, agricultural production in Russia was maintained at the pre-war level, although no less than 40 per cent of the *able-bodied* male peasants were in the army.[36] The same phenomenon occurred in Rumania during World War II. Whenever agricultural production collapsed in Eastern Europe during the World Wars it was solely because of the extreme requisition of draught animals, the difficulty of replacing worn-out implements, and, of course, the disturbances caused by the movement of armies. Even the disappearance of some ten million Ukrainian peasants during the so-called liquidation of

[32] Cf. W. E. Moore, *Economic Demography of Eastern and Southern Europe*, Geneva, 1945, ch. iii.

[33] Ibid., pp. 55 ff.

[34] References to the earliest studies for Poland and Bulgaria in Doreen Warriner, *Economics of Peasant Farming*, London, 1939, pp. 68 f.

[35] For Rumania, one study (*Enciclopedia Romániei*, Bucharest, 1939, vol. iii, p. 60) estimated the percentage of superfluous peasant population at 48, another, at 45 (V. Madgearu, *Evolutia economiei românesti după războiul mondial*, Bucharest, 1940, p. 49). The first estimate was derived from national statistical data, but the second was checked by *direct observation* in extensive field-work covering sixty villages chosen at random. Moore, op. cit., pp. 63 f., using national data, arrived at a percentage of 51.4.

[36] Leonard E. Hubbard, *The Economics of Soviet Agriculture*, London, 1939, pp. 59, 65.

kulaks, although accompanied also by a radical disturbance of the entire economy, had only an ephemeral influence on agricultural output.[37]

Now, to say simply that part of the population could disappear without causing any decrease in output is not sufficient for a theoretical characterization of overpopulation. The national product of the United States *could* easily be maintained at the same level even though a large proportion of the population were to disappear. The *differentia specifica* between the two situations is that in the latter the national product could be increased if people simply chose to have less leisure, while in the former, not.[38] This difference reveals that the situation where the marginal productivity of labour equals zero is the starting point in searching for a definition of overpopulation. And that there exist countries where the actual marginal productivity of labour is zero for all practical purposes, has been admitted by nearly all students of peasant economies.[39]

All this clearly conflicts with Professor Schultz's categorical statement that there is "no evidence of any poor country *anywhere* that would even suggest that a transfer of some small fraction, say 5 per cent, of the existing labour force in agriculture, with other things equal, could be made without reducing its [agricultural] production."[40] Nothing is farther from my thought than to challenge the fact that the concrete cases cited by him prove that in several Latin American countries the agricultural production did fall off after some labour had been transferred to other activities.[41] But that is not sufficient to justify his well-known position, namely that the overpopulation theory of underdevelopment "as a 'theory' . . . fails in that the expected consequences are not those that one observes."[42] The situation of most Latin American countries is not identical with that of the East European or Asiatic

---

[37] Cf. ibid., p. 117. In a recent paper, "The Theory of Underemployment in Backward Economies," *Journal of Political Economy*, lxv (1957), p. 103, Harvey Leibenstein alludes to some experiences in the Soviet orbit when industrialization would have caused a shortage of labour in the agricultural sector, but fails to say to precisely which events he refers. My guess is that they exhibited only the familiar kind of *spurious* shortage caused by wholesale dislocations of persons, if they did not reflect either peasant resistance or administrative inefficiency.

[38] Marx, *Capital*, i, ch. xxv, sec. 3, p. 698, asserts that if the population of England would be reduced in the same proportion for all categories, the remaining population "would be absolutely insufficient" to maintain the same level of output in spite of England's "colossal" means for saving labour. Clearly, this implies that no skilled labour has *free* leisure, a characteristic assumption of Marxist economics.

[39] E.g. Warriner, op. cit., p. 65.

[40] Theodore W. Schultz, "The Role of Government in Promoting Economic Growth," in *The State of the Social Sciences*, L. D. White, ed., Chicago, 1956, p. 375. (My italics.)

[41] Ibid., pp. 375 f.

[42] Theodore W. Schultz, *The Economic Test in Latin America*, New York State School of Industrial and Labor Relations, Bulletin 35, August 1956, p. 15.

countries, although they all have this in common: they are underdeveloped. While overpopulation is always accompanied by underdevelopment, it is neither a necessary nor the only cause of it. The underdevelopment of Latin American countries may have other bases than overpopulation.[43] Overpopulation, therefore, cannot provide the basis for a *general* theory of underdeveloped economies, but only of those economic realities beset by it. This is concrete illustration of the point which one of the preceding sections sought to bring home.

To regard the notion of overpopulation as a myth is undoubtedly a Marxist residual. And precisely because that notion still meets with opposition in some circles, a few further remarks seem in order. If in the "so-called" overpopulated economies the marginal productivity is zero— a critic may ask—how can we explain the fact that in such economies there is a greater need for skilled labour than in the other countries? Certainly—he may continue—you are not going to say that the marginal productivity of an engineer in India or Egypt is zero. But this way of looking at the problem is to intermingle evolutionary factors with static concepts and to confuse labour with capital. An evolutionary change is bound to bring about shortages of some types of skilled labour (and surpluses of some others) in *any* economy. Thus, Italy certainly feels today a shortage of technicians for her newly discovered oilfields. This, however, represents a quasi-bottleneck, to borrow an expression coined in the Marshallian spirit by Professor Lewis.[44] If no further evolutionary changes occur, the quasi-bottleneck will disappear just as any quasi-rent will do. But once the new equilibrium is reached, will the marginal productivity of a petroleum technician become zero? Not at all. For the equilibrium marginal productivity of such a technician represents not only the marginal productivity of his labour but also that of the capital invested in his training.[45] Obviously, this line of reasoning regards labour as a uniform, plastic quality of all human beings, and is—I believe somewhat in the tradition of Classical as well as Marxist economics. But I fail to see a better way to analyse the problems raised by *population* in its *purely quantitative* aspect. Actually this view of labour is even more necessary in the analysis of economic growth than of a stationary state, where population may very well be regarded as a frozen distribution of *qualities*.

Therefore, the statement that the marginal productivity of labour is

[43] Although my knowledge of the factual situation in those countries is very superficial, I would venture to suggest that some are "underpopulated" relative to the available land resources. Professor Schultz's evidence may even corroborate such a view.

[44] W. Arthur Lewis, "Economic Development With Unlimited Supply of Labor," *The Manchester School,* xxii (1954), p. 145.

[45] Another part may reflect the "rent" of his personal talents, but that is a side aspect of the problem.

zero implies that the marginal productivity of skilled labour consists only of the marginal productivity of the capital invested in the production of skill. It is a most rational expectation that an overpopulated economy should feel a greater shortage of skilled labour than a non-overpopulated one. Everything points to the fact that a shortage of skilled labour means a shortage of capital, not necessarily of labour. It is a peculiar feature of overpopulated economies that the skilled labourer is overburdened with work while the unskilled is loafing most of the time. Further still, the real economic aspect of spreading knowledge in an underdeveloped country now appears in full light: the need for additional education competes with the need for additional physical means of production, a fact which we are apt to overlook at times and underestimate often. Where resources are very scarce, free education for all types of skills is as *uneconomic* as haphazard production of capital equipment. Some countries, like Soviet Russia, seem to have grasped this truth; others, such as Italy, apparently have not.

It is a simple matter of definition to observe now that in any economy, whether overpopulated or not, there is only one way to measure the marginal productivity of labour: at the margin, i.e., where labour appears unadulterated by capital. The marginal productivity of labour in any economy then is the marginal productivity of its unskilled labour. It is a mere factual coincidence that in poor countries agricultural labour generally is unskilled labour. But this fact throws a new light upon the constant correlation of overpopulation with the agricultural conditions in the economic literature. For clearly, if the marginal productivity of labour in a country is zero, so must be the marginal productivity of the peasant.

CONCLUDING REMARKS*

Because some conclusions of the preceding arguments have a direct bearing on practical issues, it seems appropriate to present them together in this last section.

The undifferentiating schema of general equilibrium can only divert our attention from the unique role that leisure plays in economics. For instance, man has always endeavored to discover labour-saving devices because in the long run leisure is an economic *summum bonum* (and for no other reason). In the short run, on the other hand, leisure may be economically *unwanted*. An advanced economy may very well have less

* EDITOR'S NOTE: References are made implicitly or explicitly in these remarks to the earlier theoretical sections which are not reprinted. Since the author has done an excellent job of restating and summarizing his theoretical argument in these Concluding Remarks, we think the reader can understand the article without turning to the complete article in the *Oxford Economic Papers*.

leisure than a strictly overpopulated economy. And indeed, visitors from the lands-of-plenty often point out reprovingly that the people of poor countries indulge in greater leisure than themselves. They seem to ignore the fact that in strictly overpopulated countries people have no choice: in those countries leisure is imposed upon them by geo-historical conditions, and is not the result of an opportunity choice between greater leisure and greater real income, as is the case in advanced economies. In a strictly overpopulated economy, leisure is not properly speaking an economic good, for it has no use but as leisure. Its value then can be but zero.[46] The peculiar characteristic of the strictly overpopulated economy, namely that leisure has no value although labour has a positive 'price,' bears on the definition of national income.

Walras seems to have been the first economist to include leisure in national income[47] . . . In the fact that in an overpopulated economy the feudal formula leads to the maximum national product, we have an equivalent of Barone's proposition: in such an economy the feudal formula warrants maximum welfare. . . .

Only recently, Simon Kuznets proposed to return to the Walrasian formula on grounds that recall the theoretical implications of Barone's theorem.[48] He rightly points out that by excluding leisure from national income we may obscure an important effect of technological progress. The preceding analysis yields an even stronger conclusion: in comparing the rate of economic development of one advanced and one overpopulated country, we should use in each case the appropriate definition of national income. Indeed, only for the latter economies is it appropriate to define economic progress as the increase per capita net product.

Ordinary statistical data may be highly misleading for a measure of leisure in the case of overpopulated countries. As surprising as this may seem, the overpopulated countries furnish the highest occupation ratios* (F/P).[49] On the whole, it appears that in those countries it is hard to find someone unemployed, yet almost everyone is loafing. The paradox is easily cleared up. With an excess of labour, everyone fights to establish a solid claim to a share of the national product. This leads to a social pattern which may be labelled "splitting-the-job." Several persons are on

[46] Further proof of feudal features being attributed to capitalism by Marx is the fact that in his economic theory he assumes that labour power has no use-value *to its owner*. Cf. Kautsky, *The Economic Doctrines*, p. 60.

[47] Léon Walras, *Elements of Pure Economics*, Homewood, Ill., 1954, pp. 215, 379.

[48] Simon Kuznets, "Long-term Changes in the National Income of the United States of America since 1870," in *Income and Wealth, Series II*, Simon Kuznets, ed., Cambridge, 1952, pp. 63 ff.

[49] For example the occupation ratio in Rumania before World War II was one of the highest in the world, *Enciclopedia Romániei*, vol. i, p. 154.

* EDITOR's NOTE: P equals population and F is the size of the *potential* labor force.

a job that technically requires only one person, but each one insists on being considered a full-time employee for fear of seeing his claim challenged.

This practice has been frequently denounced as the hallmark of inefficiency if not of remissness. The more scientific critic has justified the verdict on the principle that an efficient economy should pay no factor more than its marginal productivity. It is clear, however, that this argument is an unwarranted extrapolation of a law valid only in advanced economies. Indeed, as we have shown, an overpopulated economy does not operate efficiently unless some labourers earn more than their own contribution to output.

The question of the over-sized bureaucracy—an unfailing characteristic of overpopulation—also has been approached from a wrong angle. Few students have realized that in overpopulated countries (and only in these) an over-sized bureaucracy is a normal economic phenomenon. With labour used up to its technical limit, nothing can be gained from a reduction in the number of public or personal servants; such a reduction may create only social turmoil. Many an overpopulated country deserves to be censured not because it has a large bureaucracy but because its entire government class has a high standard of living amidst poverty. Undoubtedly, too high a standard of living for the government class is a deterrent to economic development, for it greatly reduces the already meagre power of capital accumulation of the economy. If in an advanced economy equality of standard of living answers to an ethical principle, in an overpopulated country it represents an economic imperative.

Glossing over academic refinements, we may regard economic development as an upward shifting of the labour productivity curves. In other words, it is quasi-certain that in its development a strictly overpopulated economy has to pass through a phase where the working class has no leisure at all. This situation with its sixteen-hour day and seven-day week is well known owing to its detailed description by the socialist literature of the last century.[50] As already pointed out, Marx erroneously took it for a basic feature of capitalism. The period in the economic history of the West that served him as a model for depicting "the calvary of capitalism" corresponds rather to the growing-pains of capitalism. For capitalism, understood as an economic system regulated by profit maximiza-

---

[50] Even in the United States the average working week was seventy hours as late as 1850. Undoubtedly, earlier it was even longer. Interesting also is the fact that the first attempt to limit the work of children under 12 to a ten-hour day was that of the Commonwealth of Massachusetts in 1842. W. S. Woytinsky and Associates, *Employment and Wages in the United States*, New York, 1956, p. 98. The ten-hour day did not become a widespread standard for the other workers until 1860. Philip S. Foner, *History of the Labor Movement in the United States*, New York, 1947, p. 218; G. Gunton, *Wealth and Progress*, New York, 1887, pp. 250 f.

tion, could really exist only after the marginal productivity of labour had reached a sufficiently high level so that it could be equated with the wage-rate. Capitalist development proper began only after this phase had been consummated. Increasing leisure (not unwanted leisure) for the working class constitutes its most distinctive feature. To wit, the forty-hour week is a relatively new institution, and the idea of a four-day week is already being aired.[51]

Strictly speaking, the East European countries have never come to know the so-called calvary of capitalism. From the middle of the nine-teenth century, if not before, these countries began instead to receive the *impact* of Western capitalism. Although usually regarded as a phe-nomenon equivalent to the "calvary of capitalism," the impact was an essentially different process. The plain fact is that the East European economies were not yet sufficiently developed to begin the calvary. The true story can be told in a few words. Increasing trade with the West revealed the existence of other economic patterns and at the same time opened up new desires for the landlords and new ambitions for the bureaucracy. Under this influence the feudal *contrat social* began to weaken. An ever-increasing number of landlords switched to the capitalist formula of maximizing profit-rent, a change which, even if it did not always increase their share, had the advantage of freeing them from their traditional obligations towards the villagers. This process was later to culminate in producing the pure absentee. From this viewpoint, the main beneficiary of the freedom of the serfs was the landlord, not the peasant. That is true also of the earliest agrarian reforms (1861 in Russia, 1864 in Rumania), which in reality sanctioned the separation of the economic interests of the landlord from those of the peasant.

Now, to regulate production by profit maximization is probably the worst thing that can happen to an overpopulated economy, for that would increase unwanted leisure while diminishing the national prod-uct.[52] To be sure, newly imported techniques alleviated the crisis, but hardly the lot of the peasant. This is the explanation of the fact often commented upon that in Eastern Europe capitalism worsened the lot of the peasant, while in puzzling contrast increasing the prosperity of other sectors. It is this situation peculiar to the countries caught lagging behind Western capitalism that gave rise to the Agrarian ideology. And this ideology remained a regional philosophy at which the West

[51] Marx failed to see that one possible synthesis of his antithesis could be precisely this. Instead he wrote that "the relative overpopulation becomes so much more apparent in a certain country, the more the capitalist mode of production is de-veloped in it." *Capital,* iii, ch. xiv, sec. 4, p. 277.

[52] Kautsky, *Economic Doctrines,* p. 235, recognizes the difficulties created by the adoption of profit-maximization, but fails to see the real explanation of the process.

looked as at a curio, precisely because in its economic development the West had not had a similar experience.[53]

In a nutshell, the main tenets of the Agrarian doctrine are:

1. Because of their geographical situation some communities will always rely on agriculture as a main economic activity. And since agriculture is an intrinsically different activity from industry, such communities cannot develop along identical lines with the industrial economies.

2. For the countries with an agricultural overpopulation, individual peasant holdings and cottage industry constitute the best economic policy.

Evolution is subject to pure uncertainty, and the most we can do in tackling an evolutionary problem is to trust the existing evidence as a basis for meeting the future. As to this evidence, we have dealt at length with the historical refutation of the law of concentration in agriculture and with the specific differences between industrial and agricultural activities. We may add, however, that nothing as yet has happened to cast any doubt upon the validity of that analysis, and hence upon the first point of the Agrarian doctrine. Besides, the economic development of Denmark and Switzerland as well as parts of Germany and Austria prove that agriculture can provide the basis of its own economic development. Moreover, both anthropology and economic history confirm that only a substantial food production (independent of its source) has led to capital accumulation.[54] Quesnay's celebrated maxim works both ways: *riches paysans, riche royaume*. The logic is surprisingly simple: Robinson Crusoe could not be available for forging a sickle before Friday could gather enough fruits for both. "Industrialize at all costs" is not the word of economic wisdom, at least in overpopulated agricultural countries.

The second point of the Agrarian doctrine clearly aims at using as much labour in production as is forthcoming. It also reveals that Agrarians were the first to feel intuitively that the economic forms compatible with optimum welfare are not identical for all geo-historical conditions *even if the technological horizon is the same*. We should recall that the real novelty of Barone's work was the proof that the controlled

---

[53] Only very recently have Western economists come to accept the view of the Agrarians that the East European countries had suffered the impact of foreign patterns not befitting their own cultures and conditions. Cf. *Méthodes et problèmes de l'industrialisation des pays sous-développés*, United Nations, New York, 1955, p. 141.

[54] V. Gordon Childe, *Social Evolution*, New York, 1951, p. 22; Bruce F. Johnston, "Agricultural Productivity and Economic Development in Japan," *Journal of Political Economy*, lix (1951), p. 498.

economy of a socialist state must imitate the capitalist mechanism, i.e. it must adopt the principles of marginal productivity theory, if it is to obtain optimum welfare. However, neither Barone nor others after him seem to have been aware of one important restriction, namely, that marginal productivity principles presuppose the existence of a well-advanced economy in order to achieve optimum welfare. And thus numerous arguments have felt secure in using the converse proposition: capitalism and controlled socialism provide the best systems for developing an underdeveloped economy. Yet this proposition is patently false, at least for an overpopulated economy.

In this light, the intuition that led the Agrarians to their double negation—not Capitalism, not Socialism—proves to have been surprisingly correct. But then, what is the theoretical schema of the Agrarian doctrine? Because Agrarians have hardly bothered with theoretical schemata, one can only attempt an *ex post* rationalization and thereby accept the risks of misinterpreting their own rationale.

The arguments presented in this paper unmistakably lead to the conclusion that the Agrarian schema is the feudal formula under a new form. Capitalism—as we have explained—came to Eastern Europe not as a natural phase in economic development, but as the result of cultural contamination. In the light of economic dynamics and positive welfare theory, there can be no doubt that this was a move against the grain. For feudalism was thus displaced before the respective economies had a chance to reach the calvary phase of capitalism, i.e., the *normal* gateway to the advanced stage of economic development. Only a tithe system can efficiently carry an overpopulated economy through that phase.

But from the Marxist viewpoint, the premature disappearance of feudalism was a step in the right direction, for it represented an earlier fulfilment of what must inexorably come (a view probably shared also by most Standard economists). Into the Agrarian ideology we can read, however, a different position, even more Hegelian in spirit: no phase of economic development can be by-passed. In particular: feudalism cannot disappear before it has completely finished its job. If artificially displaced, it will return under one form or another (barring the occurrence of Malthusian holocausts). In such an alternative, the only logical attitude is then to plan rationally for the continuance of feudalism in such a way as to make it work even better. The policy of radical agrarian reforms in overpopulated countries, by which the head of each peasant family is turned into a feudal entrepreneur, responds precisely to this logic.[55]

A very interesting question now comes up: Which of the two Hegelian-

---

[55] Engels implicitly recognized the merit of feudalism when in a letter of 1892 (*Correspondence*, p. 501) he stated that "an agrarian revolution in Russia will ruin both the landlord and the small peasant," but he clearly ignored the fact that most landlords had long since ceased to follow the feudal formula.

isms, the Agrarian or the Marxist, is supported by history? The answer must be sought in what happened in the overpopulated countries after a Communist régime took them over. Unfortunately, our knowledge of what happened is very incomplete. Because the marginal productivity formula cannot possibly work efficiently in an overpopulated economy, it is fair to assume that no Communist régime would use it in this situation. If, however, they use a formula equivalent to a tithe system, the Agrarians are fully vindicated. To be sure, in a Communist régime the distribution of income between the government and the working "groups" may follow an entirely new formula. "From each according to his abilities, and to each according to his needs" has no operational value. Only when we have learned the theoretical schema of this new formula in concrete concepts (labour productivity and labour supply) shall we be able to answer the question in a more complete way.

By chance, history supplies us with proof and counter-proof examples regarding the impact of capitalism. The consequences of the premature decay of the feudal formula are best illustrated by the economic situation of the Russian and Rumanian peasant which in relative terms continued to deteriorate all through the hundred years or so preceding World War I. The few timid agrarian reforms were not able to ameliorate the situation, a fact reflected by the frequent peasant jacqueries, some of exceptional intensity. The counter-proof example is provided by Hungary, the well-known bastion of feudalism. In comparison with all her neighbours also plagued by overpopulation, Hungary stood out by virtue of a better fate of the peasant (in most regions) and a conspicuous economic development in all fields. To a great extent this difference can be attributed to the fact that the Hungarian magnate did not succumb to the capitalist formula as his Polish and Rumanian colleagues had done on a large scale.[56] The praises uttered by the apologists of the paternalistic character of Hungarian feudalism were more often than not a *pro domo sua* argument, but they were not entirely without basis. Its undisturbed existence, brought to an end only in 1945 by extra-economic forces, is another proof of the success of that feudalism. But precisely because of this progress, Hungarian feudalism had undoubtedly ceased to represent a necessary economic formula long before 1945.

The rather surprising intuition of the Agrarians, however, failed them in one important respect. They were unable to realize that in order to

---

[56] The earlier liberation from the economic yoke of a foreign power most probably constitutes another important factor of the difference. But the exploitation of national minorities for which Hungary set a paradigm cannot have been a very important element, for even the lot of these minorities improved in some proportion. We should also remark that, until her dismemberment in 1918, Hungary had almost as high an agricultural density as Poland, Rumania, Yugoslavia, or Bulgaria; this can be seen on the map in Moore, op. cit., p. 73.

obtain the maximum output from given amounts of resources, the production unit must be of optimum size. Consequently, they could not foresee the danger of determining the size of the peasant holding according to extra-economic criteria. The principle "a holding for every peasant family" naturally led to a sub-optimum size of the production unit. And this prevented the crystallization of the existing capital in the most efficient form compatible with the prevailing factor ratio and the available techniques. The unmistakable symptom of this situation was a relative excess of capital equipment. In Rumania, for instance, before the radical reform of 1918, there was a plough for every 26 acres; after the reform, there was one plough for every 15 acres.[57] The Agrarians discovered their error only *post partum,* and when they did, it was much too late. For in East Europe at least, the historical changes of the early 1930's prevented the Agrarian parties from forming a government again.

The facts just mentioned do not justify the prejudice of Stalinist governments in favour of large and highly mechanized farms of the North American type. This prejudice errs in the opposite direction: it leads to a size far greater than the optimum compatible with overpopulation, and hence it uses labour inefficiently.[58]

Poor theorists though they have been, Agrarians have never lost sight of the most elementary principle of economic development, which is that no factor should remain *unnecessarily* idle. In overpopulated economies, this may mean using labour even to the point where its marginal productivity becomes zero. From the viewpoint of positive welfare economics, we cannot do better than to cling to this principle. The question, however, is whether we can always comply with it in practice. A small farm, a small shop, can easily be run by a family or a true co-operative, and hence follow the feudal formula. On the other hand, many current products can be produced only by large plants. And large production units requiring numerous employees who have no other ties with each other than working together, lend themselves poorly, if at all, to the feudal formula. Firstly, it is hard to see how a manager could use labour beyond the point where its marginal productivity is equal to the wage-rate and still be able to prove the efficiency of his management. Secondly, once the principle that one can earn more than his own contribution to output has been accepted, the question of everyone doing his duty becomes a thorny problem. In the continuity and closedness of

[57] Cf. N. Georgescu-Roegen, "Inventarul agricol," *Enciclopedia Romániei,* iii, p. 339. Instances of "inefficient" forms of capital were quite common. To mention one more: the cows represented less than 70 per cent. of the entire cattle stock. This was a consequence of the fact that every peasant holding needed a pair of oxen for draught purposes, while only a few could keep more than two animals.

[58] Calvin B. Hoover, *The Economic Life of Soviet Russia,* New York, 1932, p. 88, reports of farms having ten times as many workers and twice as much machinery as a farm of equal size in the United States. See also Warriner, op. cit., p. 169.

the village, these problems are easily solved by the emergence of cultural patterns in which loafing is one of the worst sins.[59] There, efficiency does not need book-keeping in order to be recognized.

The baffling problem of reconciling the requirements of modern technology with the basic principle of economic welfare is no reason for throwing the latter overboard. In every overpopulated country, at least, there are numerous sectors which either by their nature or by their tradition permit labour to be used according to the feudal formula. Agriculture is almost everywhere in this category.[60] It would be the worst economics to change the production structure of such a sector because of an ill-advised development fever. No one would dispute the truth that peasant institutions and modern industry do not fit together, but it would be a great error to sacrifice all these institutions on the altar of that truth. And if a scapegoat for failing economic policies is needed, one should find a less expensive one. Many of these institutions will still be needed if the largest output is wanted from the sustaining sectors of economic development. Besides, the iconoclast may live to regret his haste, for we should not be surprised at all if the fight of the Communist régimes against the "bourgeois spirit"[61] in reality aims at creating a "socialist man" with a peasant type of conduct.

To assume that a process that sustains the progress of advanced economies necessarily befits an overpopulated economy is an unwarranted extrapolation. The ever-growing literature on economic development, however, abounds in such extrapolations. Probably the most patent is the use of marginal productivity principles in formulating economic policies for underdeveloped economies.[62] But few of these economies do not suffer from overpopulation. And it is an obvious feature of overpopulated countries that enterprises operated by feudal formula exist side by side

---

[59] Some primitive communities—we are told—hold work in such high esteem that they produce more than they need and they destroy the excess. Cf. Richard Thurnwald, *Economics in Primitive Communities*, London, 1932, pp. 209 *passim*.

[60] By destroying the peasant holdings altogether and replacing them by book-keeping operated *kolkhozi*, Stalinism certainly made a losing deal with the basic welfare principle. A truly co-operative form of production on units of optimum size with *product ownership* and *tithe* paid in kind to the government would be by far the best welfare solution. Titoism seems to have realized the Stalinist error when it renounced collectivization.

[61] See the resolution of the 1931 All-Russian Congress of Workers in *Report of the Ad Hoc Committee on Forced Labour*, United Nations, I.L.O., Geneva, 1953, pp. 456 f.

[62] Because of the momentous importance of the problem of underdeveloped countries in world affairs, the consequences of these extrapolations may well exceed those of mere academic licences. All the more so, when the source is as high an authority as the United Nations. In *Measures for the Economic Development of Under-Developed Countries*, New York, 1951, p. 49, they urge the use of the principle of marginal productivity which—they complain—"is frequently ignored in practice."

with others managed according to capitalist rules. In such circumstances, price lines are not tangent to the isoquants of every sector and, hence, the isoquants themselves are not tangent to each other . . .

In contrast with what happened in the West during the early phase of industrialization, the cities of overpopulated countries have grown to pathological sizes through a continuous immigration of rural population. The rural exodus brings into those cities not only an enormous excess of labour but also the germ of the feudal economic spirit to which practically no sector can remain immune. The social pressure of people seeking employment for their worthless leisure is so irresistible at all times that even the most convinced "marginalist" of the entrepreneurs has to yield to it and hire more people than he should according to his own rule. In these circumstances, prevailing factor prices may be proportionate to anything except the corresponding marginal productivities. To compute the money equivalent of the marginal productivity of an investment on the basis of the prevailing prices is pure nonsense. The criteria of investment priority based on the results of such computation are therefore baseless.[63] Still worse: such criteria point in exactly the wrong direction. Indeed, except for the correction for external economies, these criteria are identical with those used by the private investor. And the result of private investment is a well-known paradox: although labour-intensive techniques are the only ones indicated for overpopulated countries, the industries developed there have generally been capital intensive. The explanation is obvious: in an overpopulated country the ratio between wages and the price of other factors is greater than the ratio between the corresponding marginal productivities.

Economic development does not mean only pure growth; in the first place it means a growth-inducing process. Investment in capital-intensive industries is a wrong move in an overpopulated country not because it fails to bring about growth—for generally it does—but because they are not growth-sustaining. The power to sustain growth then is the only valid criterion of investment in undeveloped countries. The marginal productivity principles reflect this criterion very poorly, if at all. Even for a capitalist system they cannot explain more than distribution through allocation.

The path followed by the West in its economic development can help us in seeking a policy for the development of those areas that have re-

[63] For the investment criteria based on marginal productivity one may refer to A. E. Kahn, "Investment Criteria in Development Programs," *Quarterly Journal of Economics,* lxv (1951), pp. 36–61; H. B. Chenery, "The Application of Investment Criteria," ibid. lxvii (1953), pp. 76–96, among others. Because these criteria are endorsed by some economists serving as consultants to various economic development agencies, one may infer that they are used as a guide for public policy (e.g. G. di Nardi, "Criteri e 'Indicatori' per la scelta degli investimenti," *Rassegna Economica,* July 1957).

mained behind. But it cannot show us the way. For, clearly, by this policy we do not aim to follow precisely the same route that the West followed. It would take us too long to reach the goal. Still more important: it would not even be feasible, for the opportunities the West has had at one time or another cannot be reproduced. The essential distinction between an historical and a dynamic process does not need to be re-examined here. But, at bottom, this is what Marxists and Agrarians quarrelled about. Can we, as Standard economists, learn something from this quarrel?

9. Economic Theory and Agrarian Reform*

V. M. DANDEKAR[1]

Countries with retarded economic growth are in general characterized by a large proportion of their population depending for its subsistence on agriculture. Therefore among the actions intended to release the forces which may initiate or accelerate the process of economic growth, agrarian reform usually receives a high priority. In most noncommunist countries, where an agrarian reform has been initiated, it has usually taken the form of a movement aimed at creating individual peasant holdings. This has happened in countries with such widely different historical and cultural backgrounds as Japan, India, Iraq, Egypt, Cuba, and Bolivia. Everywhere, without question, the principle seems to have been accepted that in conditions of agricultural overpopulation, individual peasant holdings is the best economic policy. However, the economic rationale of this policy is generally understood only inadequately and in fact there often exist lurking doubts whether it is all economic policy. Recently, Georgescu-Roegen[2] has provided such a rationale. In fact, he comes to the conclusion that, "the proposition that capitalism and controlled socialism provide the best systems for developing an

* From *Oxford Economic Papers*, vol. 14, pp. 69–79, February, 1962. Reprinted by permission of the Clarendon Press, Oxford, and the author. The author is affiliated with the Gokhale Institute, Poona, India.

[1] The paper was originally submitted to the International Seminar on Paths to Economic Growth held in Jan. 1961 under the auspices of the Congress for Cultural Freedom and the Gokhale Institute of Politics and Economics, at Poona, India.

[2] N. Georgescu-Roegen, "Economic Theory and Agrarian Economics," *Oxford Economic Papers*, xii (1960), pp. 1–40. [EDITOR'S NOTE: Selection 8.]

underdeveloped economy is patently false, at least for an overpopulated economy" and further that "the intuition that led the Agrarians to their double negation—not Capitalism, not Socialism—proves to have been surprisingly correct." The purpose of this paper is to examine this conclusion in the light of the theoretical schemata put forward by Georgescu-Roegen and by taking his argument a step beyond where, it seems, he has left it somewhat incomplete.

The analysis is confined to the situation of overpopulation which is recognized as a certain critical relation between the total population or total labour force and the total of available land-capital resources. It is this relation which ultimately governs the marginal productivity of labour under conditions of full employment. Georgescu-Roegen defines overpopulation to be the situation in which, under conditions of full employment, the marginal productivity of labour falls short of the minimum subsistence of the worker. In the more extreme situation, the marginal productivity of labour may even reach zero before the conditions of full employment are realized. Georgescu-Roegen distinguishes this by calling it a condition of "strictly" overpopulation. Most underdeveloped countries do show such signs of overpopulation in a more or less extreme form. The process of economic growth consists in accumulating more and more land-capital resources so that the marginal productivity may progressively rise—first above the zero and then above the minimum subsistence. It is then that the condition of overpopulation ceases to exist.

From the standpoint of agrarian reform, it should be recognized further that, in the countries concerned, the agricultural sector is usually much more acutely over-populated than is the economy as a whole. This is because the non-agricultural sector in these economies is usually organized on the capitalist principles and hence does not permit workers in unless they can contribute to the production more than the wages they receive in return. Consequently, the entire residual population is thrown on the agriculture which by its nature and tradition employs or accommodates whatever population is thrown on it without reference to the marginal productivity of labour. Conceived as a part of the problem of economic growth, the agrarian problem consists in holding on to this population until an increasing part of it is withdrawn to the non-agricultural sector and in the meanwhile in employing it usefully so as to maximize the total output of the agricultural sector.

That capitalism cannot offer a solution to this problem is easily demonstrated. Because capitalism, understood as an economic system regulated by profit maximization, cannot offer employment to labour beyond the point where its marginal productivity equals the wages paid to it. Under conditions of over-population, this means that the capitalist system cannot employ labour beyond the point where its productivity equals its minimum subsistence. A part of the labour force therefore remains unemployed. Apart from its social consequences, this is obviously not even an economic solution for, though it maximizes the profit-rent of the capitalist-entrepreneur, it fails to maximize the total output of the agricultural sector. Maximization of the total output requires that the entire labour force or at least the same up to the point of zero marginal productivity is employed. Capitalism does not provide an institutional structure to make this possible.

In this context, we should refer to the theoretical construction put forward by Leibenstein[3] with the purport of explaining how, even under the incentives of profit maximization, landlords may employ labour beyond the point where its marginal productivity equals the wages paid to it. In his theoretical construction, Leibenstein postulates that the productivity of labour depends not only on the kind of technology used and the amount of land-capital resources available per employed worker but also on the level of wages paid because it affects the amount of work effort a worker might put forth. Therefore, on this construction, there is not one curve of average or marginal productivity but several such curves appropriate to the different wage levels. Given a wage level and the corresponding marginal productivity curve, there is an optimum number of workers whom the landlords as a group would hire if they were to maximize their group income and this optimum is determined, as usual, at the point where the wage is equal to the marginal productivity of the employed workers. But the wage level is not given and the landlords as a group have the choice of so fixing it as to maximize their group income. As for the supply of labour, under conditions of overpopulation, the whole of it is supposed to be available at the minimum subsistence level. Under the usual construction where the labour productivity is not supposed to depend upon the level of wages paid, there is no incentive for the landlords to raise the wages above the minimum subsistence level. But now under the Leibenstein construction, the landlords might want to offer wages above the minimum because that might raise the labour productivity and more than compensate the landlords so that their total income might in fact rise. In general, under this construction, the group income of the landlords is maximized at a wage level somewhere above the acceptable minimum. The landlords will therefore choose to offer this wage. They will of course employ only the optimum amount of labour appropriate to that wage level and the marginal productivity of the employed workers will equal the proposed wage. Nothing unorthodox has so far happened except that the proposed wage level is above the acceptable minimum and simultaneously a number of workers remain unemployed.

[3] Harvey Leibenstein, *Economic Backwardness and Economic Growth*, John Wiley & Sons, pp. 58–76.

But now it seems that in the face of a large number of unemployed workers, the landlords find it difficult to maintain the proposed wage level even though it is in their interest to do so. The competition among the unemployed and the employed workers depresses the wages. To counter this, the landlords must offer to employ the entire labour force. This they cannot do at the proposed wage level. It seems that finally they reach a compromise solution and offer a wage somewhere below the proposed one but nevertheless somewhere above the acceptable minimum and what is more important, at this compromise wage, they offer to employ the entire labour force and not only the optimum appropriate to that wage level. In other words, they employ labour beyond the point where the marginal productivity equals the wage. Thus two things happen: In the first instance, the landlords offer a wage higher than the acceptable minimum; this they do because it raises the labour productivity and on the whole they make larger income than they would do if they employed the labour at the minimum subsistence. Secondly, at the proposed wage level, they offer to employ the entire labour; on this they lose because the marginal productivity of the employed labour falls below the wage level but, nevertheless, they do it because it enables them to maintain the wages at the proposed level and on balance they still make more income than they would otherwise do.

The crucial part of the solution is that the landlords find it profitable to pay a wage higher than the minimum subsistence and in addition to employ the entire labour force at this wage. Of course, this is not inevitable; it might happen that the landlords do not find it profitable to do so and therefore they may allow the wages to be depressed to the minimum subsistence level. If and when this happens, this is important; the landlords have no interest in employing the entire labour force or in fact any labour beyond the point where the marginal productivity equals the minimum subsistence. Leibenstein does not specify the conditions under which the landlords may find it profitable to maintain the wage rate above the minimum subsistence and in particular it is not clear whether this would be true under conditions of over-population as defined by Georgescu-Roegen wherein the marginal productivity of labour falls below its minimum subsistence or even to zero. In the Leibenstein construction, this would mean that there is no wage level equal to or above the minimum subsistence, where under full employment, the marginal productivity of labour would not be less than its minimum subsistence. Leibenstein is aware of this possibility but does not examine its consequences. But it appears that under these conditions Leibenstein's special solution would not hold good and that the landlords would offer no more than the minimum acceptable wage and employ labour only to the extent where its marginal productivity equals the wage. The rest of the labour would then remain unemployed.

It is, of course, possible to presume that under conditions of over-population, the landlords are not quite unfettered in their pursuit to maximize their incomes and that they work under some kind of institutional obligations to employ the entire labour force somehow. But then these are not quite the capitalistic institutions. We may, therefore, say that in general the capitalist system does not provide a solution to the basic agrarian problem. We should, therefore, look for some other institutional structure and it seems that it will have to be basically non-capitalistic.

In point of fact the traditional agriculture in over-populated countries has developed its own characteristic institutions which, among other things, achieve precisely the same purpose, namely, to maximize the total output by maximizing the employment beyond the point where its marginal productivity falls below the minimum subsistence, or even to zero. For instance, as Georgescu-Roegen points out, feudalism provided such an institution. For here, the entrepreneur-landlord was compensated not by profit-rent, but by means of a tithe or a share of the total produce. Therefore, for a given ratio of the share, in order to maximize the tithe, the total produce had also to be maximized. Feudalism thus did provide the needed structure. But feudalism is no longer serviceable, if for no other reason, for the reason that having come in close contact with capitalistic institutions, it ceases to be sufficiently feudal. The capitalist economy in the non-agricultural sector offers new opportunities to the landlords and they are anxious to free themselves from the obligations of a traditional society. This leads to absentee landlordism, rack-renting, and all those evils which ruin agriculture. Therefore, feudalism has to be replaced.

And replaced it is, almost with a vengeance. Its place is taken by the new agrarian doctrine of individual peasant holdings and the new doctrine seems to work, at any rate up to a point. In explanation, Georgescu-Roegen points out that the principle of individual peasant holdings meets the requirements of the situation because it is essentially the old feudal formula under a new and a better form. From the standpoint of economic theory it is still feudal because the employment of the family labour is not governed by considerations of marginal productivity but by considerations of maximizing the total output. The family labour presumably works to the full limit of zero marginal productivity and it works better because it is rewarded by the entire product of its labour, no share going to the erstwhile landlord—an echo of Leibenstein's postulate that productivity is influenced by the reward.

But, as we shall see, the principle works only up to a point and in particular does not create certain important conditions for rapid economic growth. In the first instance, the principle does not remain confined to the creation of individual peasant holdings. It soon takes the form of a wider doctrine of self-employment, namely, that under conditions of over-population, self-employment provides the most favourable conditions for maximizing the total output. The principle is easily extended to industry, and small-scale and cottage industry is recommended on grounds that it promotes self-employment. Labour-intensive techniques are thus often equated to self-employment techniques. This leads to serious consequences in agriculture. An immediate consequence is the elimination of the large peasant holdings because such holdings, even though effectively peasant proprietorships, do involve a considerable amount of wage employment. Proposals for ceiling on family holdings are not always put forward explicitly on these grounds; more often they are based on general egalitarianism and more particularly on the need to satisfy the land hunger of the landless families. Also, the ceiling limits are not always placed sufficiently low to eliminate or at any rate minimize wage employment. Nevertheless, it is obvious that it would be more rational to base such proposals on the principle of maximization of self-employment. Such a principle may also provide a more rational and meaningful basis for a fixing of the ceiling.

What concerns us here is that whatever may be the basis of the principle of ceiling on peasant holdings, it can have very serious consequences on the agricultural sector. For, whatever its justification, a ceiling on land holding is a ceiling on how far a peasant may go as long as he remains a peasant. As a result, it is feared that the ability and enterprise which cannot be contained within the ceiling limits, would sooner or later leave the agricultural sector. Thus the agricultural sector would become progressively depressed and politically weak. These fears are all genuine. Nevertheless, it should be understood that they are the consequences of the initial proposition that in an over-populated economy, the agricultural sector must be organized on some principle other than the capitalist enterprise. We should remind ourselves of the initial fact: Because, the non-agricultural sector is usually organized on the capitalist principle, the residual burden of the population is thrown on the agriculture. Therefore, if a capitalist sub-sector were permitted within the agricultural sector, its immediate consequence would be to accentuate the conditions of over-population in the remaining part of the agricultural sector. Therefore these fears regarding ceiling on holdings will have to be countered by means other than permitting or promoting capitalist enterprise within the agricultural sector.

If the advocacy of a ceiling on holdings were based primarily on maximizing self-employment, the reform would still remain within some limits. However, as more often is the case, when the advocacy of the ceiling has a pronounced egalitarian base, the process does not stop at elimination of large holdings. The reform is then aimed at not only the creation of family holdings which can be cultivated by the family labour, but of equal family holdings or more strictly of equal holdings after making due allowance for the size of the family. The streak of egalitarianism is usually strong among the agrarian reformers and it would have in fact gone longer than it has, were it not for some serious physical problems of equalization of agricultural holdings. These are not always realized and equalization of holdings or reducing of existing inequalities in them is sometimes attempted within the existing physical layout. For instance, the Cuban agrarian reform provides for bringing the small land holdings up to a certain minimum by appropriately re-distributing the land expropriated above the ceiling. The small holdings are of course too numerous and the expropriated land, even if adequate to meet the requirement, is seldom located conveniently for adding to the small holdings. Therefore the objective of bringing up the small holdings up to a certain minimum would require not only the expro-priation of the land above the ceiling, but also of the land in the small holdings and its completely new allocation—in other words a complete redrawing of the physical layout of the individual holdings. Egali-tarianism has therefore to push forward more slowly than it would otherwise. When the physical layout of the holdings has to be redrawn anyhow because of considerations of agricultural technology, as in Iraq, the reform does provide for the creation of more or less equal family holdings.

It is, of course, true that even complete equalization of the family hold-ings can be justified on economic principles by following to its logical extreme the previous argument for maximizing the total product. How-ever, this is not always done and equal holdings are advocated, somewhat apologetically, on egalitarian grounds because some other considerations equally relevant to the problem of maximizing the total output appear running contrary to the objective of equal family holdings.

One such consideration is the size of the production unit. For various technological considerations, it seems that even in agriculture, in order to realize maximum output from given amounts of resources, the production unit has to be of an optimum size. Under conditions of over-population, the principle of a holding for every peasant family and for that matter an equal holding obviously does not lead to an optimum size of the pro-duction unit. In fact, it might be argued that it puts the entire agriculture in production units below the optimum. Georgescu-Roegen recognizes this defect of the principle of a holding for every peasant family and remarks that "it led to a sub-optimum size of the production unit" and further that "this prevented the crystallization of the existing capital in the most efficient form compatible with the prevailing factor ratio and the available techniques." But he does not consider how the defect may be remedied. Instead he leaves this important point with the re-mark: "The facts just mentioned do not justify the prejudice of Stalinist governments in favour of large and highly mechanized farms of the North American type. This prejudice errs in the opposite direction: it leads to a size far greater than the optimum compatible with over-population, and hence it uses labour inefficiently." This may be so. But the fact remains that something has to be done to the individual peasant holdings in order to secure an optimum production unit and the result may not be individual peasant holdings at all.

This question of the size of the production unit is often raised in the literature on the subject, but is not always understood in the same sense as it is being raised here. It will be useful, therefore, to make the distinction clear. In the context of the principle of individual peasant holdings, the question of the size of the optimum unit is usually discussed from the standpoint of the peasant proprietor and the optimum holding is supposed to give him a minimum or a desired or an optimum family income. To the extent that it is also considered as an efficient production unit, its efficiency is judged as that of a capitalist enterprise—the peasant proprietor is supposed to behave like a capitalist-entrepreneur and offer employment on the principle of marginal productivity. For instance, it is on some such understanding of the problem of the size of production unit that the ceiling on holdings is sometimes disputed. It is obvious however that if the optimum size of the production unit is to be determined on such principles, it will not satisfy the initial requirement, namely, that in order to maximize output, the maximum amount of labour resources must be utilized. Therefore, the only result of such a determination of the optimum holdings is to show that under conditions of over-population, not all the peasant families can have optimum holdings and that their creation would only lead to the creation of a large agricultural proletariat. The point is therefore given up as a hopeless idea for it appears to run against the egalitarian principle. The peasant proprietorship and equal family holdings therefore continue to be advocated with greater egalitarian zeal and with a lurking fear that the reform in these directions might affect the total output adversely.

Therefore it should be understood that the question of the optimum size of the holding is not being raised here from the standpoint of an individual peasant proprietor. The elementary principle that in order to maximize the total output, all the available resources must be utilized and in the particular context of the over-populated countries, that all their labour resources or at least a maximum amount of them, must be utilized has to be firmly held on to. Therefore, given the quantity of land in agriculture and the number of people it must absorb and support, the size of the individual holding is automatically determined and one can hardly improve upon the principle of equal family holdings. Therefore, if the question of the optimum unit of production is to be raised, it must be clearly understood that the optimum must be determined under conditions that the optimum unit, whatever its size, must carry its proportionate burden of the population. In other words, while discussing the question of the optimum size of the production unit, one should not be discussing whether an individual should have a smaller or a bigger holding, for there is no choice in that respect; rather, one should be discussing whether the equal peasant holdings should be operated, as production units, individually or whether there is an advantage in operating them jointly and, if so, how large such joint units should be.

To be sure, the question is sometimes understood in this light. For instance, this was how the Mexican agrarian reform approached the problem in its initial stages. Also, more recently, both the Iraqi and the Cuban agrarian reforms provide for the creation of the more or less equal individual holdings and their almost immediate merger into some form of co-operative production units. However, more often, co-operation like egalitarianism is regarded as valuable *per se* and is advocated without a full realization of its economic basis and implications. When these become fully apparent, the advocates of co-operation often fight shy of their initial advocacy.

The reasons for not realizing fully the implications of co-operativizing the individual holdings is that the economic basis for the advocacy of individual peasant holdings is not firmly understood so that one does not realize fully what is lost in the process of co-operativization. As Georgescu-Roegen points out, the main advantage of the individual peasant holdings, in conditions of over-population, is that they afford conditions under which labour may be employed without reference to its marginal productivity. Once the individual holdings are put in the form of a co-operative production unit, this advantage is lost because usually the conditions of employment in a co-operative farm are governed by considerations of marginal productivity. As a result, even the family workers of the members of a co-operative cannot be employed beyond the point where the marginal productivity equals the minimum subsistence wage. In terms of the usual formulation, the co-operative organization brings to surface the unemployment which otherwise appears in the disguised form of self-employment. This formulation is correct as far as it goes but it misses the important point that, in addition, the co-operative organization also in fact reduces the employment if its decisions in this matter are allowed to be governed by the considerations of marginal productivity. This is in fact what usually happens because the manager of a co-operative farm, by training and background is more often a capitalist-entrepreneur than a feudal-landlord. Also he is called upon to function in an economy where the growing non-agricultural sector is worked on capitalist principles and conse-

quently his own management is judged by the same criteria of efficiency. It is for this reason, mainly, that the co-operative organization of
the individual holdings, in the sense it is usually understood and advocated, defeats its own purpose. There is, of course, no other method of
achieving the optimum size of the production unit, except by pooling the
individual holdings in some form of co-operative joint production units.
But for them to fulfill the original purpose, namely to achieve maximum
output through a maximum utilization of labour, the co-operative farm
has to be basically feudal and not capitalist.

In its feudal form, the co-operative organization should resemble a
household rather than a business enterprise. The members of a co-operative organization are, in fact, often exhorted to act and behave like the
members of a family. But usually, such exhortation is more romantic than
realistic. Because, logically, the primary responsibility of the manager
or the managing committee of a co-operative organization conceived as
a household, would be to feed its members and to occupy them usefully,
and it is rarely that individual households are willing to yield themselves
to a common discipline which may be necessary for the purpose. In any
case, it takes more than an occasional exhortation for them to agree to
such a submission.

Of all the responsibilities which may be put on the manager or the
managing committee of a co-operative production unit, the most serious
is that of usefully employing all its labour resources. Overpopulation,
strictly speaking, means that under conditions of full employment, the
mental to the total output. Obviously therefore all the labour cannot be
employed beyond the point of zero productivity without being detrimental to the total output. Obviously therefore all the labour cannot be
utilized in current production. Therefore, a part of it must be utilized on
capital works, that is on works which directly lead to capital creation. It
is this possibility which enables the joint production units to create additional employment and to utilize the unemployed labour resources disguised as self-employed in family farms. The superiority of the joint
production units lies in this that they alone, as distinct from individual
family holdings, can undertake certain categories of capital works. The
optimum size of the production unit must therefore be decided, not
by the exclusive considerations and techniques of current production,
but also, and perhaps mainly, by the requirements of discovering,
planning, and executing capital works. Thus conceived, it will be noted
that few individual holdings, including even those above any proposed
ceiling, can be regarded to be of the optimum size. In fact, thus considered, the optimum production units will be sizeable agricultural regions. This is not what is usually conceived by way of a co-operative
organization of individual holdings.

With the accumulation of capital in the agricultural sector and with the withdrawal of a part of the agricultural population into the growing non-agricultural sector, the ratio of land-capital to labour in the agricultural sector improves and causes an upward shift in the marginal productivity curve. A stage is then reached when even under conditions of full employment, the marginal productivity of labour in the agricultural sector is no longer zero—it is positive but still less than the subsistence wage. In terms of the definitions given by Georgescu-Roegen, the condition of overpopulation still persists but not quite strictly. Under this condition, the management has a difficult choice to make between capital works and current production. However, what is more important in the present context is that under these conditions, in order to maximize the total output, the labour must be used to its fullest capacity. As Georgescu-Roegen points out, at this stage of development, the working class can have no leisure at all. The co-operative organization of the individual holdings, as it is usually understood, does not create conditions compelling everyone to work to his full capacity. For that purpose, something more than the co-operative spirit is required.

It seems, therefore, that the individual peasant holdings or even these same organized in what are loosely called co-operatives do not provide a solution to the agrarian problem under conditions of overpopulation. The solution has to be found in an organization of the agrarian sector in large units of land and population, feudal in theory, modern in technology and oriented to a socialistic purpose. Because the basic production units would be large, it is inevitable that the relation between man and land in them should be much looser than the one implied in individual peasant holdings. There is another reason why this relationship should be rather loose and certainly short of proprietary rights in land. The starting-point of this discussion, it will be remembered, was the problem of how to seek an institutional structure which would hold and employ the residual population until an increasingly larger portion of it was withdrawn into the non-agricultural sector. Therefore the holding operation must be such as would facilitate the timely release of a part of the labour force when needed. In particular, while settling the whole population in agriculture, care must be taken to see that the settlement is not done in a manner which may obstruct this eventual withdrawal of a large part of the population or which may cause dislocation in agriculture when such withdrawal takes place. Individual proprietary interests in land in general create such difficulties. Therefore it will be advisable to avoid creating such rights in land. In many countries such rights in land already exist, and possibly they have to be taken cognizance of. Nevertheless, two broad principles may be enunciated: Firstly, no individual rights should be created in lands where they do not already exist or where they have been destroyed for one reason or another, such as by expropriation or by the application of a ceiling. Secondly, granting of individual rights in land to persons who do not already have any should be avoided; in other words, permanent or long-term settlement of landless persons in agriculture should be avoided. On the other hand, those who are not yet settled on land, should receive the highest priority and preparation for being withdrawn from the agricultural sector into the non-agricultural sector.

These are some of the considerations of internal organization of the agricultural sector which indicate that individual peasant holdings do not provide the requisite structure. There are also other compelling reasons which point in the same direction. One such consideration concerns the relation between the agricultural and the non-agricultural sectors. In the process of economic growth, when the non-agricultural sector continually grows, one of the crucial functions of the agricultural sector is to produce enough food and to release it for the use of the non-agricultural sector at reasonable price. There is no need to spell this problem more fully. The conflict is well known and is known to become spiny under conditions of overpopulation and peasant proprietorship. When food is in short supply, its equitable distribution becomes crucial. In other words, if the process of growth is not to be hindered on this account, the non-agricultural sector must be able to secure its due share of the food production. Whatever the form of the institutional structure we may desire to have for the agricultural sector, it must provide for a feudal overlord who will collect the tithe and hand it over to the non-agricultural sector.

To repeat, all these considerations lead to the same conclusion, that the individual peasant holdings, though feudal in form and therefore answering the purpose up to a point and found culturally satisfying, do not meet several other requirements of economic growth. Further, this principle when it is associated with romantic egalitarianism with its doctrine of self-employment, puts a ceiling on individual achievement and enterprise, depresses the agricultural sector and makes it politically weak. The argument leads inevitably to a structure composed of large production units managed not on capitalist principles, but for collective good. It will be seen that such a structure also offers a large network of institutions, where the enterprise and ability of individuals may find the fullest scope and where it may be amply rewarded, though rather differently. In the light of this it is difficult to accept Georgescu-Roegen's recommendation of the agrarian doctrine of individual peasant holdings and cottage industry involving the double negation—not Capitalism, not Socialism.

IO. A Theory of Economic Development*

GUSTAV RANIS AND JOHN C. H. FEI†

This paper attempts to make a contribution towards the theory of growth by rigorously analyzing the transition process through which an underdeveloped economy hopes to move from a condition of stagnation to one of self-sustaining growth. Since the totality of economies bearing the "underdeveloped" label admittedly defies easy generalization, we shall be primarily concerned here with the labor-surplus, resource-poor variety in which the vast majority of the population is typically engaged in agriculture amidst widespread disguised unemployment and high rates of population growth. We hope to accomplish our task by drawing liberally on the stock of already accepted ideas and then proceeding to weave them into a general explanatory model of economic growth.

Our analysis begins with an economy's first departure from quasi-stagnation or the initiation of the so-called take-off process.[1] Rostow defines this as a period of two or three decades during which the economy transforms itself in such a way that economic growth becomes, subsequently, more or less automatic; its characteristics are a reduction of the rural proportion of the population, a doubling of savings rates and the first marked and continuous flowering of industry stimulated by the availability of surplus labor [8, pp. 25–32]. This well-known intuitive notion has been chosen as our point of departure. For our basic analytical tool-kit, however, we draw heavily on the work of Arthur Lewis.

* From the *American Economic Review*, vol. 51, pp. 533–565, September, 1961, with omissions. Reprinted by permission of the American Economic Association and the authors. Pages 533–546 have been reprinted as originally published with the exception of several changes in some of the reference numbers indicated in brackets. The authors are associate professors of economics at Yale University.

† This paper was initiated while both authors were associated with the Institute of Development Economics, Karachi, Pakistan. Comments by Bela Balassa and John M. Montias of Yale University are gratefully acknowledged.

[1] This is not to understate the importance of a prior preconditioning period (see [1] and [7]) when potentially expansionary institutional forces are being mobilized and render the system capable of a significantly positive response to a random stimulus.

In his celebrated articles Lewis [3] [4] presents a two-sector model and investigates the expansion of the capitalistic or industrial sector as it is nourished by supplies of cheap labor from the subsistence or agricultural sector.[2] Development consists of the re-allocation of surplus agricultural workers, whose contribution to output may have been zero or negligible, to industry where they become productive members of the labor force at a wage equal (or tied to) the institutional wage in agriculture. This process continues until the industrial labor supply curve begins to turn up.

Lewis, however, has failed to present a satisfactory analysis of the subsistence or agricultural sector. It seems clear that this sector must also grow if the mechanism he describes is not to grind to a premature halt. Pursuit of this notion of a required balance in growth then leads us to a logically consistent definition of the end of the take-off process.

Finally, the economy must be able to solve its Malthusian problem if the process of development along a balanced-growth path is to prove successful. Considerations of this nature have given rise to the so-called "critical minimum effort" theory [2], which deals with the size of the effort required to achieve a more-than-temporary departure from stagnation. We shall show, in the course of our analysis, that the concept of a critical minimum effort does not presuppose some absolute magnitude of effort but contains a built-in time dimension permitting the size of the effort to vary with the duration of the take-off process.

The contribution of this paper, then, is to construct a theory of economic growth of which the above ideas, rigorously formulated, constitute component parts. In Section I we present the basic structural assumptions of our model with emphasis on analysis of the role of the "neglected" agricultural sector. Section II generalizes the previously "static" analysis by admitting the possibility of a change of productivity in the agricultural sector. In Section III we introduce changes in industrial productivity and the notion of a "balanced growth criterion" by means of which the termination of the take-off process is formally defined. Section IV* proceeds with a precise mathematical formulation of our theory which enables us to make certain quantitative conditional predictions as a first test of its empirical relevancy. Finally, in Section V,* we integrate population growth as well as some other real-world complexities into our model and investigate the notion of the critical minimum effort in relation to the length of the take-off process.

---

[2] We wish to underscore the absence of any necessary one-to-one relationship between the subsistence sector and agriculture, or between the capitalistic sector and industry in most less-developed economies. The existence of substantial islands of commercial production in the primary sector and of sizable subsistence enclaves in the small-scale and service industries does not, however, bar Lewis, or us, from using this short-hand terminology.

* EDITOR'S NOTE: Sections IV and V are not reprinted.

I. THE BASIC ASSUMPTIONS

Our formal explanatory model is presented with the help of Diagram 1. Diagram 1.1 depicts the industrial sector and Diagrams 1.2 and 1.3 the agricultural sector. The first is the familiar Lewis diagram measuring industrial labor on the horizontal axis OW and its marginal physical productivity (MPP) on the vertical axis OP. The demand curve for labor (i.e., the MPP curve dtf), together with the supply curve of labor $(Stt'S')$, determines the employment of the industrial labor force (St). Since the marginal physical productivity curve depends on the size of the capital stock cooperating with the labor force, an increase in the capital stock leads to a shift of the MPP curve to the right, e.g. to $d't'f'$. Lewis' "unlimited" supply curve of labor is defined by the horizontal portion of the supply curve, i.e., St. When this supply curve turns up, unlimitedness comes to an end. Our first problem is to investigate the conditions of this turning point. This leads us to focus attention on the agricultural sector.

In Diagram 1.3 let the agricultural labor force be measured on the horizontal axis OA (reading from right to left), and let agricultural output be measured on the vertical axis OB (downward from O). The curve $ORCX$ describes the total physical productivity of labor (TPP) in the agricultural sector. This curve is assumed to have a concave portion ORC showing a gradually diminishing marginal productivity of agricultural labor and a horizontal portion XC where marginal product vanishes. The portion of any labor force in excess of OD may be considered redundant in that its withdrawal from agriculture would not affect agricultural output.

At the initial (or break-out) point let the entire labor force OA be committed to agriculture, producing a total agricultural output of AX. Let us assume that the agricultural output AX is totally consumed by the agricultural labor force OA. Then the real wage is equal to AX/OA or the slope of OX. The persistence of this wage level is sustained by institutional or nonmarket forces since under competitive assumptions the real wage would fall to zero, at equality with MPP. We shall call this the institutional wage.

Let point R on the total output curve be the point at which the MPP equals the institutional wage, i.e., the dotted tangential line at R is parallel to OX. We can then define AP as the disguisedly unemployed agricultural labor force since, beyond P, MPP is less than the institutional wage.[3]

Note that Diagrams 1.1, 1.2, and 1.3 are "lined up." Any point on

[3] Redundancy is a technological phenomenon, i.e., determined by the production function. Disguised unemployment, on the other hand, depends upon the production function, the institutional wage, and the size of the agricultural population. In other words, it is an economic concept.

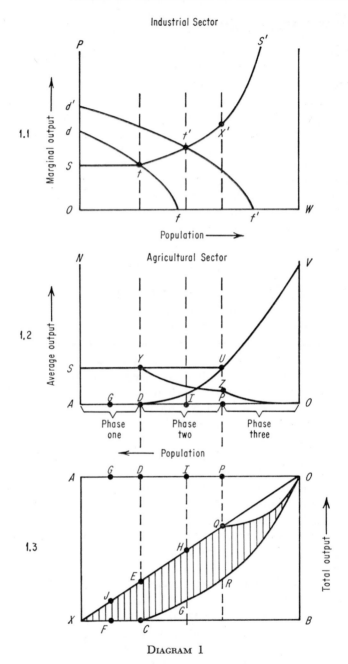

DIAGRAM 1

the horizontal axis of Diagrams 1.1 to 1.3 represents a particular way in which the total population or labor force OA is distributed between the two sectors; for example, at point P (Diagrams 1.2 and 1.3) the agricultural labor force is OP and the (already allocated) industrial labor force is AP. If, at the break-out point, the entire population, OA, is engaged in the agricultural sector, the allocation process during take-off can be represented by a series of points, A, G, D, I, P, etc., on OA, gradually moving towards O.[4]

The important concepts of disguised unemployment, redundant labor force and institutional wage can be more clearly depicted with the aid of Diagram 1.2, in which agricultural output per worker is measured on the vertical axis AN. Let $ADUV$ be the marginal physical productivity (MPP) curve of labor in the agricultural sector. Let the vertical distance AS equal the institutional wage (shown also as PU, equal to MPP of agricultural labor at U, lined up with P and R in Diagram 1.3). Three phases in the re-allocation process may now be distinguished: (1) Phase 1 is the range for which MPP $= 0$, i.e., the total productivity curve in Diagram 1.3 is horizontal. This phase marks off the redundant labor force, AD. (2) Phase 2 is the range for which a positive MPP is less than the institutional wage. Phases 1 and 2 together mark off the existence of the disguisedly unemployed labor force, AP. (3) Phase 3 is the range for which MPP is greater than the institutional wage rate assumed to prevail at the break-out point.

We assume that the institutional wage AS prevails during phases 1 and 2 and a wage rate equal to MPP prevails in phase 3. Only when the disguisedly unemployed have been absorbed, i.e. in phase 3, does the marginal contribution of labor to output become as great as or greater than the institutional real wage. As a result, it is then to the advantage of the landlord to bid actively for labor; the agricultural sector can be said to have become commercialized as the institutional wage is abandoned and competitive market forces yield the commonly accepted equilibrium conditions. Under these assumptions the agricultural real wage in terms of agricultural goods is defined by the curve SUV in Diagram 1.2, consisting of a horizontal portion SU and a rising portion, UV. This curve may be called the supply-price curve of agricultural labor. It indicates for each level of real wage the amount of labor that may be released from the agricultural sector.

The transition into phase 3 constitutes a major landmark in the developmental process. With the completion of the transfer of the disguisedly unemployed, there will occur a switch, forced by circumstance, in employer behavior, i.e. the advent of a fully commercialized agricultural sector. This landmark may be defined as the end of the take-off process. We know no other way to establish a nonarbitrary criterion

[4] The present assumption of an unchanging population will later be relaxed.

for an economy reaching the threshold of so-called self-sustaining growth.[5]

Returning now to Diagram 1.3, we see that, as agricultural workers are withdrawn, a surplus of agricultural goods begins to appear. That portion of total agricultural output in excess of the consumption requirements of the agricultural labor force at the institutional wage is defined as the total agricultural surplus (TAS). The amount of TAS can be seen to be a function of the amount of labor reallocated at each stage. For example, if agricultural workers to the extent of AG are withdrawn in phase 1 and re-allocated, JG is required to feed the remaining agricultural workers and a TAS of size JF results. The TAS at each point of allocation in phases 1 and 2 is represented by the vertical distance between the straight line OX and the total physical productivity curve $ORCX$. (For phase 3, due to the rise of the wage rate, TAS is somewhat less than this vertical distance and equals the vertical distance between the curve OQ and the total productivity curve.)

TAS may be viewed as agricultural resources released to the market through the re-allocation of agricultural workers. Such resources can be siphoned off by means of the investment activities of the landlord class and/or government tax policy and can be utilized in support of the new industrial arrivals.[6] The average agricultural surplus, or AAS, may now be defined as the total agricultural surplus available per head of allocated industrial workers.

The AAS curve is represented by curve $SYZO$ in Diagram 1.2. In phase 1 as TAS increases linearly with the allocation of the redundant labor force from A to D we can picture each allocated worker as carrying his own subsistence bundle along with him. The AAS curve for phase 1 thus coincides with the institutional wage curve SY. In phase 2, however since the MPP in agriculture of the now allocated workers was positive there will not be sufficient agricultural output to feed all the new industrial arrivals at the institutional wage level. Thus, while TAS is still

---

[5] Whether or not growth can ever really be "self-sustaining," in Rostow's phrase, is basically not a problem amenable to the tools of traditional economic analysis. The role of saving rates and per capita income levels in setting it in motion remains undefined. All we are saying here is that, after the turning point, the real wage in agriculture is determined by impersonal competitive market forces, a qualitative transformation which constitutes a necessary (if not sufficient) condition for growth to become automatic and routinized. It is this point which Lewis [4, p. 26] seems to have in mind when he speaks of "two different stages of economic development with two different sets of results" and describes the second stage as a situation in which "all the factors of production are scarce [and] . . . wages are no longer constant as accumulation proceeds."

[6] While it could easily be accommodated by the model, we neglect resource transfer costs as well as the possibility that it may be impossible to induce those left behind in agriculture to release the entire surplus.

rising, AAS begins to fall.[7] It can, moreover, readily be seen that during phase 3 AAS declines even more rapidly (and TAS also declines) as the now commercialized wage in agriculture becomes operative.

We may now consider the derivation of the Lewis turning point in the agricultural sector. Lewis himself [4, pp. 19–26] explains the turning point rather loosely as occurring when one of the following events puts an end to the horizontal supply curve of labor: (a) the worsening of the terms of trade for the industrial sector, and (b) the exhaustion of the labor surplus in the agricultural sector. But in our model any such explanation must take into account the basic determination of the entire industrial labor supply curve by the conditions postulated for the non-industrial sector.

The "worsening of the terms of trade" for the industrial sector occurs as the result of a relative shortage of agricultural commodities seeking exchange for industrial goods in the market. In our model, it will be recalled, this surplus is measured by total agricultural surplus (TAS) and, on a per-industrial-worker basis, average agricultural surplus (AAS). There is a tendency, then, for the industrial supply curve to turn up as phase 2 is entered because this is the time when there begins to appear a shortage of agricultural goods measured in AAS—causing a deterioration of the terms of trade of the industrial sector and a rise in the industrial real wage measured in terms of industrial goods. We thus see that the disappearance of the redundant labor force in the agricultural sector is a cause of the Lewis turning point.

The "exhaustion of the labor surplus" must be interpreted primarily as a market phenomenon rather than as a physical shortage of manpower; it is indicated by an increase in the real wage at the source of supply. If we assume that the real wage of the industrial worker is equal to the agricultural real wage,[8] then there is a tendency for the industrial supply curve of labor ($Stt'S'$ in Diagram 1.1) to turn upward when

[7] The following analogy with individual-firm analysis may be drawn to show more clearly the relationship between the marginal, total and average concepts involved. We may think of the total agricultural output curve (ORCX) and the total agricultural consumption curve (OX) in Diagram 1.3 as analogous to the total revenue curve and the total cost curve, respectively. Then the gap between these curves is the total profit curve which is equivalent to our TAS curve. The total profit curve reaches a maximum when marginal cost equals marginal revenue. This occurs at point U in Diagram 1.2—because SU is the marginal cost curve and ADUV is the marginal revenue curve. The AAS curve in Diagram 1.2 is equivalent to an "average profit curve."

[8] "Governed by" may be a more realistic description. Lewis [3, p. 150] points out that urbanization, transfer costs, etc. may require an industrial real wage at a constant (he believes approximately 30 per cent) margin or "hill" above the institutional wage in agriculture; while, for simplicity of exposition, our model initially maintains strict equality between the two wage rates, this assumption is later re-

phase 3 is entered. With the disappearance of the disguisedly un-employed labor force and the commercialization of the agricultural sec-tor, the agricultural real wage begins to rise (see Diagram 1.2). This leads to an increase in the industrial real wage level if the industrial employer is to compete successfully with the landlord for the use of the, by now "limited," supply of labor.

Putting the two factors (a and b) together, we can say that as labor is re-allocated from the agricultural to the industrial sector, the indus-trial supply curve turns up (i.e., the Lewis turning point occurs), in the first instance (at t), due to a shortage of agricultural goods traceable to the disappearance of the redundant agricultural labor force; and that this upward trend in the industrial real wage is later accentuated (at X') by the upward movement of the agricultural real wage traceable to the complete disappearance of the disguisedly unemployed labor force and the commercialization of the agricultural sector.

To facilitate our later analysis, let us refer to the boundary between phases 1 and 2 (i.e., point Y in Diagram 1.2) as the "shortage point" signifying the beginning of shortages of agricultural goods as indicated by the fact that AAS falls below the minimum wage; let us also refer to the boundary between phases 2 and 3 as the "commercialization point" signifying the beginning of equality between marginal productivity and the real wage in agriculture. The Lewis turning point thus coincides with the shortage point and the upward movement of the industrial real wage is accentuated at the commercialization point.[9]

There are two factors which may lead to a postponement of the Lewis turning point: (1) increases in agricultural productivity, and (2) popu-lation growth. The fact that these two factors operate very differently —one, generally viewed as a blessing, by raising surplus agricultural output, the other, almost invariably considered a curse, by augmenting the supply of redundant labor, is intuitively obvious. We shall first examine the significance of an increase of agricultural productivity. The extension of our analysis to accommodate population growth will be undertaken later.

---

laxed (Section V). In his second article [4], Lewis also refers to certain "exogenous factors," including unionization and presumably other changes in the institutional milieu. Such a dynamically growing "hill" could also be accommodated by the model but has not been considered in this first approximation.

[9] From a strictly logical standpoint the industrial supply curve of labor must be derived from the totality of conditions emerging from our analysis of the agricultural sector. The relevant conditions include (1) the agricultural real-wage curve, (2) the AAS curve, and (3) a consumer preference map specifying preferences for agri-cultural vs. industrial goods. Space limitations prevent us from rendering a rigorous derivation of the industrial real wage at each point through the terms-of-trade mechanism.

II. CHANGES IN AGRICULTURAL PRODUCTIVITY

An increase in labor productivity in the agricultural sector can be described by an "upward" shift of the entire total physical productivity (TPP) curve of Diagram 1.3. Such productivity increases are depicted in Diagram 2.3 by a sequence of TPP curves marked I, II, III . . . etc. among which the I-curve is the initial TPP curve (as in Diagram 1.3) and II, III . . . represent the TPP curves after successive doses of agricultural investment. (For the present we assume no change in industrial productivity.)

Let us make the assumption that as agricultural productivity increases the institutional wage remains unchanged, i.e., SA in Diagram 2.2 equals the slope of OX in Diagrams 1.3 and 2.3 as determined by the initial TPP curve.[10] In Diagram 2.2 we may now plot the sequence of marginal physical productivity of labor curves marked I, II, III . . . (all containing the flat portion AS_1) and the sequence of average agricultural surplus curves marked I, II, III . . . corresponding to the total physical productivity curves I, II, III . . . in Diagram 2.3. According to the method already indicated, we can now determine the three phases for each level of productivity, i.e., the sequence of shortage points, S_1, S_2, S_3 . . . and the sequence of commercialization points, R_1, R_2, R_3 . . . . Reference to these points will facilitate our analysis of the effects of an increase in agricultural productivity on the supply-price curve of agricultural labor and on the AAS curve.

As depicted in Diagram 2.2, for every amount of labor employed in the agricultural sector, an increase in agricultural productivity also shifts the marginal physical productivity curve upward.[11] As a consequence, the agricultural labor supply price curve is transformed from St_1t_1' to St_2t_2' to St_3t_3' . . . etc. with a shortening of its horizontal portion (i.e., phase 3 arrives earlier) as the sequence of commercialization points R_1, R_2, R_3 . . . gradually shifts from right to left. On the other hand, the sequence of shortage points S_1, S_2, S_3 . . . etc. gradually moves from left to right. This is due to the fact that, for each amount of labor allocated to the industrial sector, the AAS increases with the increase in total physical productivity; the amount of food consumed by agricul-

[10] It is, of course, possible that the institutionally determined agricultural wage will be permitted to rise; but as the economy becomes increasingly capitalistic it seems highly doubtful that nonmarket forces in agriculture will be strengthened and thus prevent the closing of the artificial marginal productivity-wage gap. A second, and possibly more powerful, qualification arises from the fact that the institutional wage level in agriculture may be sufficiently close to caloric subsistence so that raising it may constitute a highly productive form of investment. We do not, however, consider this possibility in the context of the present model. Concerning the relative position of the industrial wage level see footnote 8.

[11] This is a reasonable assumption if the shift in TPP is proportional.

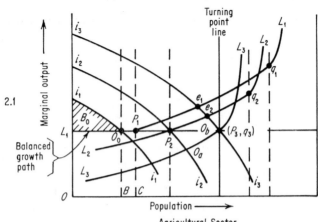

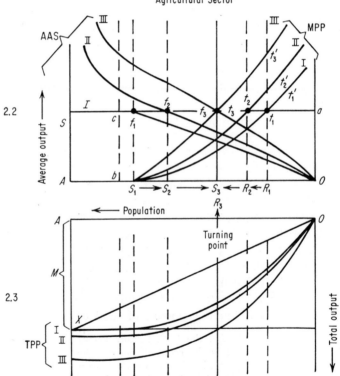

DIAGRAM 2

tural labor remains unchanged, leaving more TAS (and hence AAS) for the industrial workers. Thus the effect of our increase in agricultural productivity is an upward shift of the AAS curve (to positions marked II, III . . .).

Sooner or later, the shortage point and the commercialization point coincide, the distance S_1R_1, S_2R_2, S_3R_3 . . . vanishes and phase 2 is eliminated. In Diagram 2.2 such a point of coincidence is described by $R_3 = S_3$. We shall call this point the turning point. There exists one level of agricultural productivity which, if achieved, will bring about this turning point. (In Diagram 2.3 this level of agricultural productivity is described by TPP curve *III*.)

Let us now investigate the impact of an increase of agricultural productivity on the industrial supply curve L_1L_1 depicted in Diagram 2.1. On the one hand, the upward shift of the AAS curve will shift the industrial supply curve downward *before* the turning point. This is due to the fact that an increase of AAS will depress the terms of trade for the agricultural sector and, with the same institutional wage (in terms of agricultural goods) paid to the industrial workers, the industrial wage (in terms of industrial goods) must decline. On the other hand, the upward shift of the MPP curve which is accompanied by a higher real wage in the agricultural sector *after* the turning point raises the industrial supply curve after that point. Thus we see, for example, that the L_2L_2 curve crosses the L_1L_1 curve from below, indicating that ultimately the "terms-of-trade effect" (due to an increase of AAS) has been overcome by the "real-wage effect" (due to an increase of MPP). For purposes of this paper, we are, however, not very much concerned with phase 3 which lies beyond the turning point.

Let us now examine more closely the relative positions of the industrial supply curves before phase 3 is reached. Let the horizontal portion L_1P_1 of the initial industrial supply curve L_1L_1 be extended up to P_3, the turning point, and let us call this horizontal line segment L_1P_3 the balanced-growth path (for reasons which will be fully explained in the next section). We may then claim that all the industrial supply curves between L_1L_1 (i.e., the initial one) and L_3L_3 (i.e., the one corresponding to the turning point) cross the balanced-growth path at the respective shortage points. This is due to the fact that at the shortage point for each case (e.g., point f_2 in Diagram 2.2 for the case of industrial supply curve L_2L_2 in Diagram 2.1) the subsistence wage rate and the AAS take on the same value as that prevailing in phase 1 before any increase in agricultural productivity has been recorded. Hence the same real wage, in terms of industrial goods, must prevail at the shortage point as prevailed previously. In short, before the turning point, the industrial labor supply curve lies above (below) the balanced growth path when the

AAS curve lies below (above) the horizontal line Sa, causing a deterioration (improvement) of the industrial sector's terms of trade.

The economic significance of the equality between our turning point and the (final) shortage point is that, before the turning point, the economy moves along its balanced-growth path while exploiting (or making the best of) its under-employed agricultural labor force by means of increases in agricultural productivity. The economic significance of the equality between our turning point and the commercialization point is that, after the turning point, the industrial supply curve of labor finally rises as we enter a world in which the agricultural sector is no longer dominated by nonmarket institutional forces but assumes the characteristics of a commercialized capitalistic system.

III. CHANGES IN INDUSTRIAL PRODUCTIVITY AND BALANCED GROWTH

In addition to investment in the agricultural sector, the other major aspect of growth which must be considered is the simultaneous process of investment in the industrial sector. We know, moreover, that such activities in the two sectors do not constitute independent activities. For, from the output side, the two sectors must provide the marketing outlets for each other's products; and, from the input side, the industrial sector must provide the employment opportunities for the absorption of workers released by the agricultural sector. Consideration of this basic interdependence during the take-off process is really nothing else but consideration of the "balanced growth" problem, a key concept in the current development literature.[12] The purpose of this section is to formulate the problem of balanced growth rigorously and to investigate its significance in the context of our model.

Referring to Diagram 2.1 we see that during the take-off process the demand curve for labor, i_1i_1, i_2i_2 . . . , gradually shifts upward to the right as real capital is accumulated in the industrial sector. Simultaneously the investment activity proceeding in the agricultural sector shifts the supply curve of labor L_1L_1, L_2L_2 . . . downward in the same direction. The central problem of balanced growth concerns the synchronization through time of the shifts of the two sequences of curves. At any moment of time during the take-off process, the question is how should the total investment fund be allocated to the two sectors to ensure that they are "harmonious" from the point of view of both the input and the output criteria.

[12] See especially R. Nurkse [5] and [6, p. 192]: "Without [agricultural] reorganization the labor surplus in agriculture remains largely potential. On the other hand, reorganization may well prove impracticable without an active policy of absorbing the surplus manpower."

The output criterion, i.e., provision of mutual market outlets, specifies that the allocation of investment funds must be such as to continuously sustain investment incentives in both sectors of the economy. In the context of our model, this means that the terms of trade between the two sectors should not deteriorate substantially against either sector. The input criterion, on the other hand, specifies that the allocation of the investment fund must be such as to enable the industrial sector to demand, at the constant industrial real wage consistent with the output criterion, the precise number of new workers now freed as a result of the investment activity in the agricultural sector. We shall now proceed to show that a balanced-growth path satisfying these conditions exists as an integral part of our model.

Let the initial demand curve for industrial labor at the break-out point be indicated by i_1i_1 and the initial supply curve by L_1L_1 in Diagram 2.1, with OB units of labor already employed in the industrial sector. (While it is realistic to assume that some industrial establishment already exists during the preconditioning period and is inherited at the beginning of the take-off process, it is also realistic to assume that the initial industrial labor force OB is very small.) At this level of employment the industrial sector is making a profit represented by the shaded area B_0 (Diagram 2.1) which may be taken to represent the economy's investment fund at this stage.[13] This investment fund is to be allocated in part to the agricultural sector, thus raising agricultural productivity and shifting the industrial supply curve to the right, and in part to the industrial sector, thus raising the industrial capital stock and shifting the industrial demand curve to the right.

If the balanced growth criterion is to be satisfied, the new industrial demand curve, e.g., i_2i_2, and the new industrial supply curve, e.g., L_2L_2, must intersect at a point, e.g., P_2, lying on the balanced-growth path (L_1P_3). Otherwise the stability-of-the-terms-of-trade condition is violated. At P_2, where the balanced-growth criterion is met, the industrial sector will have absorbed O_0P_2 additional workers, which is the same number of workers which has been released by the agricultural sector (i.e., cf_2 in Diagram 2.2 equals O_0P_2 in Diagram 2.1).

Thus, as investment activity in both sectors proceeds through time, the balanced-growth path describes the actual growth path if the balanced-growth criterion is satisfied. It is, of course, likely that the actual growth path will deviate from the balanced-growth path in one direction or the other from time to time. Such a deviation, however,

---

[13] If, for the sake of simplicity, capitalists' consumption can be ignored. It should be noted that the agricultural sector (Diagram 2.2) makes no contribution to the investment fund since the entire agricultural output (area $OaSA$) is just adequate to meet the consumption requirements of the agricultural workers (area $Obca$) and the consumption requirements of the industrial workers (area $AScb$).

will call into play countervailing equilibrating forces which tend to bring it back to the balanced-growth path. The actual growth path is, in fact, likely to be oscillating around the balanced-growth path.

For example, if the actual growth path is above the balanced-growth path, say at e_2 in Diagram 2.1 (as would be the case if investment in the agricultural sector had shifted the industrial supply curve to L_2L_2 and investment in the industrial sector had shifted the industrial demand curve to i_3i_3), we have a case of overinvestment in the industrial sector. The shortage of food will result in a deterioration of the terms of trade of the industrial sector and will cause an increase in the industrial real wage. This will tend to discourage investment in the industrial, and tend to encourage investment in the agricultural sector, thus causing the actual growth path to turn back toward the balanced-growth path. Government policy may be assumed to work in the same direction if the price system proves inadequate. In this fashion, the economy, proceeding along an actual growth path which coincides with or oscillates around the balanced-growth path, moves towards the turning point, P_3, previously defined.[14] . . .

REFERENCES

1. B. F. Hoselitz, "Non-Economic Factors in Economic Development," *Am. Econ. Rev., Proc.*, May 1957, 47, 28–41.
2. Harvey Leibenstein, *Economic Backwardness and Economic Growth.* New York 1959.
3. Arthur Lewis, "Development with Unlimited Supplies of Labour," *The Manchester School*, May 1954, 22, 139–92.
4. ——, "Unlimited Labour: Further Notes," *Manchester School*, Jan. 1958, 26, 1–32.
5. Ragnar Nurkse, *Problems of Capital Formation in Underdeveloped Areas.* New York 1953.
6. ——, "Reflections on India's Development Plan," *Quart. Jour. Econ.*, May 1957, 71, 188–204.
7. Gustav Ranis, "Economic Development: A Suggested Approach," *Kyklos*, 1959, 12, 428–48.
8. W. W. Rostow, "The Take-Off into Self-Sustaining Growth," *Econ. Jour.*, March 1956, 66, 25–48.

[14] The "unlimited" portion of Lewis' supply curve of labor may thus be interpreted as an *ex post* supply curve defined as the locus of all points on our balanced-growth path under conditions of continuous increases in agricultural productivity. Neither we nor Lewis should, however, discount the possibility that the actual growth path may, in fact, be gently upward-sloping rather than horizontal. Such a growth path would imply gradually rising levels of the industrial real wage during the take-off period. (Also see footnote 8.)

II. The Ranis-Fei Model of Economic Development: Comment*

HARRY T. OSHIMA

In the September 1961 issue of this *Review*, Gustav Ranis and John Fei presented an elegant model which (together with Harrod's equation) may supply us with the best framework for thinking about macrodynamic problems of underdeveloped countries. In their two-sector model, the migration of workers from agriculture to industry is the central process around which the theory is constructed, taking into account certain basic problems, e.g., worsening terms of internal trade, disguised unemployment, institutional wages, commercialization point, balanced growth, and technological changes. I feel that these problems should be discussed further, if only to clarify the issues for empirical research.

Ranis and Fei divide the development of surplus-labor countries into three stages, assuming as a first approximation no changes in agricultural productivity and population. In the first phase farm workers who are not adding to farm output are shifted to the industrial sector with no rise in the existing wage levels of the economy since there is no reduction in farm output. In the second phase, however, farm workers producing something, but less than their wages, are shifted to the industrial sector. Farm output declines and the terms of trade between the two sectors are altered in favor of the farm sector, requiring a rise in the nominal wage of the industrial sector. If migration continues, a point is eventually reached where farm workers producing output equal to their wages (the commercialization point) are shifting to industry. This begins the third stage, marking the end of the take-off and the beginning of self-sustained growth, and "we enter a world in which the agricultural sector is no longer dominated by nonmarket institutional forces but assumes the characteristics of a commercialized capitalistic system" [10, p. 543].

With agricultural productivity increasing, the model shows that the difficult second phase can be shortened or skipped. This is because the

* From *American Economic Review*, vol. 53, pp. 448–452, June, 1963. Reprinted by permission of the American Economic Association and the author. The author is professor of economics, University of Hawaii.

rise in the marginal physical productivity (MPP) of migrating workers enables their output (1) to catch up with their wages more quickly than otherwise, and (2) to generate more agricultural surplus per migrating worker (that part of his consumption which he is not producing), lessening the deterioration of the terms of trade. (These results are obtained because wages are assumed to be unchanged although farm productivity is rising.) If the rise in productivity is sufficient, the entire second phase can be eliminated, enabling the economy to move smoothly into self-sustained growth.

In this note, I would like to raise some serious issues about the validity and empirical relevance of the Ranis-Fei model, especially with respect to problems of foreign trade, disguised unemployment and its correlate, institutional wage. At the end, the conclusions of Ranis and Fei are examined in the light of our discussion.

1. *The worsening of the terms of trade characterizing the second phase.* The worsening occurs in the model mainly because the authors have excluded foreign trade. In an open economy, industrial goods can be and are in fact exchanged for the agricultural goods produced in a foreign country, multilaterally, if not directly. In Asia, the Indo-Chinese countries have exported food to the major cities of the deficit countries to the south—Philippines, Malaya, Indonesia, Ceylon. If the Ranis-Fei model is to be of general applicability, it is imperative that the authors bring foreign trade into their model and work out its implications. Otherwise the theory will remain a very special one. It seems highly artificial to assume a closed system in a theory which makes the worsening of the terms of trade a cornerstone. For example, in Asia, if import of agricultural products is assumed, the terms of trade need not change. In Japan before the war, the import of cheap farm products from Taiwan and Korea improved the terms of trade for the industrial sector.

2. *The commercialization point which begins the third phase.* To the authors, this is a "major landmark in the development process." Enough workers have left the farms, leaving a labor shortage in the countryside. Landlords must now pay wages commensurate with MPP and must compete with industrial employers. It appears to me that in this closed model this point will be the beginning of hyper-inflation. For now, to the extent of the MPP of the workers leaving the farm, there will be a shortage of agricultural products, and this shortage will increase rapidly as the migration continues, even if some decline in the income elasticity of agricultural-product demand is taken into account.

Let us assume an open economy. A large part of the industrial product in the main cities will be exported to foreign countries and exchanged for farm products, as in prewar Japan. In this case, a large peasant economy, predominantly subsistence, can coexist with a highly industrialized sector, with MPP = W in the economy as a whole. Instead of "commercialization," we have here a dualistic economy. Thus the Ranis-Fei model shows that, even after the commercialization point is reached, there must be continual increases in agricultural productivity in the absence of foreign trade if the farm population is to continue to fall.

3. *Disguised unemployment and institutional wages.* Ranis and Fei feel that in certain countries—Pakistan, India, and Ceylon—marginal farm workers producing little or no output may be as large as 30 per cent of the farm labor force. They refer to my denial of the existence of substantial (say 5 per cent or more) zero-marginal product workers [8]. They observe that "with a fixed amount of land, there will be *some* size of population which is large enough to render MPP zero" [10, p. 547]. I would agree, but in such cases the excess population will move to the cities and in the short run will be openly unemployed, as is the case in most parts of Asia today. In due time, these unemployed workers will be absorbed into small industries and shops or will return to their villages. In the long run, the amount of land is by no means fixed, as the statistics of farm acreage for Asian countries show.[1] Extra-marginal land is brought into cultivation, e.g., hillsides, forests, and jungles. Traditionally in peasant societies the younger sons who cannot be provided with family land must go out to the cities and towns or rent out marginal land and eke out a living.[2] Though their returns are low, they are substantially above zero. Since disguised unemployment plays such an important role in many of the theories of underdevelopment, we need some empirical investigations into this matter.[3]

[1] Rice acreage harvested in the major Asian countries (excluding Red China) rose from an annual average of 52.3 million hectares in the years 1934–38 to 65.9 million for the period 1955–59, a growth rate of about 1 per cent per year, which is roughly the growth rate of the farm population in this period. See FAO [1].

[2] B. Johnston and J. W. Mellor [4, p. 568]: "The most common of these institutional arrangements is the family farm in which the unit of production is also the unit of consumption."

[3] There is one empirical study, that of J. W. Mellor and R. D. Stevens [7], of 104 farms in one Thai village. In this pioneer study, the conclusion is reached that there is substantial zero MPP farm workers. I feel it is hazardous to regard this study as conclusive for either theoretical or policy use. The spread of the data in the scatter diagram relating rice yields to labor input for each of the 104 farms suggests to me, not a linear regression line as it does to the authors, but inadequate data and/or dubious assumptions. For example, they assume that rice production functions for each of the 104 farms were the same. (Dr. Gordon R. Sitton [11] found much variability in what appeared to be homogeneous situations in a Thai village.) In estimating labor input, the authors exclude working children under 15 years old and include all persons 15 years and above, whether working or not. The concept relevant to disguised unemployment should include all labor actually put into cultivation. The labor of an owner-cultivator should not be equated with that of a hired worker, that of a male worker with that of a female worker, nor that of an

Empirical studies are also necessary to substantiate the concept of an institutional wage, i.e., a caloric-minimum wage substantially higher than MPP which the landlord is willing to pay in order to prevent wage levels from falling to caloric levels too low for efficient work. This assumes that the redundant workers have no other place to go and that cultivable land is fixed in the long run. And it contradicts the usual picture of sharp struggles between landlord and tenant in Asian countries. See, e.g., [3]. On farm wage systems, see [8]. I think a stronger case can be made for assuming wages to be below MPP.[4]

4. *Productivity changes and institutional wage.* Farm technological change is shown in the model by drawing new total productivity curves denoting an upward shift. The flat portion of the curves representing zero MPP labor force is reproduced in the new curves since the shift is assumed to be proportional.

This type of technological change is unlikely to be general under the conditions of Asian paddy agriculture. Even in the case of the intro-duction of improved seeds (which seems to fit the Ranis-Fei case best), this is likely to call for more fertilizing and more weeding, both requiring additional labor. In this situation, the flat portion of the new curves may be wiped out. Where productivity rises because of the construction of irrigation facilities, new land can be put into cultivation and double-cropping on the old land becomes feasible, both requiring more labor. And in the Japanese type of rice-growing technique which is succeeding in many parts of Asia, labor requirements per acre increased due to careful breeding of seedlings, transplantation, fertilizing, weeding, etc. In all these cases, the flat portion of the new productivity curves will disappear and there is not likely to be proportional upward shifts in other parts of the new curve.[5]

---

adult worker with that of a young worker. One of the authors, J. Mellor, in a recent study of an Indian village did not find evidence to support the thesis of disguised unemployment [6]. In fact, the data suggested "that yields can be raised by greater use of labour . . . ," a conclusion similar to that of G. R. Sitton for Thailand [11].

According to Edwin F. Jones [5 pp. 4–5], the basis for the shift to commune agriculture in Mainland China was the belief by Mao Tse-tung that there was much disguised unemployment in rural China. When it became clear that the commune movement was a failure, large masses of people were shifted back to agriculture in 1962. In Taiwan, between 1950–1956, agricultural output grew at an annual average rate of 6 per cent but this required a growth in farm labor input of about 2 per cent [2, Appendix Table]. Japan's experience in the Meiji period appears to have been similar to that of Taiwan [9].

[4] If we drop the assumption regarding disguised unemployment, the flat portion of the total and marginal productivity curve in the model will be replaced by a gently rising slope. The first phase loses its distinctive character and becomes merged with the second as far as the industrial supply curve of labor is concerned.

[5] However, it must be admitted that we know very little about the nature of the shifts in productivity curves in Asia and more studies are indicated.

The part of the model (and most crucial to it) which is most difficult to accept from an empirical standpoint is the assumption that, with the rise in farm productivity, farm wages in the first two phases remain unchanged. A general rise in Asian farm productivity will be immediately reflected in a rise of real income for the peasant-proprietor and his family, since the tax structure is such that only a small part of the increases is likely to be taxed away. The absolute share of tenants will increase because in Asia the total crop of landlord farms is often divided on the basis of percentage shares. I suspect that investigations into farm wages will show that, with productivity increases, wages do rise in Asian agriculture.

In conclusion, if the Ranis-Fei model is to be made more generally applicable by bringing in foreign trade and leaving out disguised unemployment and constant institutional wage, the following modifications are indicated: by bringing in foreign trade rapid rises in farm productivity become less urgent and balanced growth appears easier to attain; on the other hand, by excluding disguised unemployment the need for increasing agricultural productivity is enhanced. And even though (1) and (3) will mean that concepts such as shortage, commercialization, and turning points, take-off and self-sustained growth will drop out of the model, the model's service in depicting the importance of food and other agricultural products in the accumulation of capital in low-income countries is a noteworthy contribution in the literature of underdevelopment.

REFERENCES

1. Food and Agriculture Organization, *Production Yearbook*. Rome 1948–61.
2. S. C. Hsieh and T. H. Lee, *An Analytical Review of Agricultural Development in Taiwan—An Input-Output and Productivity Approach*. Taipei 1958.
3. N. Jacoby, *Agrarian Unrest in Southeast Asia*. New York 1941.
4. Bruce F. Johnston and John W. Mellor, "The Role of Agriculture in Economic Development," *Am. Econ. Rev.*, Sept. 1961, *51*, 566–93.
5. Edwin F. Jones, "The Impact of the Food Crisis on Peiping's Policies," *Asian Survey*, Sept. 1962, *2*, 1–11.
6. J. W. Mellor and T. V. Moorti, "Farm Business Analysis in 30 Farms," paper of the Balwant Vidyapeeth Rural Institute, April 1960. Mimeographed.
7. ———— and R. D. Stevens, "The Average and Marginal Product of Farm Labor in Underdeveloped Countries," *Jour. Farm Econ.*, Aug. 1956, *38*, 780–91.
8. Harry Oshima, "Underemployment in Backward Economies—An Empirical Comment," *Jour. Pol. Econ.*, June 1958, *66*, 259–64.
9. ————, "A Strategy for Asian Development" and "Non-investment Input and the Leavening Effect," *Econ. Devel. and Cultural Change*, April 1962, *10*, 294–316.

10. G. Ranis and J. C. Fei, "A Theory of Economic Development," *Am. Econ. Rev.*, Sept. 1961, *51*, 533–58.
11. Gordon R. Sitton, "The Role of the Farmer in the Economic Development of Thailand," *CECA Paper,* Council of Economic and Cultural Affairs, Inc., Sept. 1962.

The Ranis-Fei Model of Economic Development: Reply*

GUSTAV RANIS AND J. C. H. FEI

We are grateful to Mr. Oshima for his comments on our paper and heartily endorse his effort to nudge our model closer to the real world and towards a fuller empirical verification. We certainly agree, for example, now as before [3, footnote 22, p. 554], with his suggestion that the relaxation of our closed-economy assumption would represent an important next step in the evolution of our model; such relaxation would considerably soften the balanced growth constraint by relaxing a source of rigidity in the system. Similarly, it might be pointed out that foreign aid (e.g., shipments of P.L. 480 wheat) may also play a role in postponing the arrival of the shortage point. In general the importance of such open-economy aspects of the development process depends both on the size of the domestic economy and on the opportunities to participate in foreign trade under mid-twentieth century conditions. As the recent Ford Foundation's agricultural team on India indicated, the problems of large less-developed economies must basically be solved internally as the huge domestic food requirements cannot conceivably be met through major reliance on imports.

Although our article did not concern itself formally with development after the "turning point," Oshima's characterization of this landmark as "the beginning of hyperinflation" in the closed economy strikes us as somewhat misguided. To us, reaching the turning point signifies a major measure of success in the development effort in the sense that the disguisedly unemployed in the hitherto "dragging" agricultural sector have finally been productively mobilized. Thereafter we view the agricultural sector as moving towards the role of an "overly productive" appendage to the industrial sector which must be subsidized (as is typical in many

* From *American Economic Review*, vol. 53, pp. 452–454, June, 1963. Reprinted by permission of the American Economic Association and the authors.

advanced countries) rather than squeezed for the benefit of the rest of the economy.

Oshima questions four assumptions of our model: the long-run fixity of land, the existence of disguised agricultural unemployment, the level of the institutional real wage, and the nature of technological change. With respect to the fixity of land, we are simply adhering to the classical (Ricardo) assumption which we think to be particularly relevant to the many less-developed countries where a long history of population pressures has served to render rather unlikely further significant increases of cultivable acreage attainable at reasonable cost.

With respect to the disguisedly unemployed agricultural labor force, Oshima seems to have abandoned his "seasonal peak agricultural labor demand" argument [2] and now grants the existence of surplus population either disguisedly unemployed in the fields or openly unemployed in the cities. Clearly, the physical location of such unemployed workers is immaterial to our analysis as long as they are consumers of, but non-contributors to, the national product.

With respect to the level of the institutionally (or calorically) set minimum real wage, we find ourselves in more serious disagreement with Oshima's contention that such a wage is likely to lie below the MPP of labor rather than, as we assume, above it. While we certainly endorse his call for empirical research on this issue, we would like to emphasize that, if Oshima is right, what we really face here is a *shortage* of agricultural labor in the sense that landlords will want to hire additional workers to increase agricultural surplus. Under such assumptions of a Marxist-type exploitation theory of agricultural wage determination, the correct policy conclusion is the encouragement of further population increases! Small wonder that the overwhelming consensus on this issue (e.g., Lewis, Nurkse, Rosenstein-Rodan) is on our side of the argument.

With respect to the nature of technological change in the agricultural sector, it can easily be shown that the innovations which we have assumed are neutral in the Hicksian sense, i.e., they raise the MPP_L curve everywhere by the same constant multiple, leaving the horizontal (i.e., $0-MPP_L$) portion of the curve unaffected. Oshima points out that innovations are, in fact, likely to be labor-using, causing a disappearance of the horizontal portion of the curve in the course of the growth process. While we may accept the possibility or even likelihood of labor-using innovations where there exists a substantial redundant agricultural labor force, such activity would not annihilate the horizontal portion of the TPP curve immediately, but only gradually over time. The solution provided in our model really constitutes a first approximation based on the assumption of neutrality of innovations. Oshima's proposition would involve a modification of our constant T (non-redundancy coefficient) assumption and can be accommodated in our model. Clearly such modification with an equivalent upward shift of the agricultural production function would, under *ceteris paribus* assumptions, lead to an earlier arrival of the shortage point.

Finally, Oshima finds it difficult to accept our simplifying assumption of the constancy of the real wage under conditions of increasing agricultural productivity. While we do not, now as before, deny that the real wage may increase either at the source of labor supply (i.e., in the agricultural sector) [3, footnote 6, p. 538] or in the industrial sector due to a gradual widening of the "wage gap" between the two sectors [3, p. 554], the basic question is whether such increases are likely to be significant. In the case of nineteenth century Japan, increases in the real wage were extremely moderate while agricultural productivity increased sharply.[1] In the contemporary world it may well be that a combination of ineffective fiscal systems and misguided welfare emphases contributes to more substantial increases in the industrial real wage over time. It is, however, difficult to imagine how such increases can be sustained in the face of a pool of the disguisedly unemployed in the agricultural sector.

REFERENCES

1. Nicholas Kaldor, "A Model of Economic Growth," *Essays on Economic Stability and Growth*. London 1960, p. 294.
2. Harry Oshima, "Underemployment in Backward Economies—An Empirical Comment," *Jour. Pol. Econ.*, June 1958, *66*, 259–64.
3. G. Ranis and J. C. H. Fei, "A Theory of Economic Development," *Am. Econ. Rev.*, Sept. 1961, *51*, 533–58.
4. Mataji Umemura, "Real Wages of Industrial Workers," in S. Tsuru and K. Ohkawa ed., *An Analysis of the Japanese Economy*. Tokyo 1953.

[1] Referring to Umemura's data [4], Kaldor states that "in the case of Japan, real wages increased very little between 1878 and 1917, despite a one-and-a-half-fold increase in real income per head over the period" [1, p. 294].

part 4

SOME ASPECTS OF THE PROCESS
OF CHANGE IN AGRICULTURE

We turn now from the role of agriculture in overall development to an examination of change in agriculture itself. This involves two interrelated processes. The first is the procedure by which change in agriculture may be accelerated, so as to contribute more rapidly to the goals desired by the society. The second is the way in which agriculture continuously adjusts to change as a consequence of overall development. Obviously, both processes are of interest to development economists and planners.

On a number of occasions in the past, policy prescriptions have been formulated as if a single element of the rural society were the bottleneck to the development of agriculture. Among these have been landlordism, inadequate credit, and insufficient agricultural research and extension assistance to develop and communicate recent technical advances. It is recognized now, however, that change normally requires a combination of programs. The books and articles that deal with change in agriculture range from technical books concerned with soil, water controls, and varietal improvements to books concerned with social and political attitudes. Within this range, there are many gaps, both in country-by-country studies and in the conceptual integration of the key factors in agricultural development. Within space limitations, we reprint some of the significant postwar contributions, identify others here and in the Bibliography, and indicate some of the gaps which need to be filled.

As we pointed out in the Introduction, agricultural change occurs within a sociopolitical milieu; thus, study of how to initiate or accelerate change and build or create new rural institutions must be considered against the social, cultural, and political backdrop of a region or a nation. Therefore, we stress the need for students to explore the political and social aspects of agricultural development. We have not, unfortunately, been able to identify and include significant articles dealing with this important area. We hope the reader, however, will devote time to studying how these variables influence the response and performance of the traditional sector.

Since change is made by people and for people, and modifies the relationships of people to resources, we need to analyze human behavior in development discussions. Economists tend to be particularly concerned with how price changes, stemming from a new relationship between supply and demand, affect the response of producers. A few years ago it was common to hear about backward-sloping marketed commodity functions. Such irrational economic behavior by laborers and peasant producers has not been completely dismissed—sophisticated versions being found in a number of studies of marketing systems.[1] A growing body of empirical studies by Jones,[2] Berg,[3] Stern,[4] and others, however, suggests that economic motivation is present in less developed countries and that economists need not worry about the assumed differences in economic behavior between developed and less developed countries.

In the factor market too, there has been concern about how the labor market functions. D. Gale Johnson[5] has given much attention to the functioning of the rural labor market in the United States, with special emphasis on the north-south and white-nonwhite wage differentials. Schultz has studied the functioning of factor markets, including capital and credit, natural resources, and people. This has led him to a concern with human capital or investment in the human agent. The central concept is expressed in his Presidential address to the American Economic Association in a frequently reprinted article.[6] Recently a group of economists presented papers on this subject in a special issue of the

---

[1] Paul Bohannan and George Dalton (eds.), *Markets in Africa*, Northwestern University Press, Evanston, Ill., 1962.

[2] William O. Jones, "Economic Man in Africa," *Food Research Institute Studies*, vol. 1, pp. 107–134, May, 1960.

[3] Elliot J. Berg, "Backward-Sloping Labor Supply Functions in Dual Economies— The Africa Case," *Quarterly Journal of Economics*, vol. 75, pp. 468–492, August, 1961.

[4] Robert M. Stern, "The Price Responsiveness of Primary Producers," *Review of Economics and Statistics*, vol. 44, pp. 202–207, May, 1962.

[5] Reported in several articles in the *Journal of Farm Economics*, esp. vol. 33, February and November, 1951, and *American Economic Review*, vol. 43, pp. 296–313, June, 1953.

[6] T. W. Schultz, "Investment in Human Capital," *American Economic Review*, vol. 51, no. 1, pp. 1–17, March, 1961.

Journal of Political Economy.[7] Most of the literature on investment in man is readily available and focuses on advanced countries; however, Lewis[8] discusses investment in education in less developed countries. Among other items, he points to the need to relate costs and benefits of education, salary of teachers, and so on to prevailing prices and wages in the economy of the developing nation. Selection 6 is related to this discussion as it reminds us that human capital becomes more valuable only as it affects one or more of the conventional inputs in the production function.

Two other books by Schultz may be of interest to readers. The first, *The Economic Value of Education*,[9] is a further elaboration of his ideas on investment in human beings, together with some evidence on the costs and benefits of such investment. The second, *Transforming Traditional Agriculture*,[10] is not available for review at this writing. It is intended as a direct attack on the problem of economic development of agriculture in less developed countries.

Migration is often advocated as a policy to improve the frequently documented low returns to the human agent in agriculture. Migration is common in less developed countries, sometimes as a flight from the problems of the countryside, as from northeastern Brazil's frequent droughts or Colombia's rural unrest; at other times, the city is the magnet, offering electric lights, movies, excitement, and the hope that eventually it will provide a better living. Migration often results in so many new urban dwellers that some must live in shipping crates or metal shacks in urban slums. Migration data—especially short-term urban to rural flows and the social characteristics of migrants—are generally inadequate in most countries. However, Hathaway (Selection 12) examines rural-urban migration figures for the United States over the past four decades. He concludes that despite substantial out-migration from agriculture during the past twenty years, "a simple policy of rapid migration from agriculture has not, by itself, been sufficient to bring about significant improvement in the relative income position of the farm economy." A variety of views and a more detailed discussion of migration are found in a 1960 conference report.[11]

Much attention in agricultural development is given to the quality of natural resources and to institutional arrangements which affect the re-

[7] "Investment in Human Beings," *Journal of Political Economy*, vol. 70, no. 5, part 2, October, 1962.

[8] W. Arthur Lewis, "Education and Economic Development," *Social and Economic Studies*, Kingston, Jamaica, vol. 10, pp. 113–127, June, 1961.

[9] Columbia University Press, 1963.

[10] Yale University Press, New Haven, Conn., 1964.

[11] "Labor Mobility and Population in Agriculture," Iowa State University Press, Ames, Iowa, 1961.

lationship of man to land resources. Schultz (Selection 13) examines the recent history of advanced nations in light of the Ricardian-derived concept that as population grows, land resources will become a limiting factor in growth. He concludes that not enough attention has been given to the rise in substitutes for land, and that most of the increasing farm output is being achieved without increasing the quantity of conventional inputs—land, labor, and capital—at least as traditionally described. Selection 14, Dales's comment on Schultz's paper, presents a more general issue, and is related to earlier selections, especially Kuznets (Selection 5) and Dovring (Selection 4). Dales points out that the "importance" of an input in production, such as natural resources, is not necessarily determined by the percentage of income generated by the input, and that it does not tell us anything about the process of economic development. He points out also that development means more nonfarm products; consequently agricultural output declines as a percent of GNP.

The pattern of land settlement and the form of the production function influence the way in which natural resources affect the process of development. Baldwin, in Selection 15, considers the flow of capital and labor in newly settled areas, using as the prime difference the scale of operation. In one region the production function is highly labor-intensive over a wide range of relative factor price ratios, with considerable economies of scale. This is the "plantation" product and organization. A second region produces an export product also, but with a production function requiring the "family-size farm" in which the labor and capital are provided by the same individual. Both draw labor and capital from an old, established region.

Baldwin then analyzes the flow of labor and capital and subsequent path of development. The plantation area draws low income labor, a few skilled managers, and general capital resources from the old region, whereas the second area draws from the middle and upper income groups, with labor *and* capital normally provided by the same individual. He points out that plantation production does not lead to a mass market and development of a skilled labor force, i.e., the marginal efficiency of capital and the level of income remain low. The family-size farm area has a more even distribution of income, greater labor mobility, and savings which permit breaking away from an export-oriented economy.

The production function is not the only force influencing the organization of agricultural production. Kahan (Selection 16) examines empirically what happened in the Soviet Union when the new regime socialized the agricultural sector and called upon it for a substantial contribution to the process of industrialization. Following in the Kuznets framework (Selection 5), Kahan discusses both the factor and product contributions of agriculture to the growth of heavy industry. He points to both voluntary and involuntary adjustments in the agricultural sector as it reacted to the new environment.

In many of the tropical and subtropical areas of the world most of agriculture is organized into large-scale plantations or small-scale semi-subsistence units. The latter probably are smaller than those contemplated by Baldwin. These small holders or peasant producers are sometimes written off as being unimportant in terms of actual and potential changes in agricultural output, either for domestic or foreign consumption. Wickizer, after reviewing the literature on this topic, concludes that we should revise our thinking about the so-called "plantation crops" because

> A study of trends in available data reveals no tendency for the fraction of exports derived from plantations to increase. In fact, the opposite seems to be true: exports in the aggregate tend to consist increasingly of the outputs of peasant farmers.[12]

A concern for small-scale agriculturists in many countries has led to a spate of articles on land reform; the bibliography alone fills several books.[13] Much of this has little analytical value, being descriptive, filled with implicit value judgements, or assuming that a change in ownership patterns will create a miracle. The definition of land reform varies with the author. Raup[14] is one who uses a broad definition—equating land reform with a total program of agrarian development including modifications in rural credit, land division, agricultural extension, and marketing facilities. The definition used by Warriner in an out-of-print collection of essays (Selection 17) is more restricted; she examines land reform across a spectrum of social action, but uses a different set of social goals than those which Kahan identifies for the Soviet Union. Warriner points out how land reform can assist in agricultural development, thus differentiating between the two processes. She emphasizes the voluntary contributions to development following the accomplishment of the forced land reform.

Although political leadership frequently is overoptimistic about the possibilities of increasing agricultural output through opening new land to settlement, many less developed countries still have land which is unused, or used only for large-scale activities. In Selection 18, Lewis draws on his wide experience with land settlement schemes, and presents

[12] V. D. Wickizer, "The Smallholder in Tropical Export Crop Production," *Food Research Institute Studies*, Stanford University, vol. 1, pp. 49–99, February, 1960.

[13] FAO, "Bibliography on Land Tenure," Rome, 1955, and "Supplement," 1959.

[14] Philip Raup, "The Contribution of Land Reform to Agricultural Development: An Analytical Framework," *Economic Development and Cultural Change*, vol. xii, pp. 1–21, October, 1963.

a common sense approach to the key issues involved in the settlement process.

Capital is an important element in the process of agricultural change. Tostlebe's standard work on capital formation in United States agriculture[15] points out that most of the capital was formed in agriculture itself out of savings. This evidence is sometimes cited to suggest that the major source of capital for agriculture in less developed countries likewise must come from rural saving. It is frequently claimed, however, that savings are small or zero in less developed countries and, moreover, tend to be hoarded rather than productively invested. Panikar presents one of the few protests to this generalization. After examining a number of studies of farmers in three regions of India, most of them based on very small samples, he found that net (cash) savings totaled at least 8 per cent of their gross income.[16] Later Panikar acknowledges, however, that the hoarding of cash and precious metals does keep some of the savings from flowing into productive channels.

Export agriculture was an "engine of growth" in many western countries in the last century. This aspect of capital formation continues to serve as an important source of foreign exchange earnings in a majority of less developed countries today—paying for machinery and equipment vital to the overall economy. Nevertheless, most less developed countries do not place heavy reliance on increased export agriculture as the foundation of their development program. Why is this so? One reason is that raw material prices are particularly subject to wide fluctuations; a United Nations study covering the period from 1901 to 1950 indicated an average year-to-year fluctuation in prices of 14 per cent.[17] Export volume varied nearly 19 per cent and the combination of the two reinforced rather than offset the fluctuations, so that export earnings had a year-to-year fluctuation of 22.6 per cent. Cyclical movements were slightly smaller but still exceeded 20 per cent.[18] The late Professor Nurkse, in Selection

[15] Alvin Samuel Tostlebe, *Capital in Agriculture: Its Formation and Financing since 1870*, Princeton, N.J., Princeton University Press, 1957.

[16] P. C. K. Panikar, "Rural Savings in India," *Economic Development and Cultural Change*, vol. 10, pp. 64–84, October, 1961.

[17] United Nations Department of Economic Affairs, "Instability in Export Markets of Under-developed Countries," New York, 1952.

[18] To a degree, this instability in prices and earnings is comparable to the thesis that farm prices and incomes are more unstable than those in the rest of the economy, a concept very familiar to U.S. agricultural economists. T. W. Schultz advanced this thesis in one of his major books *Agriculture in an Unstable Economy*, McGraw-Hill Book Company, Inc., New York, 1945. Hanau comes to similar conclusions after examining this problem, partly in a European setting. ("The Disparate Stability of Farm and Non-farm Prices," *Tenth International Conference of Agricultural Economists*, Oxford University Press, New York, 1960.) D. E. Hathaway, in "Agriculture in an Unstable Economy Revisited," *Journal of Farm Economics*, August, 1959, reexamined this thesis, with interesting new conclusions.

19, discusses the merits of several proposed remedies for price and income instability of primary producers. One of the possible solutions, elimination of the business cycle, is largely beyond the reach of less developed countries. Closer at hand are international buffer stocks, national buffer funds such as marketing boards, and the taxing of exports for development purposes.[19]

Another approach to this problem is presented in the writings of Singer,[20] Prebisch,[21] and others associated with the Economic Commission for Latin America. They argue that the prevalence of one-crop, export economies is structurally responsible for slow development in Latin America. Adverse movements in the terms of trade and a high propensity to consume imported consumption goods combine to create persistent foreign exchange gaps. The policy prescriptions stemming from this analysis include industrialization, particularly import-substitution, and devices to strengthen the prices of food and raw material exports. Some of Nurkse's associates, participating in the two symposia reported in special *KYKLOS* volumes in 1958 and 1959, gave attention to these approaches. A number of nations have been unwilling to await the formulation of ideal solutions and have sought to ease the impact of adverse and/or unstable price changes. In Selection 20, Blau reviews the recent history of International Commodity Agreements and current thinking on what may be accomplished through such arrangements. One of the pressing reasons why development economists are concerned with world commodity problems is that an increase in foreign exchange earnings via one- or two-cent higher export prices of primary products can be as large as all present external public aid programs.

The next article on international trade issues discusses an extremely controversial policy program of the United States Government: the distribution of surplus farm products—primarily to less developed nations —through special subsidies and price discrimination in normal market channels, and through special arrangements outside such channels. In Selection 21, Witt points out that Public Law 480 and related programs have shifted the major emphasis from surplus disposal to a concern with development. If exports from less developed areas assist economic development, then how can imports into such areas also assist development? Witt points out that at least some of the agricultural exports become an addition to the regular foreign aid program. He presents the view that the impact of Public Law 480 exports needs to be judged country by country within the matrix of total development policy. Sur-

[19] See the Bibliography for a number of additional references.
[20] "The Distribution of Gains between Investing and Borrowing Countries," *American Economic Review*, vol. 40, no. 2, pp. 473–485, May, 1950.
[21] "Commercial Policy in the Underdeveloped Countries," *American Economic Review*, vol. 49, no. 2, pp. 251–273, May, 1959.

plus farm products can become a development asset in certain countries, and have little relation to development in others. Just as export earnings stimulate development only when properly used, so recipient nation policy, through appropriate measures, can use surplus products as a development asset or permit them to become a liability.

Collins and Holton (Selection 22) argue that an effective development program is dependent upon an efficient marketing system, yet many national development programs usually assume that the private marketing system will readily expand to handle the forthcoming larger volume of inputs and products. The authors contend also that a simple increase in physical facilities to improve marketing is often inadequate. More often the critical need is for a change in the organization and operation of the distributive sector. The authors draw on experience in Southern Italy, as well as Holton's earlier study in Puerto Rico.

The diffusion of new technology in agriculture has interested sociologists for a long time. Sociologists, social psychologists, and communication experts have studied how new techniques are developed or adapted by innovators. Rogers lists some five hundred studies of the diffusion of technology.[22] Economists, however, use a different approach. They have been more interested in which innovations will be profitable, and in the normative issue of what should be done. Ruttan has summarized his view of the economic interest in technical change, and indicated the gaps in present research on agricultural technology.[23] See also Johnson's comments in Selection 6. We reproduce here, however, an article by Griliches (Selection 23) in which the costs and benefits to American agriculture of a single innovation—hybrid corn—are computed.

Plans for agricultural development and policies to implement them are built upon: (1) a concept of the process of agricultural change; (2) specified goals established for the agricultural sector in the light of the overall values of the society and the goals established for other sectors; (3) empirical evidence as to where the benefit-cost ratio is likely to be favorable; and (4) some concept of feasibility with respect to external and internal resources, and with respect to social and political pressures and acceptances. Economic analysts and policy makers generally feel insecure with respect to each of these four elements. In some cases, the concepts of the process are wrong, as suggested by Selections 7 and 25. In many cases, value conflicts between the decision makers and most of the rest of society are sharp and substantial, leaving little room for compromise with respect to goals. The data problem is substantial in

---

[22] Everett M. Rogers, *Diffusion of Innovations*, The Free Press of Glencoe, New York, 1962.

[23] Vernon W. Ruttan, "Research on the Economics of Technological Change in American Agriculture," *Journal of Farm Economics*, vol. 42, no. 4, pp. 735–754, November, 1960.

any country but is particularly severe in less developed nations, as any economist who has worked in such countries knows. This is especially true for micro data on response to inputs, making decisions on overall investment plans (water control versus fertilizer versus adult education versus varietal change) little more than guesswork. Some evidence of these problems is found in Nicholls (Selection 1), where he reviews the postwar controversy on the priority which should be given to agriculture in overall planning. Oshima, in "A Strategy for Asian Development,"[24] also discusses development priorities. He argues for placing agricultural development in a central role, and against Chenery's, Mahalanobis's and Hirschman's industrialization-based program.

Nations embarked upon development programs are unwilling to wait for a more adequate conceptual framework. Plans must be completed, policies established, and investments made both on overall plans and on plans to keep agriculture somewhat in step with other sectors. It is easy to argue that less developed nations should do more careful planning, but the developed nations cannot be too critical in this respect, particularly if one examines the recent history of United States agricultural policy or the policies unfolding in other advanced nations, where clearly production in agriculture is excessive or likely to become excessive in relation to growth in other sectors.[25] Among the less developed nations, one of the best-documented agricultural planning efforts is the experience in India under three Five-Year Plans. This experience is discussed in a series of essays by S. R. Sen,[26] some of which discuss strategy while others discuss planning techniques or commodity problems. A number of United Nations agencies provide articles and comprehensive reviews of the planning or the nature of plans, some of which are listed in the Bibliography. Planning and policy for development in Latin America are less comprehensive and less well documented. There are, however, a number of partial plans or limited programs designed to change the manner in which the agricultural sector functions. Arthur Mosher examines a number of these programs for various countries of Latin America.[27] His book provides a number of case histories which help the reader develop some judgements about empirical problems and the possible results of several organizational approaches to inducing change in agriculture.

[24] *Economic Development and Cultural Change,* vol. 10, no. 3, pp. 294–316, April, 1962.

[25] See Dale Hathaway, *Government and Agriculture,* The Macmillan Company, New York, 1963.

[26] *The Strategy for Agricultural Development,* Asian Publishing House, Bombay, 1962.

[27] Arthur T. Mosher, *Technical Cooperation in Latin American Agriculture,* The University of Chicago Press, Chicago, 1957.

Perhaps the closest approach to a comprehensive view of agricultural policy in a development framework is found in T. W. Schultz's *The Economic Organization of Agriculture*.[28] This book provides an analytical approach to agricultural development problems, but largely in reference to the U.S. economy. A number of other writers have examined the process of planning, but with less attention to the agricultural sector. Among them are Arthur Lewis[29] and Jan Tinbergen.[30]

In Selection 24, Heady reviews a century-old United States policy for the development of agriculture,[31] namely, the provision of a flow of new agricultural knowledge to operating farmers.[32] In the second part of his paper, Heady suggests some of the changes in alternatives which now face this institutional matrix, arguing that new priorities are needed in the United States and, by implication, in other developed countries.[33] It is also possible that some of the strategy of the past (but not necessarily the specific institutional form) may be appropriate now in the developing nations. Nicholls presented a similar theme in his Presidential address to the American Farm Association.[34] These authors deal with institutions and programs dedicated to the "creation of nonconventional inputs."

It seems appropriate to close with an article by Hirschman (Selection 25) in which he supports the Gerschenkron theme that we should seek ways to *substitute* for what appear to be bottlenecks to development. This article was written originally as a comment on a paper by Hagen which emphasized the contribution of ejected or minority groups to development—a thesis also developed by a number of other social scientists. Hirschman also criticizes an article by Galbraith as a counsel of perfection. He suggests that nations meeting Galbraith's four prerequisites for economic aid probably do not need such aid, and that assistance may better be used to support desired programs in nations not fully meeting such criteria. He further suggests that the American people may be expecting too much too soon from the granting of capital resources to developing nations. This leads to our final comment.

[28] The McGraw-Hill Book Company, New York, 1953.
[29] *The Principles of Economic Planning*, Public Affairs Press, Washington, D.C., 1951.
[30] *The Design of Development*, The Johns Hopkins Press, Baltimore, 1958.
[31] T. W. Schultz, in *The Economic Organization of Agriculture*, pp. 255–282, provides a more analytical view of why public support should be provided to agricultural colleges, experiment stations, and extension services.
[32] For an historical approach, see James Bonnen, "Land Grant Colleges: Some Observations on the Organizational Nature of a Great Technological Payoff," *Journal of Farm Economics*, vol. 44, pp. 1279–1294, December, 1962.
[33] A fuller statement of Heady's views may be found in *Agricultural Policy Under Economic Development*, Iowa State University Press, Ames, Iowa, 1962.
[34] W. H. Nicholls, "Higher Education and Agricultural Economics: A Critical Appraisal," *Journal of Farm Economics*, vol. 42, no. 5, pp. 969–90, December, 1960.

Let us repeat that the state of economic science of the process of change in agriculture is underdeveloped, especially for underdeveloped countries. There are differences in view, and even inconsistencies among the selections used and articles cited. Until these differences are resolved through more research, it will be difficult to propose a blueprint for action. It is likely that less developed countries will be faced with a lagging agriculture so long as there are poorly conceived theories of the appropriate means of stimulating agricultural productivity. Introducing change in agriculture is a complex process. We reject as inadequate and insufficient the notion that either better seeds and more feed or more nonconventional inputs are the means to solve agricultural problems in less developed countries. Ideas are important, but conventional tools, supplies of conventional inputs, market-transportation facilities, and incentives (via favorable prices, price stability, land rights, and family patterns) are important too. Building the complex complementary package of programs is a major challenge.

12. Migration from Agriculture: The Historical Record and Its Meaning*

DALE E. HATHAWAY

The low returns to human effort throughout most of United States agriculture and the very low incomes of most persons in some regions of U.S. agriculture have long been recognized. The most common prescription offered by economists for these ills has been a large-scale transfer of labor from agriculture. It usually is argued that such a transfer would: result in a recombination of resources in agriculture that would provide a solution to the major problems of United States agriculture; increase incomes in agriculture relative to incomes in the nonfarm economy; and reduce the disparity in agricultural income between regions.

For the last four decades there has been a large out-migration from agriculture to the nonfarm economy. This is sometimes cited as having significantly contributed to the improvement of agriculture's ills, and more of the same is prescribed as the method of complete cure. Therefore, it seems pertinent to examine in some detail the impact of the recent out-migration from agriculture to help us judge whether this simple prescription is enough or whether we must, perhaps, treat some serious secondary symptoms at the same time.

THE SIZE OF THE OUT-MIGRATION

Because it has become so commonplace in our society we sometimes fail to grasp the magnitude of the migration from agriculture. Yet, for a nation lacking a positive policy to induce migration and which has

* Reprinted from the *American Economic Review, Papers and Proceedings*, vol. 50, pp. 379–391, May, 1960. The article is reprinted as originally published with the exception of two paragraphs enclosed in brackets on pp. 219–220, which were revised in light of recent data revisions. Reprinted by permission of the American Economic Association and the author. The author is professor of agricultural economics at Michigan State University.

fortunately largely avoided widespread natural or man-made disaster, the record is truly amazing. Since 1920 more than 25 million people have migrated from farms to urban areas and nonfarm occupations. Migration from farms has persisted through depressions and wars. Although the farm population in 1950 was only about two-thirds that of 1920, the absolute number of migrants during the past decade has been above earlier periods.

However, economic conditions have had a strong influence on the rate of out-migration from agriculture. In the 1920–30 decade more than 6 million people left agriculture—a rate of 19 per cent of the beginning

TABLE 1. NET CHANGE IN RURAL-FARM POPULATION BY MIGRATION, UNITED STATES AND REGIONS, 1920–30, 1930–40, 1940–50

Area	Rate of change in farm population due to migration		
	1920–30	1930–40	1940–50
United States..............	−19.3	−12.7	−30.9
New England..............	−13.0	+ 2.6	−21.8
Middle Atlantic............	−18.7	− 1.3	−20.7
East North Central.........	−19.7	− 5.3	−22.6
West North Central.........	−17.5	−17.7	−29.2
South Atlantic..............	−25.0	−13.8	−31.9
East South Central.........	−19.8	−13.2	−33.4
West South Central.........	−17.3	−19.9	−44.0
Mountain..................	−19.4	−16.3	−32.6
Pacific....................	− .3	+ 4.9	−15.1

SOURCE: *Net Migration from the Rural Farm Population, 1940–50*, Statistical Bulletin No. 176, June, 1956, Table 1, p. 16.

population.[1] During the thirties only slightly over 3.5 million migrated, a rate of about 13 per cent. In the ten years from 1940 to 1950 the net migration exceeded 9 million persons, giving a rate of 31 per cent. It appears that the number of out-migrants during the 1950–60 decade has been about the same as in the forties, so that the rate probably has exceeded one-third.

All regions of the country have experienced an out-migration from agriculture. However, the rates have varied between regions in different ways at different times (Table 1). The variation between regions in

[1] The method used to compute the rate leaves out the migration of persons born and those dying during the decade. See Gladys K. Bowles, *Farm Population—Net Migration From the Rural-Farm Population, 1940–50*, Statistical Bulletin No. 176, U.S. Dept. of Agric., June, 1956, p. 167, for the methodology used in estimating rates.

rate of out-migration was relatively low during the twenties. During the thirties, however, there was a wide variation between regions, with the west North Central and west South Central having the highest rates. During the 1940–50 period the relative variation between geographical regions was again reduced, although the entire south and the west North Central regions experienced rates of out-migration above those for other regions.

One should not conclude immediately that this has been entirely a movement of people from what we generally classify as "the low-income areas" in agriculture (Table 2). For the decade 1940–50 the net migration from serious low-income farming areas was only one-third above that of the higher income areas. Among the generalized low-income farming areas classified by the Department of Agriculture there were many geographical regions from which the rate of out-migration was below that from medium- and high-income areas. Thus the rate of out-migration from a specific area depends upon a complex of socioeconomic factors of which relative income level is but one.

A majority of the migrants from agriculture have gone to the large urban metropolitan areas of the North and West. The popular concept of large-scale movements from the South to Detroit and Chicago are based on fact. The 1950–57 net immigration to Michigan is estimated at about 520,000 persons.[2] The high concentration of the in-migrants is illustrated by the estimate that two-thirds of the in-migrants went to the three counties including and adjacent to Detroit. Other northern and western metropolitan areas have had approximately similar experiences.

What has been true generally for migration from agriculture has been particularly true of nonwhites. They have concentrated very heavily in large urban areas.[3] Thus the migration from farm areas has contributed very significantly to the growth of the labor force of the large urban areas. Some of the impacts of these movements upon the receiving areas will be discussed in a subsequent section.

WHO HAS MIGRATED FROM AGRICULTURE?

Much economic theory has as an underlying assumption that units of resources are homogeneous and that, therefore, resource transfers are neutral as to the resulting character of that portion of the resource not transferred. We know, however, that human resources in agriculture are not homogeneous, so that who migrates from agriculture has an effect

[2] J. F. Thaden, "Population Growth Components and Potential in Michigan" (Inst. for Community Devel. and Serv., Contin. Educa., Michigan State Univ., mimeographed, Jan. 16, 1959), Table 11.

[3] Conrad Taeuber, "Economic and Social Implications of Internal Migration in the United States," *J. of Farm Econ.*, Dec., 1959, pp. 1141–1154.

TABLE 2. NET MIGRATION RATES FROM DIFFERENT FARMING AREAS CLASSIFIED
BY INCOME LEVELS, UNITED STATES

Area	Rate of net migration*	
	1930–40	1940–50
Rural-farm..	−12.7	−30.9
Medium and high-income farming areas....................	−13.2	−28.0
Low-income farming areas†...............................	−12.5	−33.8
Moderate low-income farming areas.....................	− 8.3	−27.8
Substantial low-income farming areas...................	−13.9	−34.9
Serious low-income farming areas.......................	−14.2	−36.9
Generalized low-income farming areas‡		
Appalachian Mountains and border areas.................	...	−27.8
Southern Piedmont and Coastal Plains...................	...	−34.8
Southeastern Hilly.....................................	...	−34.5
Mississippi Delta......................................	...	−39.9
Sandy Coastal Plains of Arkansas, Louisiana, and Texas....	...	−49.1
Ozark-Ouachita Mountains and border...................	...	−33.4
Northern Lake States..................................	...	−29.2
Northwestern New Mexico..............................	...	−39.6
Cascade and Rocky Mountain areas.....................	...	−16.0

* Change due to migration expressed as a percentage of farm population alive at both beginning and end of decade.

† Areas delineated in "Development of Agriculture's Human Resources—A report on Problems of Low-Income Farmers." Low-income farms were classified on the basis of three criteria for State Economic Areas: (1) Farms in State Economic Areas averaged less than $1,000 residual farm income to operator and had farm-operator family level-of-living index below the regional average and 25 per cent or more of commercial farms classified as "low production." (2) Average farm-operator level-of-living index for the State Economic Areas was in the lowest fifth for the nation. (3) Fifty per cent or more of commercial farms in State Economic Areas were classified as "low production." Areas denoted as *Serious* in Table 2 met all three criteria; areas denoted as *Substantial* met any two of the criteria; areas denoted as *Moderate* met any one of the criteria.

‡ The generalized areas represent geographic groupings of the low-income farming areas.

SOURCE: *Net Migration from the Rural Farm Population, 1940–50*, Statistical Bulletin No. 176, June, 1956, Table A, p. 13.

beyond the mere numbers involved upon both agriculture and the receiving sector of the economy.

Sociologists have attempted to isolate the differential characteristics of migrants. However, no clear-cut generalizations appear possible as to whether migration selects the least able or the most able, those with the most initiative or those with less.[4]

[4] Conrad Taeuber, *ibid.*, p. 1149.

There is little question that migration from agriculture is closely related to age.[5] More than one-half of the farm population age 10–19 in 1940 had left the farm by 1950. About 40 per cent of the age group 20–24 in 1940 migrated prior to 1950. However, less than 20 per cent of those 30–49 years old in 1940 migrated from the farm during the subsequent decade.[6]

There is some relationship between the age at which out-migration has generally occurred, race, and educational attainment of the out-migrant. One study shows that migration rates from the rural farm areas for the 1940–50 decade were highest from the lower levels of education and roughly similar among those completing more than five years of schooling.[7] The migration rate from the nonwhite rural farm population aged 20–34 in 1940 was roughly similar for all educational levels up to high school. The migration rate for nonwhites with a high school education or beyond was much higher.

These conclusions for the 1940–50 period are approximately the reverse of those of Bogue and Hagood for the 1935–40 period. They found that migration during that period selected the better educated of the rural farm population, except that migration from the cotton belt contained disproportionately large numbers of the least well educated as well as the better educated.[8]

These two studies of rural-urban migration suggested that the pattern of educational selectivity has changed. This hypothesis is supported by two studies of migration over time from specific rural areas. They suggest that during the thirties there was a positive selectivity related to education among rural-urban migrants. However, during and since World War II there has been much less selectivity.[9] This probably can be attributed to the improved economic opportunities in the nonfarm economy and to a general increase in educational levels in rural areas, at least up through the eighth grade.

One final point should be made regarding who has migrated. The statistics discussed relate only to net migration, which is the result of

[5] This apparently has been true for as far back as 1920. See Carter Goodrich *et al.*, *Migration and Economic Opportunity* (Univ. of Pennsylvania Press, 1936), p. 690.

[6] Gladys Bowles, *op. cit.*, p. 17.

[7] C. Horace Hamilton, "Educational Selectivity of Rural-Urban Migration: Preliminary Results of a North Carolina Study," *Selected Studies of Migration Since World War II* (Milbank Mem. Fund), Table 3.

[8] Donald J. Bogue and Margaret J. Hagood, *Subregional Migration in the United States, Differential Migration in the Corn and Cotton Belts*, Vol. II (Scripps Found., 1953), p. 57.

[9] See B. H. Luebke and J. F. Hart, "Migration From a Southern Appalachian Community," *Land Econ.*, Feb., 1958, p. 50, and Joe A. Martin, *Off-Farm Migration: Some of Its Characteristics and Effects Upon Agriculture in Weakley County, Tennessee*, Bul. 290 (Univ. of Tennessee Agric. Exp. Sta., Aug., 1958), p. 21.

movement in both directions. Thus some of the present agricultural population are persons who left agriculture and for some reason returned. Unpublished data from the Bureau of Old Age and Survivor's Insurance (Social Security) show that about one-third of the covered farm operators in 1955 worked off the farm in covered employment in previous years but were not doing so in 1955. Many of these farmers had higher incomes in their nonfarm employment than from farming in 1955. Apparently these individuals either found values in farming that overrode income considerations, or they were unsuccessful in making a transfer to the nonfarm economy and had to return to farming. Thus it is probable that even the high migration rates of the past twenty years do not reflect all of the persons who would be willing to leave agriculture if permanent employment opportunities were available.

THE IMPACT OF THE OUT-MIGRATION ON THE AGRICULTURAL ECONOMY

One of the effects of the out-migration has been to reduce the number in the farm population, since the out-migration has exceeded the rate of natural increase. Thus an out-migration of about 25 million has reduced the farm population from 32 million in 1920 to about 21 million at the present time. Between 1929 and 1958 agricultural employment declined more than 40 per cent. The number of places classified as farms by the Census also has declined rapidly, and as a result we have had encouraging rises in statistical averages relating to per farm and per capita incomes. However, these aggregate statistics can often be misleading, and it is necessary to raise other questions as to the effects of the out-migration. The pertinent questions would seem to be: (1) Has the out-migration reduced the gap in income between farm and nonfarm people? (2) Has out-migration brought an improvement in the relative income position of areas of chronic poverty in agriculture?

[If the average per capita income of the farm population from farming is compared with the per capita income of the nonfarm population for the five years prior to World War I, five years in the late twenties, and for recent years, there is no evidence the gap is closing. From 1910 to 1914 the farm population's per capita income from farming averaged 38 per cent of the nonfarm average per capita. From 1925 to 1929 the income from farming of the farm population averaged 33 per cent of the nonfarm level, and for 1955–59 the comparable figure was 34 per cent.[10] By 1961 it had climbed to 40 per cent as a result of special government programs.

[10] Computed from Table 5H and Table 7H, *Farm Income Situation*-187 (U.S. Dept. of Agric., July 1962).

Of course, in recent years the income from farming accounts for only two-thirds of the per capita income of the farm population. Thus, the *total* per capita income of the farm population averaged 50 per cent of the nonfarm per capita level in the years 1955–59, but this was below the average of 56 per cent for the years 1945–49. Data are not available for comparisons of total per capita income prior to the mid-1930's, but indications are that inclusion of income from nonfarm sources for earlier periods would make little difference.[11] *

Since the average family size in agriculture has been larger than in the nonfarm population, comparisons of income per worker might be considered more valid. Income per worker in agriculture from farming amounted to 61 per cent of the average annual wage per employed factory worker for the years 1910–14.[12] The average for 1925–29 was 44 per cent and in 1954–59 was 44 per cent. There is no evidence of significant relative gains on either a per capita or per worker basis. Therefore, while there have been significant gains in real income in agriculture in the past four decades the rate of gain has probably little more than kept pace with that in the nonfarm economy.

Neither does the evidence support the contention that rapid out-migration has greatly improved the relative position of the low-income areas in agriculture.

It has been generally known that the poverty problems of agriculture are largely concentrated in the South so that it might be assumed that the heavy out-migration from this area would result in a sharply lower proportion of the total farm population now in that region. Surprisingly, however, the change has been only moderate. In 1920 the South had 53 per cent of the farm population and in 1958 it had 49 per cent of the total farm population. One-half of this percentage decline has occurred since 1950. Thus high birth rates in the South have partially offset the higher rates of out-migration over much of the last four decades.

Cheng found in his Michigan study that the disparities in farm income and wages between the higher income and lower income regions of the state have widened in spite of the fact that out-migration has been much higher from the low-income regions.[13]

Bishop found that despite the out-migration and increased resource productivity, net income per farm family in the southeast declined

[11] See *Possible Methods of Improving the Parity Formula* (U.S. Dept. of Agric., mimeograph, Jan. 31, 1957) for some estimates of the effects.

[12] Computed from Table 8, *Farm Income Situation* (U.S. Dept. of Agric., July, 1959).

[13] Kenneth C. I. Cheng, "Economic Development and Geographical Wage Rates in Michigan 1940–57" (unpublished Ph.D. thesis, Michigan State Univ., 1959).

* EDITOR'S NOTE: The two paragraphs enclosed in brackets are revisions of the original data published in the *American Economic Review* in May, 1960.

relative to the net income per farm family in other regions from 1939 to 1949.[14]

Figures are not presently available which give us regional and state comparisons of per capita incomes in agriculture for earlier periods. Therefore, it is not possible to determine accurately whether the heavy out-migration from southern agriculture has improved its relative income position. There are, however, some trends in the aggregate figures for regions which support the conclusions that the South has made little relative gain during the past fifteen years despite the large out-migration from its low-income agriculture.

An analysis of regional trends in per capita incomes of the total population by the Department of Commerce shows for the period 1927–29 to 1944 there was a marked reduction in the disparity in per capita incomes between regions.[15] Most of the reduction occurred between 1940 and 1944.[16] Since 1944, when the greatest out-migration from agriculture has occurred, there has been little change in the relative position of the regions. Even when the relative incomes were converging, the absolute gains in income were much larger in the higher income regions.

There are several reasons why out-migration has not resulted in significant and dramatic reductions in income differentials within agriculture and between agriculture and the nonagricultural economy. They are: the migration to date has affected commercial agriculture less than we realize; where migration has occurred its selectivity has created conditions tending to retard the recombination of remaining resources; and much more than a simple recombination of existing resources is necessary to bring an improvement in the income levels of most of the poverty plagued areas in agriculture.

Turning to the contention that out-migration has affected commercial agriculture less than might be assumed, some evidence is seen in the statistics relating to changes in numbers of farms. For our purposes it might be useful to classify farms as falling into one of three types: commercial farms (roughly Class I through IV of Economic Class of Farm defined in the last Census of Agriculture); low-production farms (Class V and VI); and rural places to live (part-time, residential, and subsistence farms). If past censuses are adjusted for changes in farm prices, the trends in agriculture are these:[17] the number of commercial

---

[14] See Charles E. Bishop, "Economic Development and Adjustments in Southeastern Low Income Agriculture," *J. of Farm Econ.*, Dec., 1954, p. 1151.

[15] U.S. Dept. of Com., *Personal Income by States Since 1929, A supplement to the Survey of Current Business* (1956), pp. 24–26.

[16] U.S. Dept. of Com., *U.S. Income and Output, a Supplement to the Survey of Current Business* (Nov., 1958), p. 37.

[17] Jackson V. McElveen, *Family Farms in a Changing Economy* (USDA Inf. Bul. No. 171, Mar., 1957), p. 20.

farms has been remarkably stable since 1929; the number of rural places to live has trended slightly upward; and the number of low-production farms has declined very sharply.

About 1.1 million of the 1.8 million low-production farms that disappeared between the 1930 and 1954 Census of Agriculture were in the South. However, this does not imply quite the degree of resource mobility for nonlabor resources that it might seem to, because about half of the reductions were of cropper farms which were not actually independent management units. Whereas the decline in the number of low-production farms has been greater in the South, the largest decline in the number of management units has been in the North and West.

There are further indications that the farms that have disappeared as people left agriculture were the smaller, less-productive farms. The decline in number of farms has been greatest among farms of ten to ninety-nine acres in size. In 1920 farms in this size group made up 54 per cent of the total number of farms, but they controlled only 17 per cent of the land in farms.[18] Between 1920 and 1954 there was a decline of 1.4 million in the number of farms between ten and ninety-nine acres. However, the amount of land which these farms contained and which, under ideal circumstances, might have been consolidated into larger units amounted to less than 6 per cent of the total land in farms in 1954. Thus the 63 per cent increase in the average size of farm in the United States from 1920 to 1954 is largely a statistical freak. Actually, there have been few increases in the numbers of farms in the various larger size groups and in the average size within the various groups.

The high degree of age selectivity in migration appears to be an important factor inhibiting the adjustment of resources remaining in agriculture. As a result of the disproportionately heavy out-movement in the younger age groups the average age of farm operators has risen. Whereas 21 per cent of the operators in 1920 were in the twenty-five to thirty-four age group and 26 per cent were over fifty-five years old, in 1954 only 13 per cent were in the younger bracket and 37 per cent were over fifty-five.[19]

Older farmers are less likely to undertake drastic reorganizations of existing resources themselves because of limits of their physical capabilities and the limited span over which they might realize returns on

[18] U.S. Dept. of Com., *1954 Census of Agriculture*, Vol. II, Chap. V. pp. 353 and 355.

[19] U.S. Dept. of Com., *1954 Census of Agriculture*, Vol. II, Chap. II, p. 83. The relative rise in noncommercial farms and the Census definition of an operator contributed to this rise.

large investments. Studies of low-income farming areas in South Carolina, Tennessee, and Arkansas all mention that the advanced age of many farm operators inhibits the adjustment of agricultural resources.[20] Apparently many older owners are unwilling to enter into contractual arrangements which will make it possible for the remaining younger farmers to organize existing agricultural resources in a satisfactory fashion. Thus institutional arrangements relating to tenure and credit, which were developed in a period of greater stability in technology and in the agricultural labor force, do not seem to be adjusting adequately to the rapid changes of recent years.

Adjustment problems in agriculture following a decline in the labor force are much more complex than a mere change in the capital-man ratio. Generally, the type of farming operation needs to be changed. New technology, new investment, and new management skills are required in order for the recombined resources to be productive. Old investments in buildings and equipment are often obsolete, requiring large additions of capital in new forms. The mere out-movement of labor from agriculture is a necessary, but not sufficient, condition to achieve these adjustments. Unfortunately, most of the people capable of making such adjustments may be among the out-migrants.

Even where heavy out-migration has occurred resource adjustments in agriculture may not tend to correct income inequalities. Bachmura found that population movements as a whole within a group of Mississippi Valley counties were not corrective in an income equilibrating sense.[21] In addition, he concluded that movements in capital investment per worker were noncorrective over the decade.[22]

Long-distance migration may be of much less help to agricultural adjustment than nearby nonfarm growth. There are indications that the adjustments are made more rapidly where the growth in nonfarm employment is local. Ruttan found that rural farm areas in the southeast which "caught up" with the national average between 1930 and 1950 were close to developing urban centers.[23] Cheng found the same tendencies in Michigan.

---

[20] See Thomas A. Burch and Charles P. Butler, *Physical and Economic Characteristics that Limit Adjustments on Full-Time Medium Sized Farms in the Piedmont Area of South Carolina* (South Carolina Agric. Exp. Sta. Bul. 453, Mar., 1958), p. 47; Martin, *op. cit.*, p. 34, and William H. Metzler and J. L. Charlton, *Employment and Underemployment of Rural People in the Ozark Area* (Univ. of Arkansas Agric. Exp. Sta. Bul. 604, Nov., 1958), p. 55.

[21] Frank T. Bachmura, "Migration and Factor Adjustment in Lower Mississippi Valley Agriculture: 1940–50," *J. of Farm Econ.*, Nov., 1956, p. 1033.

[22] *Ibid.*, p. 1041.

[23] Vernon W. Ruttan, "Discussion of Development and Adjustment," *J. of Farm Econ.*, Dec., 1954, p. 1159.

THE IMPACT OF THE OUT-MIGRATION ON THE NONFARM ECONOMY

In the nonfarm economy as well as in the farm economy the heavy out-migration from agriculture has had both positive and negative aspects. During the periods of extreme labor scarcity the migration was appreciated and encouraged, but more recently some of its negative aspects have received more attention.

The nonfarm economy has attracted over 25 million people from the farm population since 1920. A high proportion of the migrants have been in age groups enabling them to be in the productive labor force. The migration, coming as it did at a time when new entrants to the labor force were low because of low urban birth rates in the twenties and thirties, was about the only way in which a large expansion of the nonfarm labor force could occur without immigration. Ducoff estimated that one-half of the expansion in the nonagricultural labor force from 1930 to 1954 came from migration from the farm population.[24] It would have been impossible to have increased nonfarm output to wartime and postwar levels without this increase in the labor force. Without the migration from farms, the price of nonfarm labor relative to other inputs probably would have risen more sharply than has been the case.

The nonfarm economy has received through the process of migration a large transfer of capital from the farm economy in the form of investment in the rearing and educating of farm youth to the age at which they migrated.[25] As a result, the nonfarm economy has received a large and significant quantity of productive resources in the form of productive labor without having to incur most of the initial expense of its rearing and education. This should contribute to a rapid rate of capital accumulation and growth in the nonfarm economy.

Not all of the effects of rural-urban migration have been positive for either the migrants or the receiving areas. First, the assimilation of large groups of people from different cultural backgrounds has presented some of the same problems as did the earlier mass influx of immigrants. Existing educational systems, social groupings, and economic structures have been disrupted by the rapid influx of migrants into some urban areas. There has been a problem in some areas of the rapid replacement of the old population of central cities by migrant nonwhites whose economic status is low, adding considerably to the difficult adjustment problems already mounting in urban areas.

The receiving areas have become increasingly aware of the cost of

---

[24] Louis J. Ducoff, "Trends and Characteristics of Farm Population in Low Income Farming Areas," *J. of Farm Econ.*, Dec., 1955, p. 1407.

[25] James D. Tarver estimated that an investment of $15,000 in 1954 prices was required to rear and educate a farm child to age eighteen. See his "Costs of Rearing and Educating Farm Children," *J. of Farm Econ.*, Feb., 1956, pp. 144–56.

assimilating the migrants. A recent Michigan study reported that although persons born in the South make up only 9.5 per cent of the state's population, they accounted for 31 per cent of the prison commitments.[26] When a commitment rate is computed for different population groups, the rate for whites born in the South is more than twice the rate for whites born in Michigan. Approximately the reverse was true for Negroes. The heavy burden of welfare costs to migrant groups has prompted recent suggestions of sending migrants out of one city and of increasing residence requirements for welfare in several others.

The public problems that have arisen as a result of the migration to urban areas are partially because the migrants themselves sometimes have found the adjustment to the new economic and social environment difficult. They have found themselves unskilled labor in an industrial society which is increasingly replacing unskilled labor with skilled labor and machines. They have found that the impact of the nonfarm business cycle falls heaviest on the younger, the less skilled, and the nonwhite worker. They have found racial and other forms of discrimination among labor unions.

A recent paper summarized several sociological studies of the position of rural migrants in urban society.[27] It made the following points: (1) Many of the rural migrants lack the educational training or social background necessary to make them other than marginal members of the nonfarm society. (2) Rural migrants tend to move to lower standard housing areas and upgrade their housing less through moving than do urban migrants. (3) The rural migrant tends to participate less in formal and informal social and political organizations than other groups of the urban population. (4) Despite many of these less favorable aspects, the migrant generally would make the move if he had to make the decision again.

SUMMARY AND CONCLUSIONS

Migration from agriculture over the past four decades has touched virtually every community in the United States, both farm and nonfarm. Without out-migration the present problems of United States agriculture would have been magnified manyfold, and the gap between per capita incomes in the farm and nonfarm economy certainly would have widened. As yet, however, there is no evidence that the rapid rate of out-migration has appreciably closed the gap that existed in

[26] "Non-natives Cause Most Crime in State," *The State J.* (Lansing, Mich.), Nov. 3, 1959, p. 16.

[27] George M. Beal and Wallace E. Ogg, "Secondary Adjustments from Adaptations of Agriculture," in *Problems and Policies of American Agriculture* (Iowa State Univ. Press, 1959), pp. 226 ff.

per capita incomes of farm and nonfarm people. Neither has the migration from agriculture apparently significantly changed the per capita income distribution between regions in agriculture.

Despite its magnitude, the out-migration from agriculture probably has affected that portion of agriculture producing the bulk of our food and fiber relatively little. Most of the out-movement has been from farms with few resources. There are widespread indications that the out-migration has severely strained the social and economic structure of many rural communities, causing serious problems for churches, schools, and rural businesses dependent on numbers of population.

Most of the policy proposals to facilitate the migration from agriculture have been to improve rural education, job information, and human mobility. These would be of primary benefit to the migrants themselves and to the receiving communities. Few, if any, policies have been proposed that are aimed at alleviating the serious social and economic problems of communities which have been or will be rapidly losing population. Also, little attention has been given to policies to promote the new institutions that will be necessary to facilitate rapid adjustment of the resources remaining in the agricultural economy.

The farm-nonfarm migration has had desirable effects and yet has created problems for the nonfarm economy. Migration made possible an expansion of the nonfarm labor force when the pressure for increased nonfarm output was great. It has also created social and economic problems for which solutions are not yet apparent. It seems probable that the problems will become greater and the benefits of farm-nonfarm migration somewhat less evident to the nonfarm areas in the decade ahead. Unlike the past twenty years, during the next decade there will be a rising number of persons annually available to enter the labor force from within the nonfarm economy. This will be due to the marked rise in birth rates during and since 1940. Thus the need for attracting new labor from the farm population will diminish and the problems of assimilating migrants will probably weigh more heavily upon the consciousness of prospective employers.

All this is to say that even with the favorable economic and social conditions of the past two decades a simple policy of rapid out-migration from agriculture has not, by itself, been sufficient to bring significant improvement in the relative position of the farm economy. Migration has left unsolved many pressing problems it has helped create.

The total effect of the migration from farms has apparently been of value to both the farm and nonfarm economies. Therefore, it would appear that the nation could well afford some public policies to cope with the social and economic problems attendant to migration. Without such supplemental forces it is unlikely that migration will, by itself, bring about a significant improvement in the position of agriculture.

13. Connections between Natural Resources and Economic Growth*

THEODORE W. SCHULTZ

My topic is burdened by a heavy intellectual tradition based on a widely held belief that economic progress is severely subjected to diminishing returns of labor and capital against land. The belief persists despite much evidence to the contrary. Clearly the role of land in economic growth is no longer nearly as important as it appeared to Ricardo and his contemporaries. Yet, it is not easy to free ourselves from old ideas, especially so where such ideas have become entrenched behind strong doctrines.

My purpose is simply to clear the deck of these ideas that keep us from seeing the more relevant connections between natural resources and economic growth. I propose to examine three closely related questions: What is the value of natural resources as a factor in production? Are the economic growth possibilities of a country, especially so if it is poor, substantially restricted by its endowment of natural resources? Are we confronted in the case of the services of natural resources by a rising supply price?

Before turning to these questions, I do want to pay my respects to the rich intellectual history about natural resources; there is no dearth of literature. I have already alluded to the well-known concern of the older economists about land as a limitational factor in economic growth. There are also well-developed treatments of particular natural resources in mining, fishing, forestry, and agriculture and of urban uses of land. Then, too, location and transport have received much careful thought. There are now some good estimates of land as a stock of wealth and also as a factor of production. In this respect we enter an old and well maintained vineyard and our task might be viewed as simply one of gathering the fruit of these intellectual efforts.

But my purpose cannot be achieved by merely building on received knowledge. It does not, as things now stand, place natural resources in

* From *Natural Resources and Economic Growth,* Joseph J. Spengler (ed.), Resources for the Future, Washington, D.C., 1961, pp. 1–9. Reprinted by permission of Resources for the Future and the author. The author is professor of economics at the University of Chicago.

their proper economic perspective, because all too little account has been taken of the rise in substitutes, the rise in the quantity and value of other resources, and the dynamic properties of modern economic growth in developing substitutes for ever more classes of natural resources. One's conception of economic growth is not unimportant in this regard. We do well to restrict it to increases in national income that can be identified and measured. Much, however, depends on the sources of these increases in national income. If it were only the result of additions to the stock of conventional reproducible nonhuman wealth and to the number of persons in the labor force, it would be simple. But, we know that this conception leaves most of the increases in national income unexplained. I propose to think of economic growth as a particular type of dynamic disequilibrium, during which the economy is absorbing various subsets of superior resources. They are superior resources in a special sense, namely, they provide investment opportunities with relatively high rates of return; and these relatively high rates of return imply inequalities in the way resources are allocated and a lagged process in bringing these rates of return into equality; moreover, this dynamic disequilibrium will persist to the extent that additional superior resources are developed and absorbed.

I

What is the value of natural resources as a factor of production? There are presently two very different views and treatments of this measure of the economic importance of these resources. One attributes a dominating role to natural resources as is the case in the classical dynamics,[1] and the other attributes to them no role whatsoever, e.g., there is no land in the Harrod models.[2] Harrod said, "I propose to discard the law of diminishing returns from land as a primary determinant in a progressive economy . . . . I discard it only because in our particular context it appears that its influence may be quantitatively unimportant."[3]

I leave it to others to decide whether these magnificent growth models are tools or toys. What is clear, however, is that both of them are based on a grand, country-wide, macroconception of a particular economy at a given period in its history. The particular economy under consideration was England in Ricardo's day and the United Kingdom at the present time, respectively. The underlying circumstances were indeed

---

[1] William J. Baumol, *Economic Dynamics* (New York, The Macmillan Company, 1951), chap. 2.

[2] R. F. Harrod, "An Essay in Dynamic Theory," *Economic Journal*, March, 1939. See also, *Towards a Dynamic Economics* (London, Macmillan and Company, 1948).

[3] *Towards a Dynamic Economics*, p. 20.

very different, as I have attempted to show in another paper, "The Declining Economic Importance of Agricultural Land."[4]

Neither of these contrary views has any general validity. Whether we measure natural resources as a *stock* of wealth or as *flow* of productive services rendered by them, we are in the domain of estimates. For the United States we have Goldsmith's estimates which indicate that between 1910 and 1955 the proportion of national wealth represented by "all land" fell from 36 to 17 percent and agricultural land dropped from 20 to 5 percent of national wealth.[5]

When we measure the flow of productive services, we would expect natural resources to represent an even smaller fraction af all productive services than they are of the total stock of nonhuman wealth. The "Paley Report"[6] provides a clue, if we assume that there has been a fairly stable linkage between the flow of raw materials produced and the stock of natural resources on which this flow has been dependent. The value of all raw materials consumed in the United States declined, relative to gross national product, from about 23 to 13 percent, between 1904–13 and 1944–50. For agriculture, the income attributed to farm land, excluding capital structures that have been added to such land in the United States, fell from 3.2 to .6 of one percent of net national product, between 1910–14 and 1955–57.[7]

There are, so it seems to me, two general relationships between natural resources as these are traditionally defined and all resources that have strong empirical support (both of these relationships are expressed in terms of the *flows* of the productive services of these resources and not in terms of *stocks* of wealth):

1. When we compare countries as of a particular date, we observe that the proportion of natural resources to all resources employed to produce the income is greater in poor countries than it is in rich countries. (I would venture that the upper limit in the proportion of natural resources to all resources in poor countries is in the neighborhood of 20 to 25 percent and the lower limit in rich countries is about 5 percent.)

2. When a country achieves economic growth that increases its per capita income over time, natural resources become a decreasing proportion of all resources that are employed to produce the income. (It

[4] T. W. Schultz, *Economic Journal*, December, 1951. Also, *The Economic Organization of Agriculture*, (New York, McGraw-Hill Book Company, 1953), chap. 8.

[5] Raymond W. Goldsmith and Associates, *A Study of Saving in the United States*, Vol. III. Special Studies (Princeton University Press, 1956), table W-1; and Goldsmith's estimates appearing in the *Thirty-Seventh Annual Report of the National Bureau of Economic Research* (New York, May, 1957).

[6] The President's Materials Policy Commission, *Resources for Freedom* (Washington, D.C., June, 1952).

[7] T. W. Schultz, "Land in Economic Growth," *Modern Land Policy*, Harold G. Halcrow, editor (Urbana, University of Illinois Press, 1959).

would appear that during recent decades the rate at which this particular proportion has declined has been large.)

How large a contribution can natural resources make to the economic growth of poor countries? The answer to this question turns basically on the growth possibilities of poor countries. Here, too, we are confronted presently by two contradictory assessments.

There is a widely held belief among economists that primary production—mining and especially agriculture—is essentially a burden on the economic growth of poor countries. Poor countries are over committed to agriculture. Land is as a rule used intensively and the supply of land is virtually fixed. The marginal returns to labor in agriculture are at or near zero. These conditions are thought to be such that additional effort to increase the production of primary products can add little or nothing to the national product. On the other hand, large gains are to be had from a comparable effort and investment to produce industrial products. Furthermore, according to this view, backwardness is an intrinsic complement of the land-using sectors, notably in the case of agriculture; and, in addition, to add to its economic woes, in producing primary products a country is particularly vulnerable to the economic instability of rich countries. For these several reasons it is held that the natural resources sectors, especially agriculture, are less rewarding than are the sectors that contribute to industrialization on which the economic growth of poor countries, so it is presumed, is basically dependent.

The other assessment of the economic growth possibilities of poor countries holds that the endowment of natural resources in such countries, including farm lands, is a relatively important asset and that differences in stocks of these resources among poor countries are a major variable in determining the growth possibilities of such countries.

This issue is plagued by confusion and by a lack of firm evidence. A part of the confusion arises from a difference in the weight that is given to natural resources. As already noted, they are as a rule more important relative to all resources in poor than in rich countries. Most of the confusion, however, originates from a failure to distinguish between the rate of return to be had from additional reproducible capital of *the existing forms* and the rate of return that can be realized from *new and better forms* of reproducible capital.

There is first the fact that the technical properties of these two forms of reproducible capital are different, and there is the further fact that the economic attributes are also different inasmuch as the marginal rate of return from additional resources of the existing forms is low relative to the rate of return from investments in the new forms of resources. Once this distinction is made between these two forms of reproducible capital, the critical question is whether the new forms of capital are unique in that they have technical specifications that make it impossible to use any of them in primary production.

I have no doubt whatsoever that these new and better forms of re-producible capital are not restricted to industry. Many of them are applicable to agriculture and to other sectors heavily dependent upon natural resources. If the choice were only one of adding another irrigation well, a ditch, a bullock, or a few more primitive tools and pieces of equipment of the type that are being employed in a poor country, the prospects of winning a relatively high rate of return from such additions to the stock of capital would be dim indeed. But this is not the choice, whether it be in agriculture or industry. The choice that can be made and that carries with it the prospect of larger rewards entails new and better forms of reproducible capital both in agriculture and industry.

It has long been an accepted tenet of economic thought that the rates of return on additional capital in poor countries are relatively large. According to this tenet, these returns are large because poor countries have a relatively small supply of reproducible capital to use with their labor and land. The view that these earnings are relatively high has gained support from the vast movements of capital historically out of particular Western countries into many a poor country. These large transfers were in response, so it is held, to the differences between the *low rates* that had come to prevail in some of the comparatively rich countries and the *high rates* that characterized the production possibilities awaiting such capital in poor countries. What has not been made explicit in this assessment is the fact that for the most part these capital transfers were not employed simply to multiply the then existing forms of reproducible capital; instead new forms of capital were introduced into these poor countries as a consequence of these transfers.

I want to comment on still another proposition about natural resources. It is widely held to be true that the supply price of the productive services of natural resources must rise relative to the prices of the services of the reproducible factors as a consequence of economic growth. We have been taught that this is inevitable as the stock of reproducible capital increases along with the growth in population and production. Lower transport costs and improvements in the arts of production could temporarily hold the rise in the supply price of productive services of natural resources in check but that was the best that could be hoped for. Ultimately, however, diminishing returns of labor and capital against land would always prevail. This economic dictum is clearly at variance with our estimates; it is time that we relegated this dictum to our stock of folklore.

But the image of a fixed supply of natural resources and a rising supply price of the products of these resources, persists. Let me quote from another paper.[8]

[8] *Ibid.*

Yet no less an economist than Colin Clark, no longer ago than 1941, in his book, *The Economics of 1960,* came to the conclusion that the world was in for a dramatic rise in the relative price of primary products. Clark did not come to this conclusion by indulging in some easy, intuitive guesses, nor did he rely on a simple projection of past trends. He drew upon his vast stock of data; he proceeded to put them into his "analytical model" with its strong bent for diminishing returns against land, and ground out the following conclusion for 1960, ". . . the terms of trade for primary produce will improve by as much as 90 percent from the average of 1925–34."[9] To speak of so violent a rise in the relative price of primary products as an "improvement" is a neat twist . . . But what are the facts as we reach 1960? Clark missed the price target altogether; his shot went off into space in the wrong direction. What went wrong? Did he assume too large a rise in population? On the contrary, the up-surge in population has been much greater than he assumed it would be. Has there been much less industrialization than he anticipated? Again, the answer is in the negative. Clark simply assumed a lot of secular diminishing returns against land and this assumption turned out to be invalid.

A plausible approach is to treat raw (crude) materials as if they were produced under constant supply price conditions. This is the basic assumption that has made the Paley Report useful. It is a rough approximation to what has been happening, and the projections of the consumption of raw materials in the United States (to about 1975) based on this assumption have been doing quite well thus far.

I am aware, however, that there may be many a slip between the prices of the services of natural resources and the prices of raw materials. Unfortunately, there are all too few estimates of the prices of the services (rents) of natural resources; the studies that have come to my attention stop with raw materials. This led me to undertake some estimates of the changes in the prices of the services of farm land in the United States.[10]

Although my estimates are subject to a number of qualifications, they strongly indicate that the price of the service of farm land declined substantially between 1910–14 and 1956 relative to farm product prices and even more so relative to the prices of all inputs used in farming.[11] In interpreting these estimates it should be borne in mind that farm product prices receded about 15 percent, both relative to the prices of all commodities at wholesale and relative to prices of all consumer items at retail, between 1910–14 and 1956.

[9] Colin Clark, *The Economics of 1960* (London, Macmillan & Co., 1943), p. 52. A reprint of the first edition, the "Introduction" is dated May 15, 1941.

[10] T. W. Schultz, "Land in Economic Growth," *Modern Land Policy.*

[11] Of the major classes of farm inputs only the price of fertilizer did not rise relative to the price of the services of farm land.

Land as an input in farming is cheaper now than it was just prior to the first world war. This decline in the supply price of the services of farm land in the United States is not a freak event. It did not occur from a contraction of agriculture, because farm output rose about 80 percent between these two dates. Nor is it a consequence of large increases in the amount of such land. On the contrary, crop land harvested actually declined slightly, from 330 million (average for 1910–14) to 326 million acres (1956). I shall not enter at this juncture upon an explanation of

TABLE 1. U.S. FARM OUTPUT AND INPUT PRICES, 1910–14 AND 1956*

Item	Increases between 1910–14 and 1956 1910–14 = 100	Increases relative to the prices of farm products 235 = 100
1. Prices received by farmers for farm products......................	235	100
2. Prices of classes of farm inputs		
(1) Farm wage rates.................	543	231
(2) Building and fencing materials.....	374	159
(3) Farm machinery.................	329	140
(4) Farm supplies..................	279	119
(5) Fertilizer......................	150	64
(6) Farm land†		
a. Price per acre of farm land.......	158	67
b. Price per constant unit of farm land	181	77
c. Rent per constant unit of farm land	166	71

* Based on table II in "Land in Economic Growth," *Modern Land Policy.*
† In each of these three estimates I have attempted to exclude the reproducible capital structures that have been added to farm land. Also see Ross Parish, *Trends in the Use of Summer Fallow in Saskatchewan: An Economic Interpretation* (unpublished Ph.D. thesis, University of Chicago, 1959), for estimates that show the price of the services of farm land in Saskatchewan as having decreased substantially relative to the price of wheat and relative to other major farm inputs.

this decline in the relative price of the services of farm land. Suffice it merely to note that the proposition that price of the services of natural resources must rise relative to the services of reproducible capital over time as a consequence of economic growth, is demonstrably false.

II

Let me now turn to a more general view of the connections between natural resources and economic growth. Up to this point my purpose has been to show that natural resources at factor costs have been declining in value relative to aggregate value of all resources and that the supply price of the services of these resources has not been rising relative to the supply price of other major classes of resources. Implied in this treatment is the inference that the marginal contribution of natural resources over time has not been increasing. Then, too, although natural resources are mainly an integral part of so-called backward sectors of the economy of most poor countries, it does not follow that the production possibilities of these countries are such that their natural resources act as a burden on their economic growth.

The connections between natural resources and reproducible non-human capital and the labor force are being altered substantially over time by economic growth. The type of economic growth that we have been experiencing represents a form of dynamic disequilibrium brought about by the introduction of new and superior resources. These resources, among other things, have been at many points in the economy effective substitutes for one or more classes of natural resources. To see the process broadly it will be necessary to use a comprehensive concept of capital, a concept that includes both nonhuman and human wealth, in order to take into account additions to stock of capabilities of a labor force that are useful in economic endeavor, capabilities that can be had by investments in man.[12]

We are accustomed to thinking of new and better machines as a substitute for labor. Surely, in agriculture they have become an important substitute for farm land as well as for labor. Johnson's and Gustafson's study of grain yields attributes a third of the increase in the yield of corn since 1880 to farm mechanization. Improved seeds have also become a major substitute for farm land, and they appear to have contributed as much to increasing yields as has mechanization.[13] The economic effects of hybrid seed corn are noteworthy in this connection.[14]

Then, too, new forms of capital have entered into the production of fertilizer; these seem to have reduced substantially the real price of fertilizer, so that it has become a strong force not only in holding but in reducing the price of the services of farm land because of substitution. Not least of all have been the improvements in the capabilities of man (in this case of farmers and others in the farm labor force). Some of these new capabilities have also acted as substitutes for farm land.

The long established practice of treating these new and better resources as an *ad hoc* variable under the label of "technological advances," is a convenient way of covering up ignorance. Moreover, it is inconsistent with the economic logic of the properties of a production function. To assert that a production function (say in farming) has improved,

[12] See T. W. Schultz, "Investment in Man; An Economist's View," *Social Service Review*, June, 1959.

[13] D. Gale Johnson and Robert L. Gustafson, *Grain Yields and The American Food Supply*, University of Chicago Press, Chicago, 1962.

[14] See the studies of hybrid corn by Zvi Griliches, among others "Research Costs and Social Returns: Hybrid Corn with Comparisons," *Journal of Political Economy*, LXVI, August, 1958. [EDITOR'S NOTE: See Selection 23.]

or has been shifted to the right, because of an advance in technology, can only mean that at least one new resource (input) has been introduced in production, because a production function can only be derived from the properties of the resources that are employed in that production. If a production function has changed, it always means that at least one additional resource with different technical properties has been introduced in production. The analytical task, therefore, consists of developing concepts and of building models that will permit us to identify and measure the resource that provides the new technical properties and not to treat all or part of the unexplained residual by simply calling it "an advance in technology."

Lastly, the persistent and impressive economic growth that we observe in not a few countries and that we want to understand does not fit into the pattern of traditional thought. It does not fit because not all of the history of economic growth has been an exercise in stationary long-run equilibrium based on land, labor, and capital as these have been traditionally conceived. Diminishing returns, as labor and capital have been increased against a given stock of natural resources (land), is not the only game that history has been playing. In the history we want to understand, the game has been altered as a consequence of a couple more aces having somehow gotten into the deck. New and better production functions have entered from somewhere. The capabilities of labor have been improved, and the line of demarcation between capital and labor has become very blurred by investments in man. And so has the line between capital and natural resources, as new, useful knowledge has entered.

14. Comment on "Connections between Natural Resources and Economic Growth"*

J. H. DALES

I shall attempt to deny that the ratio of the income originating in Sector A to National Income is a valid measure of "importance" in

* From *Natural Resources and Economic Growth,* Joseph J. Spengler (ed.), Resources for the Future, Washington, D.C., 1961, pp. 16–19. Reprinted by permission of Resources for the Future and the author. The author is professor of economics at the University of Toronto.

the context of economic development. What the ratio measures is the importance of Sector A as a source of national income at a given time. It asserts a fact. What I wish to deny is that this fact carries around with it any implication about the process of economic development. In the context of economic development I claim that the fact is irrelevant.

The alleged measure is a simple ratio of the value of output in Sector A to the value of all output; this ratio will fall over time if the numerator declines relatively to the denominator. If we take Sector A to be the natural resource sector, the ratio will fall if a country adds to natural resource production other types of production, but this fall, far from being pregnant with economic significance, is of course nothing but arithmetic necessity. Are we to be compelled to say that if the efficiency of the natural resource sector of an economy improves relatively to that of other sectors, so that its products become cheaper, the importance of natural resources has shrunk? It is hard to maintain such a view in a discussion of economic growth since what has really happened in this case is that through greater efficiency the resource sector has freed resources to make possible production increases in other sectors. Are we to be forced to argue, too, that if the real costs of resource extraction rise resources will then become more "important"? That the natural resource sector would then provide more jobs and account for a larger share of the national income would be true by definition. That such a development would foster economic growth seems to me to be the reverse of the truth.

Indeed at this point we perceive that the alleged measure of importance can with equal reasonableness be turned around, so that the lower the ratio the greater the importance of the sector. It is certainly reasonable to suggest that areas with abundant, easily worked, and therefore cheap, natural resources facilitate economic growth; yet both *because* they are cheap and *because* they foster the growth of other sectors the proportion of national income originating in the resource sector declines. Thus the lower the ratio of income generated in the resource sector to total income the greater the importance of this sector to economic growth. This statement is of course untrue; it merely has the same specious attraction as its opposite. Since a low ratio may, with equal reasonableness, mean either great importance or little importance to economic growth, we had better dispense with it as a reliable measuring stick. It is unreliable because it is irrelevant.

Are we, in seeking to measure the importance of resources to economic development, chasing a will-o'-the-wisp; or is there a defensible measure of the relationship? I believe that there is a defensible measure, and that it is based in part on physical quantities rather than on monetary values.

The argument begins with the contention that many, and perhaps all, of the major questions about economic development can be rephrased in such a way that they become amenable to analysis in terms of location theory. The classic problem of explaining the development of England in the nineteenth century is, indeed, frequently posed in the form: "Why did the development take place in England rather than elsewhere?" This, in turn, is equivalent to asking why industry located in England rather than elsewhere. Again, if we are asked to explain the rapid economic development of, say, California, the question can be phrased as follows: "What explains the growing tendency of economic activity to locate in California rather than in, say, South Dakota?" In general, instead of asking "why growth?" we ask "why growth here rather than there?"

Put in these terms, a measure of the kind we are seeking immediately suggests itself. Location theorists have developed a measure of the "locational attraction" of different factors of production.[1] Correctly stated, this measure is a product of two factors: the physical amount of the factor used in production and the cost of transporting the factor (i.e., its mobility). The locational attraction of the factor—its "importance" in attracting industry—varies directly with the physical amounts of the factor required, and inversely with the cost of transporting it. Coal used to exert a very strong attraction to industry both because large quantities of it were required in production and because its high bulk in relation to its value made it relatively expensive to transport. Coal in the past fifty years has become a less important attraction to industry because less of it is used in producing a unit of output of nearly every commodity. Neither oil nor natural gas has ever been a major attraction to industry because their mobility has always been high. And so on.

Our problem is, I think, exactly analogous to the locational problem. I would say, then, that the importance of resources to economic development (i.e., the location of industry in a specified area) depends directly on the physical quantity of resources used in the process of production and inversely on the cost of transporting the resources from one area to another.

We can now see the folly of talking about "natural resources" as if they were a homogeneous factor of production. The locational attraction of many resource deposits has undoubtedly declined over the past few

[1] The measure is *not* the ratio of the cost of factor X to total costs. That this ratio is not a correct measure of locational attraction has been shown time and again, but strange as it may seem it is not infrequently used as such by the very authors who have demonstrated its irrelevance. It is indeed, in Fowler's language, a Sturdy Indefensible. On this matter, see my *Hydroelectricity and Industrial Development— Quebec 1898–1940* (Cambridge, 1957), chap. 8, p. 29. The present Note seeks to show the irrelevance of the ratio of income originating in Sector A to national income as a measure of the importance of Sector A to economic growth. An exactly parallel argument would apply to the ratio, cost of factor X to total cost, and would show the irrelevance of this ratio to the locational importance of factor X.

decades, and that for many reasons: improved transport, which has increased their mobility; technological change, which, in reducing waste, has reduced the quantity of them required per unit of output; technological change in another direction, which has allowed different resources, or different deposits of the same resource, to be substituted for the deposits formerly used. In all these ways the importance of a wide range of natural resources as a factor in attracting industry (that is to say, in promoting industrial development) has undoubtedly declined significantly in the last 50 years. But I very much doubt that this has been true of *all* natural resources. Climate can in part be transported, in the sense that some aspects of climate can be artificially simulated almost anywhere, but the process is usually very expensive, which is to say that climate is very immobile. I also think that food supplies are relatively immobile —they suffer a weight loss of 100% in the production process, and they are normally bulky in relation to their value. Finally, at least two energy resources which are still in wide use—coal and hydroelectric power— also have a strong attraction for industry both because they are utilized in large quantities and because they are expensive to transport. There are no doubt others. But on the strength of the argument advanced above, I confess to believing that good soil resources for food supplies, good coal or hydraulic resources, and, if you like, certain features of climate and water supply, are all natural resources that are of very great importance to economic development.

15. Patterns of Development in Newly Settled Regions*

ROBERT E. BALDWIN

I

To aid in the formulation of effective development programs, economists must seek to understand the reasons why certain parts of the "backward" world have become enmeshed in what appears to be a vicious circle of poverty. Why is it that these particular regions failed to become economically developed?

* From *The Manchester School of Economic and Social Studies*, vol. 24, pp. 161–179, May, 1956, with omissions. Reprinted by permission of *The Manchester School* and the author. The author is professor of economics at the University of California at Los Angeles.

One economic relation which may be useful for answering some aspects of this question is the input-output variation among commodity production functions. Although everyone is aware that there are significant differences among commodities concerning the nature of the physical output possibilities from different quantities and combinations of the factors of producton—as witness the frequent use of such terms as "labor intensive" and "capital intensive" commodities—these engineering differences among production functions only infrequently have been made an operational part of economic theorizing. By far, the most comprehensive use of these differences for economic analysis is the input-output studies initiated by Professor Leontief.[1] . . .

While the Leontief analysis assumes fixed production coefficients for each industry, the assumption will not be followed here, since the analysis will be conceptual rather than statistical. What will be assumed is merely that there are significant engineering differences among some commodity production functions over their input-output range. These variations concern the manner in which returns to scale behave for different factor ratios and also the manner in which the marginal rates of factor substitution vary for different output levels and factor ratios.

II

This paper will utilize the concept of these production function differences in analyzing the problem of differential rates of growth between newly settled regions. While technological conditions of production influence the pattern of growth in an economy at all stages of development, it appears that they can be particularly important in conditioning the potential for growth in newly settled regions. Consequently, the procedure to be followed will be to contrast the *hypothetical* development of two regions—both of which, initially, are assumed to be sparsely populated. The two areas are assumed to develop simultaneously within a given and constant state of technology and to draw their immigrants and capital from some common, populated region where all the inputs and outputs are represented.[2] The socio-political environment of this more populated region is assumed to be conducive to the development of the two sparsely populated regions.

Each region's economy is assumed to be small enough in its early stages of development to have no effect on the given hierarchy of factor

[1] W. W. Leontief, *The Structure of the American Economy*, 1919–1939, New York, 1951. Also W. W. Leontief and others, *Studies in the Structure of the American Economy*, New York, 1953.

[2] The effects of improvements in technological knowledge will be discussed later. In a general sense, the exploitation of these new regions may be considered a technological change.

and commodity prices prevailing in the more developed, third region.[3] Furthermore, the two regions are equi-distant from the older area and this distance is sufficiently great to make the costs of labor migration fairly substantial. It also is assumed that the economic development of each of the two sparsely populated regions begins in the export sector with the production of a primary commodity.

The differences between the two regions concern their natural resource conditions. One of the regions is assumed to possess a soil and climate highly suitable for the initial cultivation of a plantation crop in contrast to the other area which is assumed to enjoy conditions most conducive to the initial production of a non-plantation type commodity such as wheat. However, in both regions there is assumed to be an abundant supply of mineral resources such as coal, iron-ore, ferro-alloys, oil, etc. These are not exploited immediately since, initially, they are at a prohibitive distance from the export ports.

The purpose of most of these assumptions is to minimize differences among the many other factors which can cause dissimilarities between the two regions in their patterns of development. The development model to be analyzed can easily be compared with the differential growth patterns which might result by varying these initial assumptions. Some of the consequences of such other assumptions will be examined later. However, it seems that even with a wide range of possible initial conditions facing newly settled areas the effects of production function differences still emerge as an important (and neglected) determinant of development patterns.

Given the above conditions, the contention here will be that the extent to which the export sector induces the subsequent development of other sectors in the two economies depends to an important degree upon the technological nature of the production function of the export commodity (assuming there is only one major export item in each new region). For, given the price of the export commodity and the array of factor prices in the third region, this function will greatly affect subsequent development by initially influencing the nature of the labor and capital supply which flows into each region and the distribution of each economy's national income. It is from this framework that some of the many other important factors which determine the pattern of development will be introduced into the analysis.

Assume that the following conditions exist in one of the two regions. Factor and commodity prices in the populated area and the climate and soil of the new region indicate that the most profitable opportunity for initial development is the production of a plantation type commodity. Assume the production function for this particular commodity is such that for a wide range of labor/capital price ratios the most efficient

[3] The labor supply is divided into a number of imperfectly competing groups.

organization for any level of production is on a relatively labor intensive basis.[4,5] In other words, efficient production of a dollar's worth of the commodity technologically tends to require a relatively large number of laborers to perform comparatively simple tasks. Beyond a certain proportion of capital to labor, the amount of capital which must be substituted for a given decrease in labor in order to maintain a given level of output is relatively large. Furthermore, there are significant increasing returns to scale in the cultivation and processing of the commodity. Consequently, comparatively large amounts of both capital and labor are necessary for the most efficient size of the production unit. A high level of managerial and technical skill also is needed to direct large plantations effectively.

Small, family-size farms are attractive for the very low income groups in the older region, but the independent entrance of these groups is prevented by the cost of migration and the initial capital outlay on even this type of small productive unit. Nor are these people able to borrow the funds in the capital market, since severe capital rationing tends to operate against these very low income groups.

Those establishing productive units migrate from middle and higher income groups of the developed region and either possess the necessary funds for migration or are able to borrow them in the capital market. In order to produce the commodity at the lowest possible costs, these entrepreneurs in turn create a demand in the older region for the labor of very low income groups (who are assumed to possess the requisite skill to perform the comparatively simple tasks involved in production or can be trained easily to perform them). Plantation owners or their agents seek out these low wage groups and finance their migration. And they protect this investment by attempting to tie the workers to the plantations for a certain number of years.

In the second sparsely populated region assume the following conditions hold. Prices in the older area and the environment of the new region favor the development of a nonplantation agricultural commodity. The production function for this commodity differs from the plantation commodity in two respects. First, a family-size farm gives an efficient scale of production. In particular, large scale production based on the intensive use of cheap, imported labor is not the best form of economic organization. Furthermore, the absolute amount of capital required is

---

[4] Since information concerning the variability of capital coefficients among agricultural commodities is meager, it will be assumed that optimal capital requirements per dollar of output are about the same for the two types of agricultural commodities discussed here.

[5] For a general survey of the methods of production for a few plantation type products, see V. D. Wickizer, *Coffee, Tea and Cocoa*, 1951; A. Pim, *Colonial Agricultural Production*, London, 1946; P. T. Bauer, *The Rubber Industry*, 1948; and C. R. Fay, "The Plantation Economy," *Economic Journal*, 1936.

less for the optimum size of a production unit, and the level of managerial and technical skill need not be so high for a productive unit of the most efficient size. Secondly, the technological possibilities of capital intensification on the family-size farm are much greater. Varying the labor/capital price ratios over a wide range causes much more factor substitution in producing a given level of output than with the plantation crop.

As in the previous case, the very low income groups in the older region tend to be prevented from independent migration because of the costs of migration and the difficulty of borrowing funds. The level of knowledge and skill required for establishing a farm also rules out the migration of many from this labor group. Because of the assumed distance conditions, financing the movement of this type of labor is relatively costly. This fact and the wide range of alternative factor combinations prevent any extensive importation of cheap, unskilled labor by small-scale cultivators. Consequently, migrants flow from the income groups which can provide the necessary initial outlays on transportation and production. However, capital rationing also works against the latter group to some extent. The smaller scale of operations hampers the supervision of direct lending. Consequently, direct inter-regional lending is not as significant as in the plantation economy.

The agricultural development in both regions stimulates a simultaneous development of some supporting industries—such as transportation—which are directly linked with exporting the agricultural commodity.[6] The large amount of capital necessary for even a minimum amount of this type of social capital is supplied comparatively readily by foreign investors. Not only are these industries directly tied to the exchange-earning export industry and, consequently, are particularly attractive to foreign investors, but also they are organized on a large enough scale to take advantage of the established capital markets in the developed region.

III

However, the obstacles to the vigorous expansion of the plantation economy into a developed, higher per capita income economy are much greater than with the non-plantation economy. The relevant factors for an analysis of the development potential of the two regions from the stage already discussed can be grouped into demand and supply forces. First, in order to introduce domestic production of commodities for which an export advantage does not exist, there must be the basis of an internal demand for such products. And, secondly, given the demand, the natural resource situation and the supply of capital and labor must be adequate enough to meet foreign competition.

[6] See Nurkse, R., "The Problem of International Investment Today in the Light of Nineteenth-Century Experience," *The Economic Journal*, December, 1954.

For both regions the composition of the family budget is assumed to depend upon the level of income.[7] At very low levels, the budget consists almost entirely of a few basic foodstuffs, clothing, household needs and shelter. As incomes rise, the food budget is diversified and, eventually, a smaller proportion of the budget consists of foodstuffs. Durable consumer good expenditures and savings increase in relative importance.

In the plantation economy at this initial stage a large part of the population is in the very low income brackets. Consequently, most of this group's effective demand consists of a few basic foods, simple clothing and other consumer durables, and minimum shelter needs. While production of the plantation crop requires large quantities of labor, this labor is not needed throughout the entire year. Consequently, workers lease small plots of land from the plantation owners (who also usually provide the capital) and supplement their income by growing part of their food requirements. During the idle period, the choice to a laborer of working more on the plantation and less for himself does not exist. The alternative essentially is between leisure and working for himself. And since his plantation income is very low, his marginal utility for commodities is relatively high. Therefore, he is willing to devote much of his free time to growing part of his own food in a very socially inefficient manner. He drives his marginal productivity in this line down to nearly zero. The same phenomenon tends to take place with respect to part of his clothing, shelter, and durable consumption goods needs. The family unit produces many of these items.[8]

Why do not the plantation workers break away from the plantation, produce the crop themselves, and raise their income level appreciably above the plantation wage? Some do break away. However, most of these unskilled, low income workers cannot save or borrow enough to start anything but a very small, low income yielding unit of production.

In attempting to expand from such small units, the cultivators are hampered by the technical constraints of the crop's production function. They must secure more labor, land, and capital, i.e. expand horizontally, for efficient production. But this is very difficult. First, the initial income level on these farms is so low that their saving is almost insignificant. Nor are they able to borrow sufficient funds for a large scale unit. Secondly, it is difficult for this group to enlarge gradually its holdings of

[7] K. Mandelbaum in *The Industrialization of Backward Areas*, Oxford University, Institute of Statistics, Monograph No. 2, Oxford, 1947, utilizes a budget approach in estimating the flow of demand in his hypothetical model of development for south-eastern Europe. He also employs capital, labor, and commodity coefficients in computing the supply requirements for his program. Because of a lack of data, this procedure so far has been only used in a rough fashion for the formulation of actual development plans in the backward countries.

[8] For a general discussion of some of the production and labor conditions in such backward areas, see Greaves, I. C., *Modern Production among Backward Peoples*, London, 1935, and Moore, W. E., *Industrialization and Labor*, Ithaca, 1951.

good land. The fertile land is cultivated by the plantation method and its owners are reluctant to sell or lease parcels of it. Large tracts must be taken at one time. But the small farmers cannot overcome this discontinuity. The best they can do is obtain isolated parcels of good land or more contiguous but relatively poor land. However, expanded production on this type of land is not very efficient. Thirdly, the level of knowledge and skill of these people is so low that they are not capable of supervising and controlling the greater amount of capital and labor necessary for increased production. The supervision of the labor is particularly important. It is probably more difficult to direct the greater amount of non-family labor than the increased quantity of capital. Finally, the plantation class tends to develop a social antipathy towards this very low income group. It does not want the group to move into the plantation class and erects social and economic barriers in the path of the group's expansion.

All of these factors tend to prevent this group from increasing the size of its farms and thus its income level. And, because production of the crop does not require the same amount of labor throughout the entire year, these small farm families (like the plantation workers) also grow part of the food they consume (or even a market supply) and produce many of the durable consumer goods they consume. Disguised unemployment tends to arise within this sector of the economy.

Small scale planters who employ some non-family labor are another important group in the economy. These individuals either break through the exclusively family-labor type of farming or initially possess sufficient funds to establish a small plantation. They resemble somewhat the middle income migrants in the other region. However, these planters face more difficulties in reaching the optimum productive unit. In the first place, they must accumulate much more capital to attain this level. And, as in the non-plantation area, the capital rationing barrier forces the planters to rely on current saving for most of their investment funds. Furthermore, given funds equivalent to the requirements for the smaller optimum size farm in the other region, a small scale planter will not earn as high an income as his counterpart in the other region. The production unit is too small. Even if organized as efficiently as possible, he cannot use his managerial skill to full advantage. Merely directing production does not require his full time nor yield a very high income. Yet the only alternative to leisure is to perform the low productivity tasks of the hired help. Consequently, because of their low income level, these planters cannot expand their productive units as rapidly as the farmers of the non-plantation region. In addition, most of these small planters do not possess the high degree of managerial ability and technical skill required to expand the scale of operations in an optimum manner. Consequently, they tend to keep the amount of labor and land employed about the same and reinvest their savings in capital improvements which do little in lifting their level of income, because of the nature of the crop's production function.

A reasonably stable hierarchy of export producers emerges within the economy. At one end stand the plantations employing large quantities of low wage labor. The other end of the scale is composed of many small, family cultivators who operate under a tenure system or perhaps own their land. The income level of these farmers is not much higher than the plantation wage, and the possibilities for expansion by these producers is not favourable. The small scale planter who combines family and hired labor lies between these two groups. While incomes among these planters are higher than the very small farmers, they are below the level achieved with a similar investment in the non-plantation economy.

Perhaps 70 per cent of the economy's income is spent on foodstuffs.[9] The remainder is devoted to services, consumer durables (of which expenditures on items other than simple clothing and household articles are a small percentage), and saving. The effective market demand for the higher class of consumer goods and services stems largely from the middle and high income groups, who are composed of large plantation owners, those performing the marketing services associated with the export item, and to some extent the small planters. A large number of these commodities are imported from the more developed region.

Why do not efficient domestic industries quickly develop and capture both the import markets and the domestic markets which are supplied in a socially inefficient manner?

Consider the opportunities in the fields of simple, mass consumed durables and luxury durables—many of which are imported. A major obstacle confronting prospective domestic manufacturers is the problem of training the labor force to the factory system. The large, low income labor supply possess such a low level of education and skill that its costs of training represent a large, initial outlay. While there is always the alternative of recruiting skilled foreign labor, this too is expensive. At this early stage of development, the region cannot rely to any significant extent upon the voluntary migration of suitable labor. This labor migrates at its own expense only after the industrial sector has begun to expand vigorously and employment opportunities become well known. In addition, although the marginal productivity of the low income farm labor may be near zero, it is necessary to offer them a higher figure in order to induce them to move into urban factories. Both of these factors make it difficult to capture the import market.

They are particularly forceful with respect to luxury imports. Many of these items require a very high degree of labor skill. Conspicuous con-

[9] T. W. Schultz, *The Economic Organization of Agriculture,* New York, 1953, Ch. 4.

sumption also applies to some of these goods, and considerable outlays on advertising are necessary to overcome a preference for foreign commodities. Still another important factor with respect to some of these consumer durables is the internal and external economies involved in their production. The domestic market is too small to take advantage of these economies.

Most of these obstacles also apply to those consumption items produced on a household scale. However, another obstacle confronting more efficient domestic industry is one which prevents the importation of these items, namely, the high costs of internal transportation and the lack of other marketing facilities. In this region, the bulk of the population in the hinterland is so poor that the construction of transportation facilities (other than the minimum necessary for the export crop) proceeds very slowly Governments cannot raise enough revenue from these people to build adequate facilities. The higher income groups are so spread out that they cannot support these facilities either. To obtain many of the commodities and services, which they desire, they travel to a few large cities where the marketing facilities for the export commodity are located. Outside of these central cities, few other trading cities spring up and, consequently, transportation facilities in the interior remain crude. Therefore, domestic manufacturers find it too expensive to tap the interior markets for mass consumption goods.

Two other factors on the supply side, which are relevant to this discussion, are the rate of saving and the supply of entrepreneurial labor. Because of the greater income inequality the proportion of saving to national income is likely to be higher in this region than in the nonplantation economy. However, a larger share of the saving flows back to the more developed area in the form of interest and dividend returns on foreign investments in the plantations and the auxiliary service industries. The foreign earnings which are retained tend to be employed for a further expansion of the export industry, since foreign investors prefer investments which are directly linked with the foreign exchange earning ability of the economy. Furthermore, foreign investments in industries producing for an internal demand are discouraged by the lack of an adequate market in addition to the other factors already enumerated. For the same reasons, large domestic savers also tend to employ their funds in the export and import trades or in such ventures as residential and business construction. But, because of the nature of the production function for the export crop, investment in this sector does little to improve the distribution of income; it merely enlarges the existing productive structure as more cheap labor is imported.[10] Nor does

[10] W. A. Lewis employs the assumption of an elastic labor supply in his interesting article, "Economic Development with Unlimited Supplies of Labour," *The Manchester School of Economic and Social Studies*, May, 1954.

the investment in elaborate homes, office buildings, shops, etc. do much in inducing a better pattern of growth. With respect to entrepreneurship, the most obvious source of leadership for manufacturing—the large plantation owners—provides a meager supply. This group, because of the unique non-pecuniary advantage of the plantation life, tends to develop a social antipathy towards occupations in the manufacturing field. And, the low income group possesses neither sufficient training nor the social and economic opportunities necessary to provide more than the occasionally successful entrepreneur.

All of these factors tend to restrain the economy from breaking out of its predominantly export-oriented nature.[11] As transportation facilities improve, the mineral resources are tapped, but this sector too becomes export-oriented. Domestic manufacturing industries based on these raw materials are blocked by the same obstacles previously mentioned. The only real possibility for exploiting the minerals is as raw material, export industries. And, because of the general lack of technological and entrepreneurial skill within the economy, many of the firms are owned and operated by foreigners. Although these industries may provide an important source of saving in the form of royalty payments and, depending on the quality of labor they require, may help to improve the distribution of income, these effects will not be as favourable for growth as those that would result if the internal market were large enough to induce related domestic manufacturing industries.

IV

When the development potential in the other region is analyzed, a more optimistic outlook appears. The nature of the export crop's production function is an important reason for this view. As already mentioned, labor and capital requirements for an optimum size farm in this region are much smaller than for the plantation type commodity. The family unit gives an efficient scale of operations. As in the other region, the very low income families in the older regions are excluded from independent emigration by the relatively high costs of the movement. However, unlike the plantation region, the more wealthy individuals do not finance their passage, since very unskilled labor cannot be employed

[11] See Mosk, S. A., "Latin America versus the United States," *The American Economic Review*, Papers and Proceedings, May, 1951, for a discussion of some of the development obstacles in this kind of economy; H. W. Singer, "The Distribution of Gains between Investing and Borrowing Countries," *The American Economic Review*, Papers and Proceedings, May, 1950. Also on the general topic of the effect of foreign trade on newly settled areas see H. Myint, "The Gains from International Trade and the Backward Countries," *The Review of Economic Studies*, No. 58, 1954–1955.

as effectively in this type of agriculture. Instead, most of the migrants come from the income groups which possess sufficient funds for migration. In this region there are relatively fewer individuals at both ends of the absolute income scale.

Unlike the plantation economy, as this region's export sector expands, the economy does not devote a large portion of its investment to securing and supporting a greater quantity of cheap, unskilled labor. Although many of the migrants to this region originally do not establish the most efficient size unit, the limitation is not so much labor, but rather the inability to secure sufficient capital. However, these migrants do not start, like those breaking away from the plantations, at such a low level of income that their saving is almost nothing.

In the early stages of development, these farmers also produce much of their food, clothing, shelter and simple durable consumer goods. But they are not blocked from optimum expansion as are most of the small planters and the family-size farmers in the other economy. Since the marginal productivity of labor and capital is higher in agriculture than in these activities, the farmers, by reinvesting their saving, increase the output of the cash commodity and curtail the family production of food and consumer durables. Moreover, as their income level increases, the family prefers to purchase more of its clothing, food, shelter, services, and other consumer durables in the open market.

The more equitable distribution of income, which arises as the economy develops its export production, is more favorable for the induced development of domestic industry. A smaller proportion of the national budget is devoted to food expenditure. And the production of this food is undertaken on efficient, family-size farms. Furthermore, there is a relatively larger market demand for services and durable consumer goods. Profit opportunities arise in these lines of commodities. Initially, some of these goods are imported, while others are not consumed at all because of the high costs of transportation. But gradually trading centers spring up to answer the demands for medical, legal and personal services as well as to provide the marketing facilities for the imported commodities. All of this means investments in homes, offices, warehouses, roads, schools, hospitals, etc., which have a multiplier effect on the volume of trade.[12] As this development occurs, the mineral resources begin to be exploited. However, instead of merely becoming exports, these resources are also used to supply domestic manufacturers. For, the more favorable distribution of income and thus the relatively large demand for durables stimulates domestic manufacturing. Because of the relatively larger market demand for such items and the higher level of skill of the agricultural population, the problem of recruiting foreign labor or training

[12] J. S. Duesenberry, "Some Aspects of the Theory of Economic Development," *Explorations in Entrepreneurial History*, Dec., 1950, pp. 96–102.

domestic workers for manufacturing activity also is not as difficult as in the plantation area.

All of these factors and their interaction tend to induce a faster and a more balanced type of development. This economy has a better chance of climbing from its initial export orientation. Domestic industries spring up which, in turn, stimulate the further expansion of other domestic or export industries through external economies and the familiar multiplier-accelerator interactions.

V

In order to emphasize the role which technological differences among production functions can play in the process of economic development, a number of restrictive assumptions were made in the preceding analysis. When these are lifted, the factors stressed in the traditional explanations of differential growth patterns re-emerge to a more prominent position.

First, there is the matter of the production functions themselves. In the above discussion, it was assumed that the production functions in the export industries of the two regions were such as to impose rigid constraints on the nature of the development process. While I believe this factor is and has been an important element in shaping actual development in several regions, this is not to say that it always plays an important role in the development process. For example, the production functions of some crops may be such that both plantation and small scale production are equally efficient. And, there may be wide possibilities of factor substitution with relatively slight changes in the factor price ratios. In these cases the engineering constraints of the production function will not be important in determining the character of development. It was also assumed that each region drew its productive means from a common equi-distant, purely competitive market. But obviously, if the array of factor and product prices differs in the older regions which initiate development in the two new regions and the distances to these new regions vary, the patterns of development will be affected accordingly. Differences among the factor supplying regions in the state of their technological knowledge, in their entrepreneurial spirit, in their tastes and in their social, economic and political ideas and institutions generally also will play an important role in determining the nature of development within the two regions. And, of course, the dissimilarities between the new regions with respect to their natural resource conditions are highly relevant. The effects on the preceding analysis which regional differences in the above factors can cause are fairly obvious.

Another condition which has been maintained in this discussion is the assumption of an unchanged state of technology. Probably, most of the technological knowledge actually introduced over the last 200 years has been of two types: (1) those changes which required more capital and less labor (or other resources) per unit of output than previously; and (2) those changes which required less of all factors.[13] How do these types of technological progress affect economic development?

Clearly, the development problem cannot be dismissed with the assertion that technological progress will guarantee successively higher levels of *per capita* income in an automatic fashion. Three major factors should be considered in analyzing the problem: demand, the supply of capital, and the nature and growth of the population. The first factor, demand, is extremely important for those agricultural exporting nations which are so large that changes in their output affect international prices. Price and income elasticities for many agricultural products are low in the higher *per capita*, agricultural importing regions. Consequently, part of the possible real income benefits of technological progress may be lost through an adverse movement in the terms of trade. Secondly, in order to achieve the maximum growth allowed by technological progress, the requisite capital must be forthcoming. But there is no reason to assume that the saving propensities of the public and business will adjust automatically to take advantage of the new technique. In low *per capita* countries this can be an especially serious problem. Rather similar barriers with respect to the nature of the labor supply also can prevent maximum growth. Shortages of particular kinds of labor and/or general lack of entrepreneurial ability are examples of this type of bottleneck. Finally, the growth of population in relation to the increase in income will determine what happens to *per capita* income.

But, of course, technological progress does operate in the direction of encouraging a more rapid rate of increase in national income. This is especially so if the progress in technological knowledge is such that less of all factors of production are required per unit of output. However, to the extent that technological progress is such that the relative position of each commodity in the scale of labor and capital coefficients remains roughly the same, technological progress can be handled in the model by interpreting much of the development behaviour of the two regions in relative rather than absolute terms. But a radical shift in the relative position of a commodity in the labor and capital coefficient hierarchy must be treated as an autonomous change, and the analysis must be modified to take into account this new engineering relationship.

Even with the many special assumptions in this analysis, differences in the technological nature of production functions still, I think, emerge as an important factor determining actual patterns of economic development. Briefly, the argument is that the technological nature of the pro-

[13] See Grosse, R. and Duesenberry, J., "Technological Change and Dynamic Models," Prepared for the Input-Output Meeting of Conference on Research in Income and Wealth, Oct., 1952.

duction function for the major commodities initially selected for commercial production influences the potentialities for further development in newly settled regions. In conjunction with market conditions in the more developed areas, these engineering constraints affect the nature of factor migration and the early distribution of income within a region. The latter factors, in turn, affect the stimuli for further economic development. While much more empirical and historical investigation is necessary to determine the extent of the technological restraints of various production functions, these differences can, I think, prove useful in contrasting actual historical development of some plantation-type economies in the world with those regions which at an early stage specialized on such commodities as livestock and grains. Furthermore, they must be carefully considered in the formulation of plans for future development.

16. The Collective Farm System in Russia: Some Aspects of Its Contribution to Soviet Economic Development*

ARCADIUS KAHAN

INTRODUCTION

The Soviet economic organization is marked by its ability to direct economic activity toward economic growth. The preoccupation with problems of economic development and growth in Russia antedates the Soviet period. Even during the Czarist period, since the 1870s, most of the industrial and mercantile interests assumed a favorable attitude toward accelerated economic development which they considered as a means to eliminate a major cause of political and cultural backwardness.

During the Soviet period the attitudes toward economic growth have been shaped by Marxian economic doctrine and by the political objectives of the state. The ability of the Soviet economic organization to produce economic growth was greatly enhanced by the priorities assigned to such goals by the dictatorial political regime. The full weight of the political regime was called upon to impose general compliance with the economic objectives and demands as defined by the policy makers. In the process of adjusting Soviet society to the goals of the regime, a

* An original contribution. The author is associate professor of economics at the University of Chicago.

multiplicity of institutions was established and various organizational forms were devised to facilitate the attainment of the economic objectives. The adoption and subsequent modifications of the organizational framework of Soviet agriculture can, in part, be explained by the policy makers' design to make agriculture provide the maximum contribution to the forced pace of industrialization.

The purpose of the following discussions is to analyze the contribution of the collective farm system, the prevailing form of Soviet agriculture for over thirty years, to the overall economic growth of the Soviet Union.

SOCIALIZATION OF AGRICULTURE

The organizational framework for Soviet agriculture is in part predetermined by the decisions to nationalize land and socialize most capital assets in agriculture. Nationalization of land took place in 1917 and the socialization process was started on a mass scale in 1929 and 1930. The rationale for socialization of agriculture ought to be sought in the Soviet leaders' political and economic analysis of the performance of peasant agriculture. Among the multitude of arguments in favor of socialized agriculture were (1) achieving economies of scale by amalgamation of small fields and use of agricultural machinery, (2) changing the terms of trade between the state and the agricultural producers without impairing the agricultural output or its product-mix, and (3) attaining more effective political control over the peasantry, to prevent the "breeding of capitalism."

By 1935 the socialization process in Soviet agriculture was completed except for the territories which were later incorporated into the Soviet Union and went through this process during the years 1945 to 1950.

In 1962 about 97 per cent of the arable land is cultivated by the socialized agricultural enterprises and only about 3 per cent is tilled privately. Moreover the socialized sector possesses all the farm machinery and most of the livestock. In terms of relative shares of agricultural output, the socialized sector accounts for an estimated 70 per cent of the total production and about 83 per cent of the marketed production. Therefore, any discussion of the problems of Soviet agriculture involves primarily those pertaining to the socialized sector.

Within the socialized sector we encounter two types of farm organization, the collective and the state farms. While the collective farms were originally based upon the general principle of cooperative use of resources of a particular unit (village or group of villages) by applying different degrees of socialization, the state farms were from their inception organized and managed according to the model of industrial state enterprises. The typical features of the state farm organization were the large size of the farms, an appointed management subordinated to central authorities, the employment of hired labor, and the extensive use of farm machinery. The state farms were considered a "superior" socio-economic form of farm organization because of the principle of hired labor (which provided for the classification of the employees as workers). They were considered economically more advanced because of a higher capital-labor ratio than in the collective farms.

State farms have existed in the Soviet Union since 1918, but for most of the period until about 1954 their share in total agricultural output was less than 10 per cent. The share of the state farms in total agricultural output began to rise only after 1954, in connection with the expansion of the sown area in the "new lands" of Siberia and Kazakhstan. This tendency was strengthened by the conversion of a substantial number of collective farms into state farms. By 1962 the state farms produce about a fifth of the total output and this share will probably increase in the future. However, for the purposes of our analysis, the past experience of the collective farms and their contribution to economic growth are more significant, since the rise of the state farms was to a large extent a consequence of an advanced stage of the general economic development of the Soviet Union.

THE COLLECTIVE FARM SYSTEM: 1928–1953

The particular characteristics of the collective farm system that made it fit into the Soviet pattern of economic growth were:

1. Collective farms were defined as cooperative associations, set up on government land given to the farms on indefinite tenure. They were obligated to deliver a major part of their produce to the state at prices fixed by the government.

2. The goal of collective farms was to maximize agricultural output. Special emphasis was put upon the maximization of a particular product-mix of the marketed output.

3. The distribution of the collective farm output, as outlined in the collective farm charter, conformed to a set of general priorities. In descending order, these were

   a. Deliveries of the share of output claimed by the state
   b. Payment of direct taxes to the state
   c. Reimbursement of the production costs of output
   d. Distribution of the residual (which constituted the wage fund) among the members according to their labor contribution to production.

4. The members of the collective or "agricultural cooperative" were obligated to render labor services for which they were paid in two forms:

   a. By the assignment of a small plot of land, primarily a truck crop garden, and *b.* By an unspecified volume of products in kind and an unspecified money payment out of the total wage fund, reflecting the worker's relative share in total labor expenditures.

5. The major decisions of the collective farms were subordinated to the administrative direction of state authorities and the execution of the directives was subjected to state control.

6. The state constantly interfered in the internal affairs of the farms in order to assure compliance with the general and particular policy objectives.

Any analysis of the collective farm system must also consider the motivation of collective farm members. The collective farm system by itself is mostly "neutral" with regard to incentive policies. The freedom to apply incentives whenever they considered it necessary was reserved for the state policy makers acting as an arbiter between the farms and the farmers. Thus they were, at times and at their own discretion, able to counteract the system's failure to establish a relationship between increased labor efforts of the members and the rewards for such increased efforts. The original assumption of the policy makers was that lack of alternative income opportunities for the collective farm members was a satisfactory substitute for an incentive system. However, the government soon found itself compelled to make exceptions to this rule and selectively apply incentive methods to facilitate the achievement of the general economic objectives of the state.

Factor contributions, the case of labor. It is convenient, following Kuznets' distinction, to classify the contributions of agriculture to economic growth into "factor contributions" and "product and market contributions."[1] "Factor" contribution to economic growth rather than "product" contribution was typical for the first period (1928–1953) in the history of Soviet socialized agriculture. A program of rapid industrialization usually requires a large increase in the nonagricultural labor force. The demand for labor can be met either by utilizing potential urban labor resources (often used up quickly) or by drawing upon a part of the labor force previously employed in agriculture.[2] The socialization of agriculture and the accompanying loss of land property rights accelerated the separation of the existing industrial labor force from agricultural pursuits. It effectively cut off the remaining ties between the industrial laborers and an agricultural milieu from which they were not far removed psychologically, culturally and socially. Since the collectivization of agriculture in the Soviet Union was accompanied by mass deportation of a whole rural stratum, the "kulaks" (an arbitrary classification

---

[1] Simon Kuznets, "Economic Growth and the Contribution of Agriculture: Notes on Measurement," in *International Journal of Agrarian Affairs*, vol. 3, no. 2, April, 1961. [EDITOR'S NOTE: See Selection 5.]

[2] In some countries, e.g., the United States, immigration has provided an addition to the domestic supply.

of well-to-do peasants), both their labor and that of their hired farm workers automatically became available for nonagricultural employment, although some of the farm laborers joined the collective farms.[3]

In Czarist times, much of Russia's agricultural labor force sought seasonal employment in construction, transportation, forestry, road and railroad construction, and even in mining and manufacturing. This seasonal employment outside agriculture supplemented the incomes of millions of peasants. The phenomenon of seasonal employment to the extent of a yearly average of 3.1 million for the years 1924 to 1926 existed also under Soviet rule.[4]

Collectivization of agriculture made possible a more organized form of rural labor recruitment for industry. The state authorities established the so-called "organized recruitment" (Organizovannyi Nabor) among private peasants and collective farms which in turn designated certain members to work off the farms for various time periods. The available data for the "organized recruitment" drives are the following:

TABLE 1. "ORGANIZED RECRUITMENT" DRIVES, 1931–1940

Year	Number recruited (in thousands)
1931*	5,454
1932*	3,642
1933	1,887
1934	3,247
1935	3,124
1936	3,104
1937	1,570
1938	2,011
1939	2,315
1940	2,373
1931–1940	28,727

* Includes all types of peasant seasonal employment outside of agriculture.
SOURCE: M. Ia. Sonin, *Vosproizvodstvo Rabochei Sily v SSSR i Balans Truda*, Moscow, 1959, pp. 182–83.

Since the average time period for collective farm workers performing seasonal industrial work increased from about four to five months in 1924 to five to six months during the years 1933 to 1935 to about eight to nine months in 1940,[5] the above data do not indicate a declining trend for this kind of work when the numbers are multiplied by the average duration of empolyment. Other available evidence suggests that the de-

[3] There are no direct reliable data for the number of exiled kulaks, although some private estimates for the exiled kulak population run in the millions.
[4] L. E. Mints (ed.), *Otkhod Sel'skogo Naseleniia na Zarabotki v SSSR*, Moscow, 1929, p. 11.
[5] *Ibid.*, p. 185. The average for unskilled laborers was 5.9 months in 1926 and 1927. See Akademiia Nauk SSSR, Institut Istorii: *Izmeneniia v Chislennosti Sovetskogo Rabochego Klassa*, Moscow, 1961, p. 146.

mand for this type of labor was declining. This can be explained by the decrease in demand for unskilled labor in general, the increase in labor recruitment through the vocational schools[6] and the rising demand for permanent rather than seasonal labor in industry. As a result of these factors the organized recruitment system was transformed into a system of recruitment for *permanent* nonagricultural employment during the post-World War II period. Collective farm workers employed off the farm decreased from about a half-million annually during the early 1950s to about 200,000 by the end of the 1950s.[7]

Interindustry mobility of labor. The collective farm organization combined with the state administrative system tried to match the flow of labor from agriculture with the demand in the nonagricultural labor market. Given the existing urban-rural income differential and the objective conditions for increased mobility (as a result of abolishing private land property rights), one would expect the supply of agricultural labor either to exceed the demand or to fluctuate with changes in agricultural income. In order to avoid such possibilities the Soviet government introduced a number of administrative measures. Collective farmers and private peasant farmers were deprived of the right to move freely. Their mobility was dependent both upon (1) permission to leave issued by the farms and local village councils and (2) the requisitions of industrial establishments and urban authorities. The system of contracts between the organized recruitment setup and the collective farms also made the release of labor less dependent upon the changes in the peasants' incomes.[8]

The increase in nonagricultural employment can be reconstructed both from the available employment data and from the data on population transfer from rural to urban areas. The annual average of employed wage and salary earners outside of agriculture grew very rapidly from 9.9 million in 1928 to 20.1 million in 1932, to 35.5 million in 1950 and 58 million in 1961.[9] The same trend is apparent when we examine the data reflecting the transfer of the rural population to the urban areas. During the years 1926 to 1939, 18.7 million people transferred from rural to urban areas and between 1939 and 1959 another 24.6 million transferred, for a total of 43.3 million against a net increase of the urban population of 73 million during the years 1926 to 1959.[10] As a result of the decline of

---

[6] See Arcadius Kahan, "The Economics of Vocational Training in the USSR," *Comparative Education Review*, vol. 4, no. 2, pp. 75–83, October, 1961.

[7] Sonin, *op. cit.*, pp. 186 and 207.

[8] The collective farm output distribution system under fluctuating output levels had a leveling income effect of its own.

[9] TsUNKhU SSSR, *Socialist Construction in the USSR*, Moscow, 1936, pp. 354–355. TsSU SSSR, *Narodnoe Khoziaistvo SSSR v 1961 godu*, Moscow, 1962, p. 567.

[10] Sonin, *op. cit.*, pp. 144–146, and TsSU SSSR, *Narodnoe Khoziaistvo SSSR v 1960 godu*, Moscow, 1961, pp. 9, 24, and 26.

the birthrate in the rural areas (peasants' households decreased in size from 5.84 in 1917 to 4.42 in 1939) the natural population increase of the rural areas was absorbed by the transfer to the urban centers.

A more detailed analysis of the data on migration and occupational change of rural and agricultural labor reveals some interesting features. For example, the paths from agricultural to industrial occupations lead very often through employment in forestry, peat-production, and (primarily) urban construction. These occupations could be considered transitional for later permanent industrial employment and urban living for the rural migrants. Although the majority of migrants from rural areas possessed no industrial skills and little education,[11] the development of the training program of the so-called "mechanizers" in agriculture facilitated their adjustment. In their attempt to substitute mechanical power for animal power in agriculture (in order to raise the productivity of labor and to save the grain fed to horses for human consumption), the Soviet authorities started to train tractor drivers, combine harvester operators, and truck drivers in the socialized sector of agriculture. According to incomplete data,[12] about 3,191,000 trainees acquired these skills during 1930–1939. However, at the end of the period, less than a million of these trained people were employed in agriculture. The following table shows that the majority of trainees used their newly acquired mechanical skills as a means of eligibility for industrial employment.

TABLE 2. TRACTOR DRIVERS, 1932–1939
(*In Thousands*)

Year	No. at beginning of year	Trained during the year	II + III at end of year	Actual no. at end of year	Probable transfer to industry
1932	107	227	334	171	163
1933	171	261	432	235	197
1934	235	248	483	364	119
1935	364	281	645	493	152
1936	492	368	860	589	271
1937	589	343	932	685	247
1938	685	268	953	690	263
1939	690	268	958	695	263

SOURCE: Iu. V. Arutunian, *Mekhanizatory Sel'skogo Khoziaistva SSSR v 1929–1957 gg.*, Moscow, 1960, p. 46.

[11] The average number of years of education per worker in industry in 1932 was smaller than in 1928 as a result of the influx of rural migrants into the urban labor force.

[12] See Iu. V. Arutunian, *Mekhanizatory Sel'skogo Khoziaistva SSSR v 1929–1957 gg*, Moscow, 1960, p. 46; A. Kahan, "The Economics of Vocational Training in the USSR," *Comparative Education Review*, vol. 4, no. 2, p. 76, October, 1961.

One aspect of Soviet mechanization of agriculture was utilized to expedite the labor transfer from agriculture. Planned mechanization of the various phases of agricultural work in the Soviet Union was biased in favor of plowing and grain harvesting. This left a number of labor-intensive tasks in industrial crops and in livestock production untouched for a very long period. It would appear that the bias was in the direction of freeing as many prime male field hands as possible. The concentration of machinery in grain production had as its goal a substantial decrease in the peak seasonal agricultural employment and the freeing of male labor. This was consistent with the preferences of industry for a particular sex and age distribution of the entrants into the labor force.

Labor contribution to social overhead construction. In terms of the contribution of agricultural labor to the economic growth of the country, the collective farm system served as a convenient organizational framework. The utilization of agricultural labor for the social overhead construction was a typical feature of the Soviet scene. The collective farm system facilitated the concentration of the labor effort of large masses not only on projects serving agriculture,[13] but also on road construction, and road and railroad maintenance. The statutory obligation of each peasant to render six days of work per year for road construction was synchronized by the collective farms and state authorities. Collective farms supplied some of the equipment and thereby effected a substantial contribution to the social overhead construction. The average yearly contribution of labor was equal to about one million yearly workers; the fact that this labor was rendered without compensation was an important feature. During the postwar period, additional contributions to the social overhead were required of the collective farms. The claim that such contributions as the construction of schools, kindergartens, and day nurseries were made for the benefit of the rural population does not change the nature of the contributions. That is, the contributions were charged against the incomes of the collective farms and executed primarily by collective farm labor. This type of contribution is likely to increase in the future in order to counterbalance the increasing gross income of the collective farms.

PRODUCT CONTRIBUTION

Analysis of the contribution of agriculture to economic growth should include a discussion of the Soviet ability to provide food for the growing nonagricultural labor force and urban population. In a sense, it can

[13] For the digging of the Fergana irrigation canal 165,000 collective farm members of the Uzbek and Tadzhik republics were mobilized. Tens of thousands were mobilized for the construction of the Uralo-Kushumskii canal in Kazakhstan, for the Samur-Divichinskii canal in Azerbaijan, etc.

be treated as an import substitution problem. But on its own merits it may be treated as a problem of adjusting agriculture to rapid industrialization and to the ability either to produce a higher agricultural output or to increase the share of its marketable output.

From the previously mentioned characteristics of the collective farm system it follows that it was well designed for the collection of the marketable surplus. The collection of the marketable output was facilitated by *two features* of the collective farms:

1. The collection was (in the normative sense) made independent of the "terms of trade" between the industrial and agricultural sectors.[14] Since the collective farms had to accept the size and prices of the marketed output set by the state, any "terms of trade" problem between the agricultural producers and the state could be resolved by the government unilaterally.

2. The collective farm organization enabled the size of delivery quotas to be determined independently of the size of output. As a result, the fluctuations in the level of output, containing an independently determined marketable component, had a destabilizing effect upon the collective farmers' home consumption. This effect can be illustrated by the official data in the following table pertaining to the distribution of the total grain output of the collective farms during the years 1937 to 1939. It shows that the state deliveries as a percentage of net output increased from 41 per cent in 1937 to 57 per cent in 1939.

TABLE 3. DISTRIBUTION OF THE COLLECTIVE FARM GRAIN CROP, 1937–1939
(*In Percentages and in Million Tons*)

Item	1937	1938	1939
Total output (in million tons)....................	87.02	67.09	67.35
Deliveries to the state (in million tons)............	25.1	22.7	24.4
Deliveries to the state (in % of total output).......	28.8	33.9	36.2
Distributed for labor services (in million tons)......	32.2	18.6	16.0
Distributed for labor services (in % of total).......	37.0	27.7	23.7
State deliveries as % of net output*..............	41.4	51.5	56.8
Distribution to farmers as % of net output.........	53.2	42.1	37.2

* Net output assumed equal to gross output minus seed and feed.
SOURCE: *Istoriai SSSR*, no. 1, 1962, pp. 43 and 46.

Although the collection of the marketable output was *technically* simplified through collective farms in comparison with procurement from a multitude of small peasant producers, and only involved the

[14] During the precollectivization period the Soviet government had a disappointing experience whenever it had tried to impose terms of trade unfavorable to agriculture. The agricultural producers, in most cases, limited the agricultural marketable output in order to raise agricultural prices.

transfer of agricultural commodities from the collective farm granaries to the state warehouses and elevators (under the administration of the procurement authorities), the growth of the marketable output was far behind the growth of the urban population. As a result, during the 1930s the urban per capita consumption of most food products was below the level of the late 1920s. The data in Table 4 illustrate the decline in the urban per capita consumption of meat, milk and milk products, and eggs, over the 1927–1937 period.

TABLE 4. URBAN PER CAPITA CONSUMPTION OF SELECTED FOOD PRODUCTS
(In Kilograms)

Product	Actual 1927–1928	Actual 1937
Meat......................	49.1	21.0
Milk and milk products.......	218.0	132.0
Eggs......................	90.7	44.1

SOURCE: Gosplan SSSR, Piatiletnii Plan Razvitiia Narodnogo Khoziaistva, for 1927–1928; Naum Jasny, Soviet Industrialization 1928–1952, University of Chicago Press, Chicago, 1961, p. 163.

Per capita consumption was below the 1927–1928 level not only in urban areas but also in rural areas.[15] Simultaneous decreases in the consumption level of the urban and rural population preserved the differential between nonagricultural and agricultural incomes and stimulated the transfer of labor resources into the growing industrial sector. It is likely, however, that the level of consumption (inclusive of manufactured consumer goods) of the newly recruited industrial workers from the rural areas was in fact not lower than their previous consumption level in the villages. The decrease in consumption levels which reflected the overall decrease of the levels of real income was imposed by the political regime and provided some very important sources for capital formation.

The contention that the food supply was insufficient to meet the demand of urban consumers during most of the post-1928 period could be surmised not only from the data pertaining to the size of marketable output but also from the fact that the government encouraged private agricultural production of urban dwellers at various times. In fact, the urban dwellers and nonagricultural labor force supplemented their food diet from their own food output.[16] Soviet economists have argued that

[15] The 1937 urban per capita consumption was as follows: meat, 21.0 kg; milk, 132 kg; and 44.1 eggs vs. the 1927–1928 rural per capita consumption of: meat, 22.6 kg; milk, 183 kg; and 49.6 eggs.

[16] In 1954, the urban population consumed about 4.5 million tons of potatoes and vegetables and 2.2 million tons of milk from its own production. The per capita consumption out of their own production in 1954 was reported as 44 kg of potatoes, 11 kg of vegetables, 27 liters of milk, and 5 kg of meat (except poultry). See Sovetskaia Torgovlia, no. 6, p. 11, 1956.

it was efficient to force the urban people to raise vegetables, pigs, chickens, etc., in their gardens because this additional output was secured by using the type of labor that did not have alternative employment opportunities.[17] Indications that this situation may be changing became apparent during the late 1950s, but since the income derived from such activity might still exceed the wages of unskilled labor, the policy of liquidating the urban "kitchen gardens" might encounter a resistance that could disappear only with increased supply of food and/or decrease of the relevant food prices. As of 1962, and for the livestock products for which long-term data are available, the 1927–1928 level of urban per capita consumption was regained for only one product —milk. However, it would be fallacious to evaluate the success or failure of the collective farm system solely by its ability to provide livestock products or vegetables for urban consumption.

Within the earlier period of development of the collective farms the composition of both gross and marketable output underwent a substantial change. The share of crop output increased and the share of livestock output decreased. Within the crop category, except for increased output of some industrial crops and increased share of wheat output among the grains, a shift from higher value products to lower value products took place. In terms of delivery of the marketable output of grain and increasing the output of most industrial crops (such as cotton and sugar beets), the collective farms have fulfilled their functions within the realm of possibilities.[18] They contributed to an increase of about three times in the volume of marketings from 1928 to 1961.

The measurement of sheer size of the total marketable output foreshadows another interesting development. Soviet economic growth was very much tainted by accompanying goals of autarky or economic self-sufficiency. The Soviets substituted domestic production for imported products of low priority to harmonize the conflicting objectives of rapid economic growth and autarky. The process of import substitution

[17] The labor intensity of private agricultural production is indicated by some available data. The total employment in private agricultural production in January, 1959, was reported by the census data as being 9.86 million, of which 8.95 million were women, or a total of 6.9 million year-equivalent workers. The urban component of this labor force constituted a fraction of the total, perhaps 25 per cent. The labor input per hectare of truck garden (93 per cent potatoes and 7 per cent vegetable area) was officially estimated at 328 man days in 1956. When the urban labor input involved in tending about 1.5 million cows, over a million pigs, and about 2 million goats and sheep is added, the total must be of considerable magnitude.

[18] The share of marketable output in the total agricultural production of the private peasant economy was about 30 per cent in 1928. The share increased in the late 1950s to about 50 per cent and the socialized sector accounted for about 83 per cent of the marketings. Among the industrial crops cotton and sugar beets are the most successful.

had to be synchronized with the achievement of a maximum rate of economic growth through the commodities exported. The Soviets, for example, substituted domestic cotton output for cotton imports so that the proceeds from exported grain could be used to import capital equipment instead of cotton. The government facilitated import substitution through its ability to determine the output-mix of the collective farms. The most successful examples of import substitution were cotton and tea. Within a relatively short time, imports of both commodities were reduced to insignificant quantities while the industrial consumption of cotton did not decrease.[19] On the other hand, economic failures of various import substitution schemes demonstrate the economic perils of a centralized decision-making authority which determines the product-mix for agriculture and sets the prices as well.[20]

[19] The government was able to prevail upon the collective farms in Central Asia and Transcaucasia to raise cotton as a monoculture and to reduce the output of grains (including rice) to insignificant quantities. It might be noted, however, that after 6 to 7 years the system of command in cotton growing was substituted by an incentive system. The relatively high prices for cotton and tea turned out to be more conducive to raising output than the methods originally applied. The following data indicate the decrease of imports of cotton and tea.

COTTON AND TEA IMPORTS, 1928–1939

Year	Cotton (tons)	Tea (tons)
1928	145,000	28,100
1929	115,037	28,590
1930	57,876	24,227
1931	53,749	20,708
1932	24,299	15,949
1933	22,552	19,307
1934	24,875	25,812
1935	44,219	23,638
1936	16,664	12,258
1937	22,054	15,191
1938	16,507	16,742
1939	3,988	9,500

SOURCE: TsUNKhU SSSR, *Socialist Construction in the USSR*, Moscow, 1936, pp. 432–435. Ministerstvo Vneshnei Torgovli SSSR, *Vneshniaia Torgovlia SSSR za 1918–1940 gg.*, Moscow, 1960, pp. 321, 327, 355, 360, 389, and 394.

[20] Out of a long list two examples are worth mentioning. One was the extension of cotton on nonirrigated lands. The second, a classic example of the autarky craze, imposed upon agriculture in the 1930s, was the mass planting of uneconomical rubber-yielding kok-saghyz to substitute for natural rubber imports.

TAXATION

The collective farm organization has played a decisive role in capital formation. The obligation to deliver a share of the agricultural output at fixed prices to the state enabled it to determine (within limits) the volume of taxation levied upon the agricultural sector. The delivery quota originally was set as a volume of product per unit of land for a given crop; later the quota was set independently of the acreage, in order to prevent any decrease of acreage.

In order to establish the tax incidence in the collective farm deliveries one would have to prove that the price level of these products differed measurably from the price level of other goods and services. Thus, while between 1928 and 1937 the average prices for agricultural deliveries rose about 2.5 times, the average gross money wage increased over four times and the retail prices about ten times. By 1952, the agricultural delivery prices were about five times the 1928 level while wages were ten times higher and retail prices about thirteen times higher. The above data indicate that, in fact, the tax incidence in the agricultural delivery prices was quite substantial. The policy of taxation in kind of the agricultural sector was applied under conditions of rising inflationary pressures, resulting in the decreased purchasing power of the money income the agricultural population received from the sale of the agricultural products procured by the state. Thus the agricultural population was affected by government policy in more than one way: first, by the high delivery quotas, which left a limited volume of products in kind for home consumption; second, by the low prices for the agricultural procurements; and third, by the high prices for manufactured consumer goods. Each of these policies incorporated a built-in element of taxation, generally designed to increase the agricultural producers' contribution to economic growth. In fact, a large share of the investment expenditures for industrialization was generated through agricultural taxation in kind and direct money taxes upon farms and the farm population.

The government policy, carried out through the collective farms, of limiting payments in kind and money, and thus keeping the incomes of the agricultural population low, facilitated Soviet economic growth. The low incomes of the peasants, which declined from their pre-collectivization level, coupled with the high prices of manufactured consumer goods, resulted in a diminished demand for manufactured consumer goods. Thus, the Soviet government could (1) curtail investment in consumer goods industries and center most of the investment in capital goods industries, thus increasing the growth rate of the strategic sectors of industry, (2) assign a higher proportion of the manufactured consumer goods to meet the demand of the industrial labor force, compensating to some extent for the decrease of food consumption, and (3) keep the output of manufactured consumer goods limited in the absence of capital investment in those industries, as well as shift labor to employment in construction, mining, and other capital goods industries.

SUMMARY OF THE PRE-1953 PERIOD

The results of pre-1953 Soviet policy for socialized agriculture in relation to the general economy can be summarized as follows:

1. According to official Soviet statistics, gross agricultural output was below the output level of the pre-collectivization year 1928[21] for all years from 1929 to 1953, except for the 1937 bumper crop year.

2. Input substitutes for land were not developed and the increased area under cultivation could not compensate for the decrease of yields.

3. The labor transfer from agriculture to industry was the main contributing factor to economic development on the part of the agricultural sector.

4. Apart from the labor transfer facilitated by the organization of socialized agriculture, the system of taxation (directly by the state and indirectly through the collective farms) was effective in channeling resources away from agriculture, increasing the volume of marketable farm output, and lowering the prices paid by the state for this output.

5. In spite of the growth of the marketed share of agricultural output, neither the supply of food for the nonagricultural population nor the supply of raw materials for consumer goods industries was sufficient to increase the living standard of the population.

THE COLLECTIVE FARM SYSTEM: 1953–1962

The second period in the development of Soviet agriculture roughly coincides with the post-Stalin period in Soviet history. In some respects it represents persistence of the basic features of the first period, but with significant deviations and changes that justify a distinction between the two.

While the structure of the collective farm system remained basically constant, changing general economic conditions altered the demands for agricultural contributions to economic growth. War losses of population, chiefly among males of rural origin, and the very low rate of population increase coupled with the steady outmigration from rural areas, diminished the role of the agricultural sector as a supplier of labor. The demand upon agriculture to increase its marketable output of food and indus-

[21] The reference is to gross agricultural output on a comparable territory and excludes the output produced on the territories incorporated in the Soviet Union during the years 1939 to 1945.

trial crops became more pressing because of urbanization and industrial growth. Soviet policy makers during the 1950s realized that the increment of labor productivity in industry depends at least in part upon increases in the real incomes of the industrial labor force. This discovery has led to the observation (implied or actual) that the income elasticity of demand for food in the Soviet Union is about 0.7 to 0.8 and consequently requires a substantial increase in size of the marketable agricultural output. During the previous period the growth of the marketable output fell behind the growth of the urban population (and even further behind if the increase of non-agricultural rural population is taken into account). This tendency had to be reversed and a new policy implemented. In terms of the results of the policies the distinction between the period 1913–1953 and the subsequent period becomes clear from the following official data.

TABLE 5. INDEXES OF MARKETABLE OUTPUT OF AGRICULTURE
AND URBAN POPULATION, 1913 = 100

Year	Marketable output of agriculture	Urban population
1913	100	100
1940	165	215
1953	190	*
1958	293	347
1961	300	380

* Not available.
SOURCE: TsSU SSSR, *Narodnoe Khoziaistvo SSSR v 1961 godu*, Moscow, 1962, pp. 7, 8, and 296.

Note that while the urban population increased 77 per cent between 1940 and 1961 the marketable output increased 82 per cent. Out of the total increase of the marketable output during the period from 1940 to 1960 almost 82 per cent of the growth took place between 1953 and 1961. It became clear, however, that a further increase in the marketable output would be impossible without a simultaneous increase in the total agricultural output. In order to bring about this desired result, another long ignored economic relationship had to be explored, namely the price and income elasticity of supply in agriculture. The supply elasticity of farm output with respect to price and income operates within the collective farm system as follows: The yield from an increase in price of farm products has to be passed on to the collective farm members in order to have an income effect because there is the alternative of utilizing the price increase for other than personal income purposes, especially investment. A policy to increase farm prices paid to collective farms therefore included a provision to increase the incomes of the collective farm members. This policy was carried out in a few successive moves between 1953 and 1958 and resulted in a threefold increase of the average price of state deliveries of agricultural products.[22] It resulted in an increase of the real incomes of the collective farm members. The increase in payments to collective farmers was mainly an increase of money payments.[23] The collective farms were, with respect to specific crops, under obligation to pay to their members a percentage share of the payments from government deliveries. A further step to improve the income position of the collective farmers was the growing practice of guaranteeing them a minimum income. This constituted a departure from past practice, under which industrial or even hired farm workers had a degree of income security in the form of minimum wages during employment, while the collective farmers received only a residual income.

There can be no doubt that the increase of farm output during the 1950s was to some extent a result of the material incentives provided both to the farms and to the farmers through these price and income increases. Therefore the second stage of Soviet agricultural development is marked by the realization that the welfare of the nonagricultural labor force is important and that increased farmers' incomes aided economic growth. Although the Soviet policy makers are still wrestling with the many problems involved in this interrelationship, recognition of the dependence of increased food output upon the increased income level of agricultural producers became an established feature of Soviet policy during the last decade. One can question the degree of consistency in pursuing the goals, even question the proportions in the allocation process. But the basic undercurrent of an understanding of the relationship cannot be denied.

THE RECORD OF SOCIALIZED AGRICULTURE

When we analyze statistical data, we ought not to overlook the qualitative features which are reflected in the quantitative measurements. One of the most surprising features of Soviet agriculture, at least to the uninitiated, is the still sizeable share of the private producers in the gross agricultural output. The private sector accounted for 98.6 per cent of total agricultural output in 1928, for 46.9 per cent in 1940, 33.7 per

[22] The officially reported index of the average level of agricultural prices paid by the state to collective farms and private individuals was 302 in 1959 (1952 = 100). TsSU SSSR, Sel'skoe Khoziaistvo SSSR, Moscow, 1961, p. 117. Livestock prices were increased again in 1962.

[23] The share of money in the total receipts of the farmers from the collective farms in the Ukraine has increased from 33.7 per cent in 1940 to 53.6 per cent in 1953 and to over 65 per cent in 1958. Sotsialisticheskii Trud, no. 8, 1960, p. 20.

cent in 1959, and had declined further by 1961.[24] The share of the collective farms in gross agricultural output was 46.5 per cent in 1940, reached its peak of 54.3 per cent in 1955, and declined to 46 per cent in 1961. The total share of the socialized sector (collective and state farms) in gross output of agriculture increased from 53.1 per cent in 1940 to 66.3 per cent in 1959 to about 70 per cent in 1961.

By 1940 the gross agricultural output reached approximately the level of the pre-collectivization year 1928.[25] However, the gross agricultural output during the years 1955 to 1959 exceeded the 1940 level by 41.5 per cent, as shown in Table 6. Among the factors that contributed to this growth, land and capital should be emphasized. The total sown area increased from 113 million hectares in 1928 to 150 million in 1940 (including the new territories) and 204.6 million in 1961.[26] Capital stock in agriculture (excluding livestock and net depreciation) was officially reported by Soviet sources for 1959 as about six times larger than in 1928.[27]

While there exists, at the present, a marked difference between the levels of labor productivity in the collective farms and state farms, attempts are being made to raise the level of labor productivity in the collective farms and narrow the existing gap. The output per unit of labor input for all agriculture during the 1955 to 1959 period was about 42 per cent higher than in 1928. Almost all of the increase took place during the post-1953 period.

These are the most general indicators of the performance of Soviet agriculture, a performance that ought to be judged both within the context of the existing political system in the Soviet Union and by its actual or potential contribution to economic growth.

Agriculture's ability to contribute to economic growth in its own right depends upon several factors.

Land. One factor is land or the ability to substitute other production factors for land. It is interesting to note that throughout the whole

[24] The private sector includes about 17 million households of collective farm members and about 17 million agricultural and nonagricultural workers and employees in rural and urban areas. The 1940 and 1959 figures were derived from a calculation of gross output of eleven major commodities, using 1958 purchase prices as weights. It is believed that the private share would decline by about one-tenth if the list of commodities were greatly expanded.

[25] The 1940 output on the expanded territory of the Soviet Union was approximately 17–18 per cent above 1928. The newly acquired territories accounted for 14–15 per cent of the total output.

[26] The expansion of sown area in the Soviet Union continues. The 1962 sown area was reported at 214 million hectares.

[27] The inclusion of livestock would substantially reduce the increase in capital. Within the total reported capital stock increase, agricultural machinery and equipment represent approximately a sevenfold increase and farm structures represent a more than fivefold increase.

period of Soviet socialized agriculture numerous attempts were made, with differing degrees of success, to increase the land area under cultivation. A large share of the additional land was used for rather low-yielding fodder crops. Some crop redistribution results were of substantial significance within the sown area. Although work to improve the varieties and selection of seed and the improvement and enlargement of irrigation and drainage systems were substitutes for land, they cannot be counted as major achievements of Soviet agriculture. Bringing new land under cultivation is still considered a major means to increase farm output. The problem of crop rotation as a form of resource improvement of land

TABLE 6. INDEX OF GROSS AGRICULTURAL OUTPUT
(*1913 = 100*)

Year	Official Soviet index	Estimated*
1928	124	116
1932	107	89
1937	134	127
1940†	141	122
1950	140	118
1953	146	127
1955	170	151
1958	218	191
1960	224	188
1961	230	190

* Estimated by the author.
† Inclusive of new territories.
SOURCE: TsSU SSSR, *Narodnoe Khoziaistvo SSSR v 1961 godu*, Moscow, 1962, p. 292.

has remained unsolved during the second period as it did during the first. During the first period the insistence upon state authorities to determine the product-mix for collective farm output, and incessant drives during the recent years to introduce new crops in various areas (the corn campaign, the present campaign to introduce pulses on a large scale) have interfered with the collective farms' desire to introduce a crop rotation that would both be economical in the short-run and also increase the long-term fertility of the soil, in the absence of an adequate supply of fertilizer.

Capital. A substantial change took place in the area of supply of capital to agriculture. The supply of farm machinery has increased substantially during the post-1953 period. However, the non-compensated decrease of human labor and animal draft power are still felt in Soviet agriculture. For example, the present availability of machinery, at the prevailing intensity of utilization, is insufficient to assure a timely harvest and thus minimize losses involved in the postponement of certain types of field work. While the state farms (receiving priority in the supply of equipment and farm machinery) are also using extensively the pool of machinery and personnel which moves northward and eastward with the advance of the harvest period, the collective farms are benefiting relatively less from machinery. But with respect to the change of management (and also formal ownership) of farm machinery, the collective farms are now in a better condition than before 1957. Since 1957 the collective farms have become the owners of the farm machinery, which was previously owned and managed by a state institution, the Machine-Tractor Stations (MTS). The tax in kind, collected for the services of the MTS, was abolished (although the collective farms now pay for the machines and their operating expenses), and unity of management was established in one authority, the Collective Farm Administration. This meant a gain for the farms. Reports regarding the performance of machinery under collective farm management are divergent. There is no clear evidence that a gain in productivity has been achieved. Perhaps a real gain has resulted from qualitative changes such as the introduction of smaller row-crop tractors, which have replaced inefficient models on certain types of work.

Soviet attitudes toward supply of capital in agriculture have a distinctive character. Decisions for an all-out commitment to provide capital for a particular task in agriculture are very reluctantly made. It seems as though the decision makers are waiting for a new technological breakthrough in the machinery field, or a scientific discovery in a related field, that will substitute for the heavy investment involved. This hesitation to supply capital on a broad front is true for machinery as well as for fertilizer. Postponement and the use of stopgap measures enables such capital funds to be used elsewhere in the economy. But there is no doubt that the lack of complementary actions in the agricultural investment field greatly diminishes the total effect of new investment. While the collective farms were previously ignored (during the period of MTS) with regard to their choice of machinery, at least they now have the freedom of choice within the available supply of machinery. Whether the new arrangement will assure the required continuity in investment is still an open question. Soviet marketing has a poor system for communicating the preferences of the consumers.[28] And the impact of the farm demand upon the volume and mix of farm machinery production is not likely to become very effective within the existing farm supply organization. It could, therefore, be concluded that the contribution of agriculture to economic growth by increasing output and decreasing unit costs depends to a large extent upon a sizeable increase in capital

[28] See Marshall Goldman, *Soviet Marketing: Distribution in a Closed Economy,* The Free Press of Glencoe, New York, 1963.

per worker and per unit of land and the raising of the complementary effects of various capital expenditures to higher levels. Without the expansion of capital outlays, the domestic and foreign demand for food and agricultural raw materials (particularly from the countries within the Soviet bloc) will not be met.[29]

Other Factors. A few more problems which have emerged recently are of considerable interest. One deals with the levels of skill and education of the agricultural labor force. Skill and education levels of the agricultural labor force are increasing even though the levels are still low compared to those of the industrial labor force. Major impediments to progress in the agricultural sector, apart from the general environmental conditions, have been the lower rate of investment in education and skill training in rural areas and, to some extent, the sex distribution of the labor force employed in agriculture (over 61 per cent female). The next ten to fifteen years may witness a rapid rise in educational level for rural laborers, as the present labor force is replaced by the new generation. This will stimulate a rise in marginal value productivity levels, simultaneously broadening the range of employment opportunities and bringing about higher rates of growth.

The second problem, related to the first, is the quality of management on farms. Apparently the educational level of farm managers has increased and their average technical competence has improved. This should improve decision making at the farm level. The main obstacle to effective use of improved farm management has been the primacy of political considerations in the appointments of such officials. There is no indication that pressure in favor of the political criteria is subsiding. However, cases of sheer managerial incompetence might become less frequent due to the increased supply of managerial talent and experience.

Another interesting and still undecided problem of economic organization that has plagued Soviet agriculture is the one of arriving at an optimal size for farm operations. Indeed, the optimal size of the collective farms has not yet been established. In fact, discussions on this topic were only begun after 1958. Beginning with the early 1950s the amalgamation of collective farms has proceeded almost without interruption; the number of collective farms declined from 240,000 in 1950 to about 40,000 in 1961. The average sown area of collective farms increased from 492 hectares in 1940 to 2,665 in 1960.[30] In a market economy, the optimal

---

[29] Another problem is whether, at the existing stage of economic development, the Soviet Union should strive for self-sufficiency in most agricultural commodities. At present, the cost of domestic sugar is above the imported price. Perhaps a policy based purely upon economic considerations of economic growth would dictate a different course of action. This problem, as well as the problems of the costs of autarky to economic growth, is outside the scope of this essay.

[30] TsSU SSSR, *Narodnoe Khoziaistvo SSSR v 1961 godu,* Moscow, 1962, p. 419.

size of farms of particular production profiles or within certain regions is determined by the interrelation of various factors and ultimately by the farms' relative profitability. Within the Soviet economic framework, the guides for the establishment of an optimal size are obscured, thereby making such a determination difficult. The collective farm system, as it now exists, is not flexible enough to let the farms establish or decide the optimal farm size. Such decisions are still reserved for the state.

Possibilities of future development of the collective farm system. The basic decision, arrived at during the post-Stalin period, that agriculture ought to contribute to the growth of the other sectors of the economy and to its own, calls for a solution to problems similar to those facing economies with a different organizational structure at a similar stage in their economic growth. Whether the collective farm system will be able both to fulfill the demands which the economy sets for it and to adjust to the changing conditions without itself undergoing significant changes is very much a matter for speculation. In the past, Soviet policy makers repeatedly exhibited a tendency to retreat in the direction of administrative centralization and control whenever reliance upon decentralization did not quickly produce the expected results. Soviet agriculture has not responded to the post-1953 challenges with a continuous upward movement of output and productivity. It has responded instead with a series of short-run spurts, which petered out as soon as the various incentives, so to speak, were "absorbed." Therefore, increased centralized control might well be the choice of some Soviet decision makers in the near future. Predictions run in opposite directions: (1) further conversion of collective farms into state farms, and (2) return to more privately oriented farm organizations. This last prediction reflects primarily the preferences of some Western observers. In addition, the likelihood of a transformation to truly cooperative farming should not be dismissed. When Soviet policy makers recognize the conflict between their objectives of economic growth (with the prevailing disregard for short-run welfare considerations) and the *necessity* for incentives to fulfill successfully the tasks of agricultural production, they may settle for a compromise solution. A truly cooperative farm organization might be acceptable to them under such circumstances.[31] Given the Soviet commitment to sustained economic growth, and the gradual recognition of difficulties associated with the present agricultural system, one might reasonably anticipate further organizational changes in one of these directions.

[31] The acceptability will depend largely upon the degree of confidence that any change of this sort will not erode the political power of the Party.

17. Land Reform and Economic Development*

DOREEN WARRINER

LECTURE I HISTORICAL

Introduction

My excuse for the choice of this ambitious subject can only be that it is an important one. Land reform is the most important social change now taking place in the world. That statement may seem to be an exaggeration, but reflection will convince us that it is so. No contemporary social change in the industrial countries is comparable in scope. The great new advances in social life are now happening in agricultural countries, above all in Asia; and they affect the people on the land.

We stand too near to these changes to be able to understand their full significance. No one can possibly hope to survey the results in all the different countries. The question which I propose to consider is the relation of these social changes to economic development. The subject of land reform has frequently been discussed in recent years in the General Assembly of the United Nations, and in the Economic and Social Council, in relation to the development of under-developed countries. The United Nations reports have put forward the contention that land reform, in these countries, must be regarded as a condition of economic development. On the face of it, this statement seems simply untrue. It certainly requires investigation, and it is for that reason that I have chosen the subject.

At the outset, it is necessary to define the term "land reform," for definitions are now confused. Land reform, in the traditional and accepted sense of the term, means the redistribution of property in land for the benefit of small farmers and agricultural workers. There is also a wider definition now in use, in which "land reform" is understood to mean *any* improvement in agricultural economic institutions. This definition originates in the United States. The object of using this broader defini-

* From National Bank of Egypt Fiftieth Anniversary Commemoration Lectures, Cairo, 1955, pp. 1–42 with omissions. Lectures I, II, and III of the four lectures have been corrected by the author and reprinted in entirety. Reprinted by permission of the National Bank of Egypt and the author. The author is reader in economic and social studies of Eastern Europe, University of London.

tion is to widen the conception of reform policy, in order to emphasize that Governments which undertake reform measures should not confine their policies only to the redistribution of land, but should also undertake many other things—the regulation of rents, conditions of tenancy, and farm wages, the improvement of farm credit systems, methods of land taxation, co-operative organisation, agricultural education and so on. We must all agree with that view in theory, and in Egypt it has been put into practice.

None the less, we need not confuse the definition of a concept with the conception of a policy. To use the term "land reform" in this wide sense confuses the real issues. The redistribution of property in land is a very difficult change to carry through, far more difficult and controversial than the other measures, and we cannot really put it on the same level as other institutional improvements. The order of magnitude is too different, and we take the edge off if we ignore this fact.

So for reasons of proportion and clarity I propose to use "land reform" in the sense in which the term is generally understood. When terms in common use have a clear meaning, it is better to adhere to them. I shall therefore limit the subject to this quite specific and most important type of institutional change.

We must next consider the method of treatment.

Everyone who has discussed the subject of land reform must have noticed that it is extremely boring. It is repetitive. The same old arguments for and against are brought up again and again, the same old platitudes are re-iterated. There is a continuous confusion of different issues.

The confusion arises precisely because land reform is important. Land systems affect the life of a country in many ways. They determine the distribution of incomes and the use of land. But their influence goes far beyond the economic sphere. There are times in the life of every country when it must forget about economics. Land systems determine social attitudes, social satisfactions. They are interwoven with national tradition, even with national character.

So inevitably there are different ways of looking at land reform. People who argue about it disagree usually because they are talking on different planes, within different frameworks of reference, and using different standards. They are really arguing about which standard should have priority.

For example, there often appears to be a conflict between the demand for greater social equality and the need for increasing efficiency in agriculture. The kind of society we should like to live in is not necessarily the kind of economy that will feed us best. Which should be the standard, social justice or economic efficiency?

Then there is the baffling demographic side of the question. It is sometimes said that Egypt cannot undertake land reform because it is over-populated, while Syria, because it is under-populated, does not need reform. If this argument is true, there is no case for land reform anywhere. Somehow we must fit the demographic factor into its right perspective.

Most important of all are the political arguments. Some people think that the object of land reform should be to defeat communism, and that this object should over-ride all other considerations. Others will assert that land reform *is* communism. Political arguments of this kind can easily overwhelm us, if we cannot keep them in their proper place.

We shall not be able to make any real advance in the study of the subject unless we can sort out these different angles, and distinguish between the standards which are relevant for each approach.

To do this, we must recognize that the conflict of priorities is really a conflict between different ways of studying human society. It is what Germans call a *Kompetenzstreit*, a dispute between different sciences or different academic disciplines about their rights to study a subject. The reform of the institutions of land tenure, and its relation to economic development, is not a subject in its own right, but lies between different studies—economics, history, geography, anthropology and sociology. Each of these could claim to map out the whole territory. But they have not done so.

Economists have neglected the subject, because it concerns the institutional framework which they accept as given; and this neglect is unfortunate, because it means that we have no accepted methods of analysis, and lack even proper terminology. Historians ought, of course, to be interested in the long term effects, and in the secular processes which are development. But apart from the French, who have done wonderful work, most historians simply do not know enough about agriculture to give us much help. Geographers are good—Weulersse, for example, whose book, *Paysans de Syrie et du Proche Orient,* is a masterpiece in the synthesis of geography, sociology and history.

Sociologists and anthropologists are also concerned. In the vast literature dealing with land tenure in colonial territories, it is the anthropologists who hold sway. But when we are thinking about development, the anthropologist gives no guidance. His strong bias in favour of the static leads him to regard all change as disintegration, even if it is the kind of change that the economist would describe as progress.

So for the present, the territory is an academic no-man's-land. No single science or study has yet established its claims, and each has its limitations. No single method of approach can take us all the way. The subject remains what Americans call inter-disciplinary, and the English call borderline.

If it is true that knowledge grows at the points where different studies intersect, the best way to advance is to try to use several different methods of study. This is of course difficult. It is clearly impossible for any one person to survey the territory with the full equipment needed for each approach. We cannot use the "powerful tools" of the economist, or the sharp eyes of the demographer, or the accumulated learning of the historian. But we might make a few excursions into the territory to make a preliminary reconnaissance, even if we have not the necessary equipment or the time to prepare a complete expedition. We can consider the kind of questions that these real authorities might ask, and consider possible answer[s], as seriously-minded amateurs. We can then consider whether the different methods can be co-ordinated. This will give us, if not a systematic treatment, at least some kind of ordered perspective.

Among the various possible academic approaches, I shall select three, the historical, the economic and the demographic, as the most important, and in considering these shall attempt to isolate the political aspects. Land reform is inevitably a political question. It involves a conflict of interests between the "haves" and the "have-nots." But it seems important, particularly when the economic effects are under discussion, to try to keep political bias out of the way, and to discern how far any argument is influenced by class apologetics. For this reason, it is best to keep politics to the end. It is best kept to the end also because it is in the last resort decisive.

The Historical Aspects

Our first approach should be an historical one. Clearly economic history ought to throw light on the question of the relationship between economic growth and institutional change. We must ask whether there is any historical evidence to show that the re-shaping of agrarian institutions has been a condition of development in the past.

In attempting to answer this question, we must limit our survey to economic development in recent times. It would, of course, be interesting to go back further and speculate about the influence of land system on the rise and fall of civilisations. In this part of the world, Ibn Khaldun interpreted history as an endless struggle between nomads and farmers— an interpretation still illuminating for the Fertile Crescent. In Roman times, Pliny propounded his admirably concise theory that large estates destroyed the Empire—a view which may be true of empires other than Rome. But in Egypt, the miracle of continuity in time, such speculations seem presumptuous. We do well to remember that the question is not a new one; but we need not go back so far.

If we consider the recent economic history of the countries now called advanced, we must admit frankly that there is really no evidence at all to suggest that land reform has been a condition of development.

First, it is obvious that several countries which achieved very rapid development in the past did not do so with help of land reform. On the contrary, England, Prussia and Japan progressed at the expense of their peasant farmers. In England and Prussia large landowners expropriated peasant farmers and turned them into farm labourers. Japan advanced by taxing its farmers very heavily. In the history of these countries there obviously was a conflict between social equality and economic efficiency at the time of their most rapid expansion.

However, we should not be justified in arguing from their experience that expropriation and oppression of peasant farmers is a necessary condition of progress. There have been other ways of expansion in which this conflict did not arise. Western European countries have reached high levels of development with peasant systems of farming; Switzerland, for example, with the highest standard of living in Europe, and the Scandinavian countries, with their high levels of productivity in agriculture.

Moreover, the countries which today have the highest levels of output per man in agriculture—the United States, Canada, Australia and New Zealand—have done so on the basis of family farming and State control of land use. Looking at the history of these countries, we could conclude that family farming can promote very rapid expansion, and very rapid technical progress.

Thus there have been different patterns of development. We should be justified in concluding that the experience of the advanced countries shows that some countries have advanced very far and very fast without large landowners, and with a very equal distribution of ownership in land. But it also shows that others have used methods of capital accumulation which oppressed small farmers and farm labourers. So we cannot conclude that land reform is a condition of development.

Nor will the historical approach tell us that there is any one type of land system which will best promote investment and so favour development. Peasant farmers can achieve small miracles of careful and gradual improvement which in the course of time add up to big miracles. But landowners too can show great enterprise in introducing new crops and new techniques. Equally, both peasants and landowners can fail to invest —peasant[s] can remain bound in traditional routine, landowners can neglect their estates.

However, the historical approach should enable us to draw some conclusions about the effects of reform on development over a long period. To investigate these effects, it would be necessary to compare the rates of economic growth in countries which have carried out land redistribution and in countries which have not. The difficulty in making such comparison is that it is usually impossible to isolate the effects of land reform from the effects of other factors which have influenced economic growth. We should have to compare countries with the same general economic background, but with different agrarian structures. This is difficult, for history never works under laboratory conditions. The agrarian structure of a country is the outcome of a long historical process, and countries with different institutions are therefore not likely to resemble each other in other respects.

In Eastern Europe, however, we can find countries with similar natural conditions and types of agriculture, and with different agrarian structures, so that some comparison seems admissible.

We can compare, for example, Hungary and Bulgaria, two small agricultural countries in the Danube basin, in the years between the wars. In Hungary, there had then been no land reform, and the distribution of land ownership was extremely unequal with about half the land in large estates. Bulgaria had reformed its land system in 1880 when it got rid of the Turkish land system, and thereafter the distribution of land was extremely equal with all the land in small farms.

This early land reform, it is worth noting, was extremely well carried out. All the things that the United Nations recommended Governments to do in 1951, Bulgarians began to do in the early years of this century. They set up co-operative credit societies to break the grip of the money-lenders, and later they invested co-operative savings in canning factories and power stations. They were skilled in intensive types of farming. Within the social system they had chosen, they made good use of their resources. After centuries of Turkish rule, equality and independence were what they wanted, and these benefits were provided by the farm structure. But in the years between the wars, the well-built house was getting rather too small for their needs. Agricultural production only just kept pace with increase of population.

Hungary, on the other hand, was an extremely stratified society, with great wealth at the top, and great poverty at the bottom. About half the farm population had no land, and the casual labourers on the estates and the small peasant owners were wretchedly poor, worse off than the average Bulgarian farmer. Inequality produced rigid social attitudes of snobbism and servility. Socially, Bulgaria was better, because its people were happier.

Yet, in comparing development, the advantage must go to Hungary. In Hungary the productivity of land and labour was higher than in Bulgaria. Output per man was about 30% higher, because grain yields were higher, and there was more land per head. Hungary maintained a higher level of productivity, at the same time as much unemployment, and not disguised unemployment either. But, on the other hand, the wealth of the great estate owners had financed the growth of industry which had absorbed labour as it was driven off the land. Bulgaria's equal farm system tended to keep people working on the land and did not promote a high rate of investment.

This comparison suggests that countries which carry out land reform must make great efforts to increase investment, particularly if the rate of population increase is fast. It does not show that reform prevents development; but it does show that, if incomes are very equally distributed, it will be necessary to find types of farm organisation which will mobilise savings and promote progress in agriculture, and also in industry.

So the historical approach can tell us something of value. But it does not point to any general connection between land reform and development. So far its outcome is negative.

If, however, we frame the question on broader lines, and understand the re-shaping of agrarian institutions to mean the abolition of feudalism, rather than the re-distribution of ownership, then it seems possible to be more positive about the relationship to economic development.

There are, of course, difficulties of interpretation here, so many that it is impossible to discuss the question adequately in this brief amateur expedition. But the conception of feudalism is part of the historical approach to the subject, and we must consider it because it influences policies as well as ways of thinking. One difficulty is that the conception itself is not clear. Professional historians use the term feudalism in different senses. Some understand it to mean service tenure, the grant of land ownership in return for military service. Marxist historians understand it to mean serfdom, the exaction by landowners of compulsory labour from serfs who were tied to the land. It would be possible to argue at length about which of these features should be regarded as the more essential. Other historians would include both serfdom and service tenure in the conception of feudal order, as a system in which public function (military power) and private rights (over land and labour) were integrated. If we accept this view, then by the abolition of feudalism we can understand the process by which an economic and social order based on status turned into an order based on contract.

This institutional change in Europe was certainly a condition of economic progress, for it was a necessary preliminary to expansion in trade, industry and agriculture. There is a correlation between the dates when this change took place and present economic levels. In the countries of Western Europe which have advanced to high levels, feudal relations disappeared early. In the countries of Eastern Europe, including Russia, feudal relations survived in the form of serfdom until the second half of the nineteenth century; and the development of these countries lagged behind that of Western Europe.

Yet it is also true that economic progress conditioned the change in institutions. In Western Europe, it was the earlier expansion of trade and town life and the influx of bullion which hastened the break-up of service tenures and labour services, while Eastern Europe preserved its rigid social structure because these influences were much weaker. The most that we can conclude from the European pattern is that the relation between economic development and institutional change has been reciprocal with a slight lead for "development."

How far can we regard this past European experience as relevant to the question of land reform in the under-developed countries today? Is there any parallel between the abolition of feudalism in Europe and the contemporary abolition of large landownership in Asia and Latin America, which would justify the inference that land reform may be a condition of development in the same way?

This is a difficult question indeed, and one which admits of no definite answer. It would perhaps be better if we could avoid the term "feudal" altogether, because it is so ambiguous. But this parallel is often drawn, and so must be considered. In popular discussion, particularly in America, land reform is often identified with the abolition of feudalism, and for American opinion this is its great sanction. But unless the term "feudal" is used loosely, to mean any form of large landownership which gives rise to social stratification, it seems quite wrong to compare the forms of landownership in the under-developed countries with the institutions of feudalism in Europe. There are strongly marked resemblances in some features, most noticeably in the Latin American countries where serfdom still exists and where the great *latifundia* originated as land grants from the Crown. But if we use the term feudal in any of the precise senses used by historians, we cannot apply it to most Asian systems, nor to most Middle East systems. Nor, of course, can it be applied to plantation estates which are commercial enterprises. On the whole—and here of course there must be difference of opinion—the comparison with Europe seems misleading, even erroneous. At any rate, we certainly cannot conclude that there are any economic forces at work causing the break-up of these systems, or that their removal will set in train the same kind of expansion that followed the break-up of feudal systems in Europe.

None the less, land reform in the modern world does represent a turning point which is comparable in importance to the abolition of feudalism. Many Governments in Asia and Latin America, when they formulate their policies for agrarian reform, are conscious of the past history of their countries. When they describe the features of the existing agrarian structure, they do so by reference to its historical origins. Mexico, for example, looks back to the Spanish conquest, and so does Bolivia. India and Pakistan look back to the land systems established under British rule in the eighteenth century. Their land systems are rooted in the past; in the present, needs have arisen which make them obsolete. These countries are confronted with the need for getting rid of institutional hang-overs in order to re-shape their national life on new lines.

The historical significance of these turning points is, for many countries, the abolition of colonial land systems. The old systems have been associated with foreign rule, or established by foreign conquest. In several Asian countries, land reform is linked with the achievement of national independence, in Latin America with emancipation from the legacy of Spain.

The conception of a break with the past can be a powerful stimulus in national life. Because land systems are deeply rooted in custom and tradition, and preservative of social attitudes hostile to change, and because the cultivators of the land are at the bottom of the social hierarchy, the decision to carry out a land reform crystallises the determination to break with the past in an irrevocable way. That decision may well be one of the strategic factors in development.

But in agriculture there can be no break with the past. Continuity is the essence of its growth. For the world's agricultural countries, the maintenance and increase of agricultural production are now quite literally a matter of life and death. If Governments and peoples wish to break with the past they must find ways of doing so which will increase the incentives to produce more and invest more in the land. This brings us to the economic aspect, to be considered in the next lecture.

LECTURE II   ECONOMIC

Professional economists neglect the subject of land reform, because it concerns the institutional framework of society, which economic analysis accepts as given. The study of change in economic institutions, it is assumed, can be left to the historian. Yet, as we have seen, the historical approach can tell us only about the experience of advanced countries: it does not serve as a guide for the countries that are now commonly described as under-developed. If we are to consider the effects of land reform on agricultural production, investment and employment, in these countries, we must attempt to use the methods of economic analysis. These methods include the theory of competition and monopoly, the theory of the firm, and the theory of investment.

The economist's approach is valuable, because it forces us to define the assumptions underlying any general argument for or against land reform. Most of the economic arguments commonly used against land reform are really political arguments in disguise. There is, for example, the argument that land reform will lead to a fall in production. In Egypt, this argument has been proved false by experience; economic analysis can show the conditions in which it does not apply even in theory. If we use the methods of economic analysis, and are careful to define our assumptions, we can perhaps show that there is a positive relation between reform and development, in the conditions of "under-developed countries."

Before going further, I must define this phrase. The "under-developed countries" are, of course, not under-developed, and they are not countries. They are continents—Asia, Latin America and most of Africa—the agricultural continents in the world's tropical regions. They are not under-developed in regard to the utilisation of natural resources. Some of them are really under-developed in this sense, (as for example the Latin American countries) but many of them, from an agricultural standpoint, are very highly developed indeed, producing higher yields to the acre and making much fuller use of their land than the countries which are now called advanced. Nor must the term "under-developed" lead us to suppose that these countries exist on lower levels of development because they are passing through earlier stages in a process of development similar to that which the advanced countries have already experienced. This view would be quite false to the facts; many of the countries now called under-developed are very old countries, and were already old when the advanced countries were new. The essence of their situation is not that development is delayed, but that it is extremely difficult. They cannot expect to advance through any automatic or inevitable process. They are not on lower steps of the same ladder; they are not on a ladder at all.

The term "under-developed" is a euphemism for "poor." Under-developed means poor, and under-development means poverty. There is nothing new in poverty; it is the human condition. What is new is that the economists, in all simplicity, are beginning to call it a "problem." That may be an advance, even though they mean only that it is a problem for somebody else.

This poverty is usually measured by the level of national income per head. The classification of countries into three groups, according to the level of national income per head, is by now familiar. The first group, that of the advanced countries, includes the United States, Canada, Australia, New Zealand, Western Europe and Great Britain. It also includes the Sheikhdom of Kuwait, which now has the highest national income per head of any country in the world. The second group includes Russia and Southern and Eastern European countries. The third group includes the three great agricultural continents. The question of whether these measurements of income are comparable need not concern us; they are obviously only rough approximations which serve to show an important contrast in living standards. Other indices of poverty, such as the level of nutrition, the extent of illiteracy or the incidence of disease, can be used to show the same broad contrast.

This is a definition in descriptive terms. Since "under-development" is regarded as a problem, we must define it not only descriptively but also conceptually. Inevitably, conceptual definitions differ. One eminent authority maintains that the concept of under-development is identical with overpopulation, and is really only a new dress for this old conception—the state of chronic and cumulative poverty which may become a retrogressive condition.

To a very great extent—to the extent of 90% perhaps—under-development is co-terminous with overpopulation, for Asia dominates the whole picture. However, this conceptual definition does not quite fit with the descriptive definition, which includes some regions in Africa and Latin America which are not at present overpopulated. For these countries, we require another conception, that of unbalanced or lop-sided development. We may use the two situations defined by Professor Nurkse: the vicious circle and the lop-sided economy. Both are conceptions of capital shortage. In the first, no net capital formation is occurring, in the second, net capital formation occurs principally in one branch of the economy, leaving the rest primitive and backward. (The countries of the Fertile Crescent, with their modern and highly efficient oil industry and their primitive agriculture, are an obvious example of the second situation.)

The primary fact is poverty. I once asked the late Sir Bernard Binns, the FAO authority, how he would compare living standards in the tropical countries which he knew so well. He considered the matter carefully, and replied: "A poor Indian village is about the same as a good African village; but a Brazilian village is worse than both." Few of us know the world well enough to be able to make such comparisons from experience. This comparison, based on an unquestionable accuracy of observation, is interesting because it shows how little difference there is between countries with very different resources, and with very different histories.

We have to ask what land reform can do for these villages which take up such an enormous percentage of the world's population.

We must be clear that we are generalising about the land systems of three vast continents. There is great variety in institutions, in types of farming and natural conditions, and it is dangerous to generalise too broadly.

Each country has a land system peculiar to itself, though it is not so peculiar as it is believed to be. At first sight we seem to be confronted by sheer multiplicity. In fact, there is much more uniformity than appears at first sight. If we compare the different forms of land tenure, three distinct patterns emerge, and we can say that from the standpoint of economic analysis there are really three distinct problems of reform. We can leave out some land systems altogether as irrelevant to our subject—the peasant systems, in which land ownership is more or less equally distributed, and communal tenure systems, in which the land is communally owned (mainly prevalent in Africa). These may need other types of reform—reforms of the agrarian structure—but they do not need redistribution of ownership. We can concentrate on the land systems in which the large estate is the predominant form of tenure.

We must, however, distinguish sharply between the different types of large estate. One of the great difficulties in the study of this subject is that we have no accepted vocabulary. Much confusion arises from lack of precise terminology. "Large estate" itself is an ambiguous term, referring to at least three different forms of tenure and three different types of economic organisation. The three types are:

1. The type of ownership characteristic of Asian countries, in which the land holding is only a property and not a large farm or large producing unit. The property is leased in small units to tenant cultivators, either on the basis of money rent or on a basis of share-cropping rents.

2. The large estate, characteristic of South European countries and of Latin America, which is both a large property and a large enterprise. This type of estate is managed by salaried officials and worked by labourers and people of indeterminate status, squatters or share-croppers. Estates of this kind are usually extensively cultivated, or used as cattle ranges. We may call them latifundia, since this is the term used in the countries where they prevail; they are the direct descendants of the slavetilled ranches of the Roman Empire.

3. Plantation estates. These are also both large properties and large enterprises. They are usually owned by a company with foreign capital and foreign management, though estates of a plantation type may also be found in private ownership. The methods of cultivation are usually intensive.

Many countries have agrarian structures which include estates of two or even three of these types. The land system of Egypt in certain features resembles the Asian form of ownership, while in other features it is a plantation system.

These forms of ownership and enterprise have very little in common with the types of large-scale farming found in advanced countries, i.e. in countries with an industrialised economy and commercialised agriculture. The Asian system is found principally in subsistence economies, while latifundia and plantations produce mainly for export.

From the standpoint of economic analysis, the most obvious feature of all these types of ownership is the existence of an institutional monopoly. In Asian countries, where demographic pressure is high, the level of rents is determined not by the fertility of the land, but by the fertility of human beings. Land is a scarce factor of production, and would command a high price in terms of its produce, whatever the system of land tenure. The existence of institutional monopoly allows the landowner to raise rents to a still higher level. In latifundian systems and in plantation systems, the estate owner is a monopoly buyer of labour, controlling the use of land rather than its price, and he uses his monopoly power to keep wages low.

The main economic argument for land reform is the need for securing a more equal distribution of income by eliminating these monopoly elements. In the first case the aim is to reduce the price for the use of land, i.e. a reduction in rents, and in the second case, the aim is to subdivide big holdings and secure a fuller use of land, an increased demand for labour, and higher wages for the farm worker.

But, it may be objected, will not this redistribution of ownership reduce productivity by dividing up efficient large estates? If we wish to use this argument, we must consider in what sense these estates are to be regarded as efficient. The theory of the firm is always difficult to apply in agriculture, and as far as the under-developed countries are concerned, it seems to have very limited application.

The argument that the division of large agricultural enterprises will cause a decline in productivity is true on two assumptions: 1) that there is competition between the factors of production and, 2) that there are economies of large scale production. These assumptions are generally valid in industrialised countries. In England, for example, a large farm has generally become large because it is a more efficient producer, i.e. it produces at lower costs; it can compete more effectively for the factors of production and combine them more efficiently, using more capital and using it more fully; it can also use more efficient management and more specialised labour. In such conditions there is a presumption that the size of farms is more or less adjusted to an optimum scale of output for certain types of farming. This optimum scale of output is difficult to define precisely, and in practice means the minimum area needed to utilise power-driven machinery. In Sweden and France, for example, agricultural economists are now much concerned with the problem of farm sizes, because farms in the smaller size groups are not large enough to use modern technical methods, and the farming structure is not so well adjusted to technical advance as it was 50 years ago. Even in advanced countries, therefore, there may be institutional factors which prevent adjustment to larger scale production. But the conception of an optimum scale of output is always valid, simply because capital equipment plays a large part in farming.

When we try to apply this argument about the scale of production to the under-developed countries, we shall find that over a very wide range of conditions it has no validity at all. In Asian land systems, large estates are not large producing units. Land reform in such systems simply means the transfer of ownership from the landowner to the cultivator of the existing small holding. The size of the farm is not affected, for there are no large farms. When the Governments of India and Pakistan speak of "uneconomic farms," they mean farms which fall below a subsistence minimum, not below a technical optimum. Nor does the argument about efficient large estates apply generally to latifundian systems. The haciendas in Mexico and many of the latifundia in Southern Italy were not efficient large estates on any standard. They wasted both land and labour.

So generally speaking, the argument about "efficient large estates" does not seem to apply to the first type or the second type of estates which we have distinguished. It does seem to apply to plantation estates which use intensive methods of cultivation and modern methods. Every plantation system is a special case. Where there is reason to believe that sub-division of the estate would lead to a decline in production, then the monopoly effect on labour must be tackled by a policy for raising wages, and taxing profits to secure reinvestment in other types of farming producing for local needs. Or the estate may be divided with safeguards for maintaining efficiency, as under the Egyptian Land Reform.

I have examined this argument at some length because it serves to illustrate the danger of using the methods of economic analysis without making explicit the assumptions on which the analysis is based. The assumptions of competition and economies of large scale production which are valid in advanced countries are generally not valid in relation to the land systems of the under-developed countries, simply because capital plays so small a part in production.

Several other arguments used against land reform are false because they are based on projections of conditions in advanced countries, and do not take these basic differences into account. One argument frequently encountered in international discussions is that because tenancy works very well in England there can be no reason for Asian countries to abolish tenancy by redistribution of ownership: what they need is legislation to improve the security of tenure for tenants. This argument overlooks the monopoly influence in Asian countries. It is true that tenancy works well in England, because the conditions of tenancy are regulated by law, and also because land is only one of the many forms of holding wealth. If a landowner attempts to take too high a rent, the tenant will prefer to invest his capital in other ways. But in Asian conditions tenancy laws will never suffice to counteract the effects of monopoly ownership.

Another argument of this kind is that there is no need for expropriation by compulsion. This argument runs as follows: "If governments wish to encourage ownership, they can do this by giving tenants special credit facilities enabling them to buy their holdings. In Switzerland (or Denmark or Sweden) the land system has evolved itself by gradual adjustment to modern conditions, and Asian countries should therefore adjust their systems gradually, without drastic legislation to expropriate owners of land." The logical fallacy in this argument is obvious. In advanced countries, an improvement in the economic position of agriculture will enable the tenant to buy his land, and special credit facilities can encourage the acquisition of ownership. In the United States, the proportion of ownership to tenancy rises when agriculture is prosperous, and special legislation aids farm purchase. In European countries, particularly in Scandinavia, governments have helped tenants to become owners by giving them easy credit terms. But in Asian countries, the market price of land is too high in terms of what it produces to allow the tenant to purchase his land. If agriculture becomes more prosperous, either as a result of higher prices or better harvests, the share-cropping tenant will not be able to buy his holding, because the landlord benefits equally from the increased income, and the tenant's position in relation to the landlord has not improved. There is no price which the tenant can afford to pay which the landlord will be willing to accept. If the tenant is to acquire ownership, the price of land must be fixed at a level which he can pay, and this will inevitably be much lower than the market value of the land. All land reforms involve expropriation to some extent for this reason.

In economic terms, there can be no ground for paying compensation at all, since the existing prices of land are monopoly prices. The price that is actually fixed in reform legislation is determined by political bargaining power.

We can conclude therefore that the existence of institutional monopoly creates a strong argument for land reform on the ground of equalizing incomes. We can conclude that in Asian systems and in latifundian systems the redistribution of ownership will not have adverse effects on production through the division of efficient large units, though in plantation systems sub-division may have bad effects, and other ways of equalizing incomes may have to be used.

These arguments, however, tell us nothing above the positive effects of reform on development. They are negative arguments which show it will not do harm. If we are to consider the effects on economic development, this is not enough, and it is the investment aspect that must be considered.

The general economic argument for land reform as distinct from the social argument for more equality is that these systems of ownership give rise to large incomes which are not reinvested in production. They give rise also to social attitudes inimical to investment. Landowners spend conspicuously; buy more land; or invest in urban house property; or lend at extortionate rates of interest to cultivators for non-productive purposes. This argument applies with great force to Asian tenancy systems and to latifundian systems. It does not apply generally to plantation systems. These may have bad social consequences, but whatever their defects may be, failure to invest productively is not one of them, or not generally one. (There are exceptions where plantations keep land out of cultivation, and these systems cause trouble.)

In general, the land systems of Asia and Latin America are strong deterrents to investment and aggravate the shortage of capital by draining capital of agriculture. They undervalue the future. The landowners' preference for land as a form of holding wealth can be explained simply as a result of the secure and high return on capital which results from institutional monopoly, there is no need to introduce the Keynesian liquidity preference analysis.

The crucial question is whether land reform—the change to small ownership—will give better results in the future. Can it promote more investment?

The traditional view of peasant ownership, based on the European experience, is that it does promote investment through the incentives of individual enterprise. Ownership, said Arthur Young in the eighteenth century, is the magic which turns sand into gold. But we cannot universalise this European view. The peasant economies of Western Europe have evolved in very favourable natural conditions, and in a very special historical environment. These conditions have enabled them to reach their present high level of productivity through gradual improvement in grain yields and cattle raising. But the peasant is not a basic universal type, a sociological constant. Where cultivators have been small tenants, and have had no example of better farming to follow, we cannot expect that ownership will suddenly transform them into real farmers.

Even in Europe, experience is not uniform. In Eastern Europe, under the recent communist reforms, peasants tend to eat more. I have even seen peasants in Yugoslavia engaging in conspicuous consumption. In the winter of 1945, when food was very short in the capital, they would bring cooked chickens to eat in the cafés in order to annoy the "bourgeois reaction." That could happen only in a very remarkable country.

In Italy, farm labourers who receive land under the reform like to spend on manufactured goods, and even go so far as to form cooperatives to buy television sets.

In India, Professor Krishnamurti tells us, peasants who come into money may do several things; repay debts; buy a bit of land or a bit of gold; or exceptionally, they buy a diesel pump. In order to foster the habit of investment, the Indian Government promotes the community development schemes. Other countries use cooperatives for the same purpose.

All we can say as to the investment effect is that results depend mainly on what can be done to give inducements to invest, through special credit facilities and special forms of village organisation. We cannot say that reform will *cause* more investment: but we can certainly say that it is a condition, for without more income in the hands of the cultivator, no investment programme for agriculture is likely to have much effect.

Can we say anything about the production effects of reform, when there is actually sub-division of the land?

Here too we can only say that results will depend on how far the new owners can intensify farming, either by the use of more labour on the land, or by the use of more labour and more capital. The inter-war reforms in Finland, Czechoslovakia and Poland, were followed by increased livestock production on peasant farms. This investment was aided by the farm credit system.

In the Balkan countries in the inter-war years, the results also depended to a large extent on the credit and cooperative systems. In Bulgaria, with a good farm credit cooperation system, farm production was intensified through the special crops, tobacco, vines, vegetables, roses, and oilseeds. Grain yields rose somewhat, though they remained low. In Yugoslavia and Rumania, intensification took the form of increased production of maize. This was the result of the increase in population on the land, which necessitated greater production of maize as a food crop, by more input of labour. The increased production of the main food crop was not of course only a result of the land reform, but was a general tendency on all peasant farms. The land reform facilitated the change by transferring land from the latifundia, which had produced more wheat by extensive methods. In Yugoslavia, maize yields rose quite considerably during the nineteen-thirties and reached a fairly high level, but in Rumania they rose very little. Thus the reforms were followed by an increase in labour-intensive production which sufficed to feed more people at a low standard. Had the peasants been able to invest capital, they could have fed the increased output of maize to pigs, and have increased the output of wheat for human consumption. Chiefly because the farm credit system was inadequate and cooperative organisation weak, there was not enough impetus to expand in ways which would have meant better use of the land and a higher standard of living.

Judging by the East European experience, an increase in production of the staple subsistence crops might be expected to be the chief result of reform. Yet in Mexico the reform has produced no such results: on the contrary, the production of the subsistence crops has increased less than the production of fruit and vegetables, and less than livestock production. If the results are considered up to the year 1945 it could be said that in economic terms the reform was a failure. During the period of the reform—that is the whole period from 1910 to 1940—production appears to have remained much below the level in the years before the revolution. Shortage of credit was the main adverse factor. How much of the decline can be attributed to the reform is impossible to say, since up to 1934 conditions were chaotic, and the early thirties were the period of the world crisis when production of grain declined by much the same proportion in other countries in Latin America and in North America. Still, the reform certainly did not promote an increase in production of staple food crops. Throughout the whole period up to 1944 the production of maize and beans remained below the pre-reform level. It did, however, lead to much diversification through the expansion of new intensively cultivated crops. The crops which showed a spectacular rate of increase were bananas, pineapples and tomatoes, while large increases were also shown in the production of rice, peanuts, sugar-cane and cotton. Most of these crops were unknown or grown in very small quantities before the reform. The new peasant holdings show higher yields than other farms in bananas, beans and cotton, lower yields in coffee, barley, wheat and maize. Livestock production rose over the reform period. Cattle increased in number from 1902 to 1940 by 55 per cent, pigs by 87 per cent and sheep by 23 per cent.

Since 1945, however, agricultural production has increased very rapidly, doubling the level of 1929. Most of the increase is still in the production of fruit and vegetables, the irrigated crops, while the increase in staple food crops lags behind the increase in population.

So we can say only that the production effect depends on what can be done to promote more investment.

It would be possible to carry the investment argument very much further. We might regard these three types of land system as the institutional framework for the typical development models set up by Professor Nurkse, the vicious circle situation and the lop-sided economy.

Asian tenancy systems, in certain conditions, though not universally, might be regarded as a determinant of the vicious circle situation. The *zamindari* system in India seems to have been such a determinant. This system was instituted by Lord Cornwallis, at the end of the eighteenth century, in an attempted imitation of the English landlord system. It conferred rights of ownership on tax collectors, the *zamindars*, and under the permanent settlements, fixed the tax on land in cash in perpetuity. As population and production increased, the zamindars could increase

their demand for rent from the cultivators, but the state could not increase its demand for revenue. Monopoly ownership, low taxation and
a high propensity to consume, add up to a vicious circle condition.
Asian tenure system need not have this effect, if the state practices a
policy of financing development from land revenues obtained through
a stiff tax policy, as it did in Japan.

In Latin American countries, the latifundian system promotes lop-
sided development. The great inequality of incomes prevents the expansion of the internal demand for food, while the great inequality in
farm sizes prevents an expansion of supply of food for the home market. So far as investment takes place in agriculture, it is concentrated
in the branches producing for export. Many examples might be quoted
of the distortions in the land use pattern reflecting this one-sided development, as for example in Venezuela where fertile land round the
capital is used for cattle grazing, while food for the city is grown on
remote small holdings.

If these situations are to be changed, then clearly the institutional
framework of society must be changed also. Of course, institutional
change will not reverse the course of development and repair the
damage done in the past through the loss of capital. It can only be the
first step towards breaking the circle or getting a more balanced development. But it is, in such conditions, an essential first step. We can
therefore conclude that land reform, in the conditions of many underdeveloped countries, is certainly a condition of development.

LECTURE III   DEMOGRAPHIC

We have so far considered demographic factors only as settings for
typical land systems, i.e. as static, not dynamic, conditions. Since rates
of population growth are high in the under-developed countries,
whether or not they are over-populated, our discussion of reform in
relation to development must include some reference to demographic
change.

Two questions must be considered:
1. How does the growth of population affect the need for land reform?
2. Can land reform help to mitigate the effects of over-population?

It would be unrealistic to suppose that it could provide a remedy,
but it might, by offering more employment, help to reduce an excess
of labour on the land.

The first question can be answered straightforwardly. The countries
which have carried out important reform measures in recent years have
high densities of rural population. In Asia, they include Japan, China,
India and Pakistan. These are among the world's most densely populated

agricultural countries. Egypt belongs to this group and may now rank first with the highest density of agricultural population per acre of agricultural land in the world.

In Europe, South Italy has a high density of rural population and much unemployment. The East European countries, with the exception of Hungary and Czechoslovakia, have rather high rural densities. In Latin America, Mexico and Bolivia, the only countries on that continent which have so far carried out measures of land distribution, are both densely populated in relation to their land resources.

All these reforms have been carried out in very different ways, and with different ideologies behind them. Some are communist, some nationalist, some Americanist, while others, like the Mexican, arose from spontaneous upheavals, revolutions in the genuine old-fashioned sense. The factor they have in common is shortage of land.

The reason for this relationship between land shortage and reform is obvious. It springs from the influence of institutional monopoly in its various forms. As population on the land increases, the landlord's monopoly power increases also. In Asian systems, the level of rents rises, and rent takes up a larger share in the national income. In latifundian and plantation systems, the demand for labour is inelastic, and as population increases, wages fall. In all three types of large estate systems growing population results in growing inequality of income.

Thus the growth of population gives rise to a demand for reform. There are some densely populated countries which have not yet carried out reform measure—as for instance the Philippines—but there social unrest centres on the land system, and will not be allayed until it is reformed.

Conversely, in countries which are sparsely populated—Syria, Iraq, Persia—the need for reform is not felt. These countries have enough land, water and money, and so could carry out reforms very successfully. But as yet there is no agitation for it, except in regions of close settlement.

Thus we may regard the growth of population as giving rise to agrarian unrest and so creating a demand for reform. Perhaps demographers could calculate the level of rural population density which detonates the explosion.

We may now turn to the second question, and consider whether land reform can mitigate the effects of over-population.

This question is a difficult one, because over-population is not as clear a conception as it should be.

We must distinguish between three conditions, all of which are currently described as over-population:

i. Surplus labour on the land, i.e. an excessive number of workers in relation to the labour requirements of the existing system of farming. This is a static condition.

ii. Falling output per head, resulting from declining productivity of labour, i.e. the Malthusian model, the rate of production lagging behind the rate of reproduction.

iii. Falling output per acre, which results from failure to maintain soil fertility. This is by far the most serious condition of the three.

In recent years, economists have tended to concentrate on the first condition, that of surplus labour. "Disguised unemployment" in agriculture has become popular, because it seems to fit in with Keynesian economics. Much time has been wasted on calculating its extent, chiefly in Eastern Europe. Professor Nurkse, in *The Problems of Capital Formation in Under-Developed countries,* has built up a theory of economic development on the assumption that this condition exists all over Asia.

This emphasis on over-population as "disguised unemployment" is most unfortunate, because it concentrates on pure guess-work and diverts attention away from the ascertainable facts—the fall in output per head resulting from pressure of population on the means of subsistence, and the destruction of soil fertility. These are the real things at the back of most of the discussion about under-developed countries, and there is nothing hypothetical about them: they are happening. These are retrogressive conditions, and so far more serious than disguised unemployment which indicates waste of labour, not declining productivity. Professor Nurkse is right in arguing that surplus labour as a static condition ought to be an advantage to an under-developed country, since it represents waste which could be avoided. But his argument falls to the ground if the real situation is falling productivity. We can learn more about the meaning of over-population in India, for instance, from a diagram showing the fall in total grain production, and the increase in total population over the last ten years, than from calculations of the amount of surplus labour on the land.

In some parts of tropical Africa, destruction of soil fertility is now a terrible problem—although population density is sparse.

So it is extremely important to distinguish between these three different conditions. My main argument, in attempting to answer the question of the effects of land reform, depends on making a sharp distinction between them.

When there is real over-population, i.e. falling output per head, or declining fertility of the soil, land reform cannot do much, and perhaps cannot do anything to remedy the decline in output. It is necessary, of course, to undertake reform in order to increase investment, but if we are realistic, we must recognise that the increase in output achieved in Asian systems, where there is a transfer of ownership to the cultivator, just is not likely to be quick enough to be more than a minor offsetting factor. Economic remedies for falling output per head must be investment on a much bigger scale in industry and large scale projects for agricultural development, irrigation and land reclamation. Obviously anything that can be done to improve methods of farming through community development projects or co-operatives will be a help, even a great help. But such things cannot suffice. Perhaps no *economic* policy can suffice.

Nor can we consider that land reform, in the sense of redistribution of property, is relevant to the problems of soil exhaustion under communal tenures. In some African territories, these systems of communal tenure are based on shifting cultivation. So long as populations were small, the method of shifting cultivation could produce enough food and protect soil fertility, but with the growth of population, the period in which the soil is left fallow grows shorter, and soil fertility is threatened. Eventually there is no more land to clear, and the community is faced with the destruction of its habitat. The need is to find a way of transition from shifting cultivation to permanent agriculture with crop rotations which can be done only through settlement schemes and entirely new forms of tenure—and through measures to control erosion. Reform of the agrarian structure is a crucial need, though land reform, in our sense, is not. We are here entering a wider field which I expressly excluded from the definition of the scope of these lectures, but here it is necessary to refer to African conditions, because they show what over-population really means, at its most intractable.

But where over-population exists in its least harmful form—a surplus of labour on the land in relation to a given system of farming—then land reform can mitigate the conditions. Dividing up big estates into smaller farms can increase employment.

At this point we run into a highly controversial issue. Is there really any validity in the conception of surplus farm population at all?

It has recently been subjected to a devastating attack in an article by Mr. N. Koestner, *Marginal Comments on the Problem of "underdeveloped countries."*[1]

This attack is timely, because the monster of surplus labour (or disguised unemployment) is now proliferating everywhere. Mr. Koestner would like to kill it altogether, and return to Malthusian over-population, i.e., falling output per head, as the true explanation of the situation in under-developed countries. He attacks the conception of surplus labour on two grounds. One is the method used to estimate the surplus, and the other is the assumption on which it is based.

The surplus farm population is defined as that proportion of the farm

[1] *Randbemerkungen zum Problem "unterentwickelte Länder,"* Wirtschaftsdienst, Hamburg, May, 1954.

population which could be removed from the land without reducing agricultural production, under given technical conditions and given social relations. It does not, that is to say, include the number of workers who would become surplus if machinery or other technical changes were introduced.

Various methods of calculating the surplus have been applied. The absolute density of rural population is not a possible basis for calculation, since some types of farming have higher labour requirements than others.

One method used by economists and demographers (chiefly Professor Wilbert E. Moore) has been to calculate the surplus of labour by reference to a standard level of productivity. The number of workers required to produce a given volume of output in Denmark, for example, is compared with the number of workers who actually produce the same volume of output, in, say, Yugoslavia, and the surplus is the difference between these numbers. Of course the fallacy in this method is that it abandons the assumption of the given system of farming. It assumes that Yugoslavia, if it had the Danish capital equipment, and technical knowledge, and the same imports of feed grain as Denmark, would have a surplus of this amount. But since Yugoslavia did not fulfill these conditions, the surplus remains purely hypothetical. This method does not show the extent of the actual surplus at all. All that it shows is a lower level of productivity.

On this point, therefore, Mr. Koestner's objections are well founded, for this method is certainly wrong.

The method of calculation, however, is not an insurmountable difficulty. It is possible to calculate the surplus of labour in any one country on the standard of the labour requirements of agriculture in that country. In practice, this is difficult, because there is much variation in cropping patterns and combinations of crops. But land settlement authorities ought to make such calculations. In Italy, the land reform authorities calculate the labour requirements of different crops and fix farm sizes accordingly. In this case the calculation is easy since they themselves decide what crops are to be grown so that the difficulties in an overall country calculation are avoided.

If we use this method of calculation, however, we must be careful to include in the estimate of labour requirements not only the amount of labour required to cultivate the crops, but also the amount of labour needed to keep up the farm capital. This point may be illustrated by reference to Professor Cleland's estimate for Egypt, which shows that 50 per cent of the rural population is surplus to the labour requirements of Egyptian agriculture. This estimate was quoted in my book *Land and Poverty in the Middle East,* without verification, and I would like to take this opportunity for correcting it. The error lies, of course, in the omission of the labour requirements for capital maintenance. One need only look out of the train between Alexandria and Cairo to see that maintaining the irrigation ditches and canals requires an enormous amount of man-power and time. Camels and baskets are labour-intensive methods, and perhaps labour requirements at such low levels of productivity are not calculable.[2] But whether they are calculable or not, the omission of all this labour puts Cleland's estimate of the surplus right out. This shows how easy it is to be misled by methods of calculation which are apparently exact.

However, Mr. Koestner's objections to the concept of surplus population relate not only to the use of wrong methods, but also to the assumption of given technical methods and social relations. He points out that it is illegitimate to assume that technical methods and social relations are given, because they adjust themselves to increasing demographic pressure. They are variables. As population increases, more labour-intensive methods are used, and more labour-intensive crops are introduced. Cultivation is intensified up to the point where the marginal productivity of labour is less than the cost of the extra energy expended. There is no unemployment, because if cultivators do not work more, it is because the return is not worth it. The farm population may be fully employed at a low level of productivity—or at a falling level of productivity. There may be no surplus labour, although the country is over-populated. The monster of surplus labour gives way to the Malthusian devil, pressure of population on the means of subsistence.

Obviously if land systems do adjust themselves in this way, it is illegitimate to take the technical methods and the social relations as given. So the success of the attack depends on whether it is true that methods of farming and tenure systems adjust themselves to growing population.

As regards Asian land systems with share-cropping tenancy, it is certainly true. These systems are elastic in offering employment on increasingly unfavorable terms. As population grows, cultivation is intensified, farms are sub-divided into smaller units, rents rise, debts increase as cultivators borrow to buy food and eventually yields must fall also.

It is also true of African communal systems which allow free access to land, and allow over-cultivation to destroy soil fertility.

So for these land systems—and they cover an enormously wide range —we must admit that Mr. Koestner's attack is successful. In such systems we cannot regard the methods of farming or social relations as given, and therefore cannot estimate the amount of surplus labour.

[2] The Statistical Department of the Egyptian Ministry of Finance is engaged in preparing an estimate of labour requirements in Egyptian agriculture, including capital upkeep.

The practical application of this argument to Egypt is, presumably, that on the present cultivated area there is no possibility of increasing output per acre by further intensification of labour. Output per head has been falling for some time. There are certainly technical improvements which would increase output—through the use of more capital and knowledge and better seed and fertilisers. But these probably would not increase the demand for labour, which some such improvements might even displace it so that there may be no changes in methods of farming or in social relations which could increase employment. So if there is a surplus of labour (and its existence is too undisguised to be denied) it is surplus not in relation to a given system, but to any system, since methods are already adjusted to the maximum possible extent. The land of Egypt might be said to be over-populated absolutely, not relatively. The only way of increasing output sufficiently to maintain the present level of consumption with the present rate of population increase, is, so I am given to understand, the extension of the cultivated area, which will involve large scale investment in new irrigation projects.

We have to distinguish between this situation, in which the marginal productivity of labour is zero, and the situation where it is negative. This apparently exists in African territories where there is absolute over-population with existing methods, and where further cultivation reduces output per acre by reducing soil fertility. With a completely different system of farming, and some investment, the land might be under-populated; but to make this change lies beyond the powers of the community, as it is now constituted.

Thus Mr. Koestner's argument for abolishing the conception of surplus labour has great practical importance, since it shows that only very large scale and fundamental changes are able to provide solutions to the problem of over-population. It is valuable, because it focuses attention on the really grave problem, the fall in the living standard, rather than on the existence of unemployment.

None the less, though we can agree to abolish the conception of the surplus as a general phenomenon, it seems necessary to keep it as a useful method of analysis in some cases. There are other types of land system which do not adjust themselves to growing demographic pressure, because the social structure is inflexible, the type of farming fixed, and the demand for labour inelastic. Here, the conception of a surplus of labour in relation to a given system is surely valid, as some examples may show.

In the South of Italy, large estates (of the latifundian type) do not adjust themselves to the growth of population. They grow grain by extensive methods or leave the land uncultivated, as poor grazing. Landowners as a rule will not, or cannot, find the capital needed for more intensive cultivation. When they do, they supply citrus fruit to export markets—and this is both risky and costly. There is certainly a large surplus of labour in that region.

Then there is the East European example. In Russia, Rumania and Hungary before 1914, great estates concentrated on grain growing for export, using primitive rotations. They carried on prairie farming in regions where full employment required pig and poultry farming and market gardening. "Land hunger" and "hunger exports" were inseparable features of these land systems.

This failure to adjust may arise from rigid social institutions and attitudes, or from economic factors. Landowners prefer to hold on to land for prestige or power, or find it more profitable to supply export markets with the products of extensive farming. Cheap labour does not give sufficient incentive to invest in better farming or to rent the land to cultivators.

In these conditions, therefore, the concept of a surplus is relevant. There is unemployment or under-employment on the land. Technical methods and social relations can be taken as given, for they are in fact highly inflexible.

Conditions of this kind produce situations of maximum political tension. If land systems do not adjust to growing population, there is likely to be a period of prolonged crisis and even anarchy, as in Ireland, in Mexico and in Eastern Europe. When land questions have acquired great historical importance of this kind, they have usually been part of a wider question, a division of race or nationality which reinforces the conflict between absentee landowners and the under-fed and under-employed farm population.

Can land reform increase employment in such situations? Certainly it did in Ireland, in Mexico and in Eastern Europe. Access to land is likely to promote more labour intensive cultivation, if cultural conditions favour it.

Redistribution of land may not, however, suffice to give full employment, or to raise living standards, if there is only an increase in labour-intensity and no increase in the use of capital. In Mexico, where reform has been carried out on an enormous scale, agricultural production has increased, but it still does not keep pace with the growth of population. In Eastern Europe, in the inter-war years, though farms were subdivided by inheritance and by the reforms, the peasants continued to farm on much the same lines as the large estates had done, with a change in cropping; they were not able to invest enough to change the type of farming completely. In the nineteen-thirties, there was a surplus of labour on the land, partly as a result of real over-population (i.e. falling output per head and per acre) in the poorest regions, and partly as a result of a one-sided type of farming in the richer regions, where there were great possibilities of technical improvement, through invest-ment, by which both employment and productivity could have been increased.

These examples suggest that the gains of reform can be dissipated, and fairly soon, if there is not, at the same time, an effort to change the type of farming with the help of more capital investment.

In answer to the second question, therefore, it is probable that reform will increase employment where farm systems are inflexible and de-mand for labour inelastic, though it may not provide full employment. Experience suggests that it would be better to undertake reform be-fore political trouble arises, and when there is a chance of establishing more productive types of farming before rural population density is too high.

Two other points arise from consideration of the demographic aspects.

The first is that in Asian systems it appears to be very difficult to make ownership stick. Because farms are so small, and because con-sumption perpetually tends to outrun production, the cultivator is al-ways under pressure to resell his holding. In Egypt, I understand, the law foresees this danger. However, so long as the pressure on the land increases, it must be difficult to make ownership secure and permanent. The expansion of other occupations is needed to make it so.

The other point concerns a common objection to land reform. In over-populated countries, it is often said that land reform is useless because it cannot provide enough land to give farms of adequate size to all the farm families. It is true that there is never enough. Most land reforms do not give enough land to all, just because the demand for reform does not become acute until there is a land shortage. But this is not an argument against reform. The fact that everyone cannot benefit does not prove that no one should benefit. The social argument for land reform is based on the need for breaking monopolies of land ownership, by giving easier access to land, or by reducing rents. It im-plies greater equality, not complete equality.

In densely populated countries, the decision as to the size of farm to be granted is inevitably very difficult. But redistribution is not a failure because it does not provide for all. It is not until some families have received land that the question of what is to happen to those who do not receive any is ever asked.

That, of course, is the important question.

Thus from the demographic standpoint we can regard the relation of reform to development in a new light. To make reform successful, development—i.e. investment in agriculture and in industry—is needed. And once a reform is undertaken, the interests of the rest of the farm population will oblige Governments to go further, and to provide wider opportunities of employment through development.

18. Thoughts on Land Settlement*

W. ARTHUR LEWIS

These thoughts are occasioned by my wanderings around the under-developed countries of the world, either in person, or through the medium of books and reports. In practically all these countries land settlement is a major activity. Their populations are growing rapidly, and they are having to bring large new areas of land into cultivation—perhaps I should speak of "colonisation" rather than "land settlement," though in some countries the breaking up of estates for the settlement of small farmers is also occurring, and the problems are in any case much the same. There is great enthusiasm for this work, and much money and effort are going into clearing forests, or controlling river systems, or other preliminaries of settlement. But there is also everywhere some disillusionment. The expense is very heavy; or it proves unexpectedly difficult to get settlers for the land; or if settlers are found, to prevent them from abandoning their settlements within two or three years; or, if they stay, to prevent them from ruining the fertility of the soil. It is the universality of these problems which causes me to ask whether enough experience of land settlement has accumulated in the various countries of the world to enable us now to lay down a set of rules for the success of land settlement. I have visited areas of recent settlement in the West Indies, in Nigeria, and in Malaya, for the purpose of investigating these problems in the field, and I have also read a great deal about experience in some other parts of Africa and of Asia, but I claim no real expertise, and am hoping rather to stimulate you to give of your experience by opening this discussion tonight.

It seems that success depends on the following factors: (*a*) choosing the right place; (*b*) choosing the right settlers; (*c*) physical preparation of the site before the settlers arrive; (*d*) settlers' capital; (*e*) the organisation of group activities; (*f*) the acreage per settler; and (*g*) the conditions of tenure. I propose to go systematically through each of these factors, but I shall dwell lengthily only upon those which seem to me to raise the more difficult questions.

* From *Journal of Agricultural Economics*, vol. 11, pp. 3–11, June, 1954. Reprinted by permission of the Agricultural Economics Society and the author. The author is professor of economics and international affairs at Princeton University.

The place. It is pretty obvious that settlement must fail if the place chosen is unsuitable, whether because of poor soil, or uncertain rainfall, or its unhealthiness, or for other such reason. This, though obvious enough, has not always been taken into account, and many elaborate plans have been frustrated for no better reason. The place must also be reasonably accessible, so that settlers can hope to get their produce out cheaply. Such things are easily said. The trouble with most land settlement is that the best lands are already settled, so that land settlement officers are almost by definition working with areas which the people have rejected for centuries, because of the difficulty of making a reasonable living there. Sometimes the area can be transformed: you can suddenly wipe out the malaria from the dry zone of Ceylon, or you can irrigate what was previously uncultivable for lack or uncertainty of water. But you cannot always make these transformations, and if population is doubling every forty years, as it is in many places, people just have to move on to lands which were formerly sub-marginal. One cannot therefore say, settle only good lands; all one can say is do not settle lands which are on the face of the matter not suitable for settlement.

I have been impressed, particularly in West Africa, with the large areas of land between the forest belt and the desert, which are now sparsely settled, which will have to be fully occupied one day, and in which contemporary efforts at settlement are frustrated more by our not knowing what to do with such lands than by anything else. For example, the Colonial Development Corporation and the Nigerian government have started a settlement scheme at Mokwa,* in the middle belt of Nigeria, which I have visited. The problems there are as much problems of pioneering in agriculture as of pioneering in settlement. There is a complete lack of knowledge as to what crops can be grown there economically; what the soil requires by way of fertilisers; what rotations are appropriate; what protections the soil needs against the sun, wind, and rain, and so on. One cannot help feeling that such questions ought to be decided on pilot farms before the expense is undertaken of clearing large areas for colonisation. But the British taxpayer knows to his cost how seldom this is done. In all the under-developed countries governments are anxious to get a move on with opening lands up for settlement, and it is almost universal practice to settle the lands first and find out what they will grow economically afterwards.

The settlers. To say that one must choose the right settlers for colonisation violates the principle on which most of the world has been brought into cultivation in the past—namely that anyone who wished to clear and farm virgin land was welcome to do so, either freely, or on payment

---

* EDITOR'S NOTE: This project failed in 1954. For an account of the problems encountered see K. D. S. Baldwin, *The Niger Agricultural Project*, Harvard University Press, Cambridge, Mass., 1957.

of a small price or rent for the land. It is still reasonable, I think, that
if there is unlimited land available, it should be had for the asking. In
most of these countries, however, settlement is possible only on lands
on which a great amount of money has been spent to make them cultivable. Such lands are scarce and valuable, and it is only common sense
to restrict their use to the best persons whom one can find for the purpose. One can list the principles most often violated. First, preference
should be given to agriculturists of experience. In the nineteen thirties
in this country there was a curious doctrine that you could take unemployed men from towns and turn them easily into successful farmers,
and the same doctrine is still applied in such places as Jamaica, where
land settlement is thought of as a means of reversing the drift from the
land into the towns (I should say "was thought of" since much more
careful selection of settlers was started in 1950). All "back to the land"
movements are economic nonsense. As productivity per head grows, every
country needs a smaller proportion of its population in agriculture, to
feed itself, the proportion falling from around 75 per cent in the most
backward to around 15 per cent in the most advanced agricultures. The
purpose of colonisation is not to remove people from the towns to the
land, but to make more land available to those who are already in agriculture. I do not deny that individual townsmen should be permitted to
qualify for settlement; but they should do this by first going to work in
training centres or on other farms, and demonstrating that they have
acquired sufficient skill, and are attuned to the rural way of life. Ideally,
no person should be accepted until his record as an agriculturist has
been checked and found satisfactory; but this is a counsel of perfection,
for it is not always easy to make this kind of check in the under-developed
countries, where the agricultural officers are spread very thinly on the
ground and cannot possibly know or report upon all applicants for land.

A second principle of settlement is to choose for each new area people
of similar social background, i.e., speaking the same language, if there
are language differences, or belonging to the same tribe, or coming
from the same group of villages. Thus sources of social tension are reduced to a minimum, and a new community life is quickly built. Settlers
depend very much on each other's co-operation, especially in the early
stages, and this is helped if they are acquainted even before arriving
on the settlement.

A third and more debatable principle is to choose only settlers who
have some capital of their own. This also may seem a counsel of perfection. All the same, new settlement requires an immense amount of
capital, and a settler who has no capital of his own to start with is
gravely handicapped. It is true that the settlement agency can lend
him capital, or provide him with tools or livestock—if it has the money,
but it seldom has enough to be able to provide him with all the capital

he needs. One way out of this proved very successful in Indonesia before the war. New recruits for settlement were transported from Java to the Outer Islands just before the harvest. They were lodged with established settlers, and they helped with the harvest, for wages. The money thus earned, plus the experience, the period of acclimatisation, and the formation of new friendships, all proved invaluable when the recruit moved on to start his own farm. You will no doubt recognise the resemblance of method, if not of objective, to the proposals formulated by Edward Gibbon Wakefield over a century ago.

Preparing the site. In the good old days each settler had to prepare the land himself. He cut the forest, or diverted streams, or built tracks, or built his house, or whatever was required. Millions emigrated from Europe to people the Americas on this basis in the nineteenth century, and millions of shifting cultivators are doing this to this very day, say in the African forests or in Sumatra. At the other extreme we can find today, say in Wisconsin, or in Ceylon, settlement agencies which not only clear the ground, lay in water, build roads, and build houses before the settlers arrive, but also stock up the place with equipment or cattle or other needs. Where should the line be drawn?

In the first place, some preparations are better done by a central agency than by the individual settlers, and there is no doubt that these should be done by the agency. Making the land accessible by roads or otherwise is one of these. Controlling or diverting rivers, building irrigation channels, or piping water, supplies (if feasible) is another. So would the provision of electricity supplies if this were feasible, as it usually is not. On the other hand, the settler can often clear his own land, build his own house, or dig his own wells just as economically as the agency. This is not always so. Where modern bulldozing techniques are appropriate, the agency may be better at clearing the land, cleaning it of stumps, and preparing it, though our African experience shows that mechanical clearing is not always effective or cheap. Digging tube wells is also a specialised occupation which is probably best done by an agency. I confess to peculiar doubts about housing. In all my travels I have never found a government agency which could build cheap rural houses. Their houses cost more than the house the settler would build for himself, and only too often become a burden round his neck and that of the Minster of Finance. So in under-developed countries I always feel that there is much to be said for leaving the rural people to put up their own houses, at any rate until government agencies solve the problem of cheap rural housing.

The advantage of doing as much as you can for the settler before he arrives—including clearing the land and building his house—is that it makes the settlement more attractive, and therefore makes it easier to get and to hold settlers. If the settler has to do these things for himself after he arrives, it will be some time before he can get down to the business of farming, and he may have to spend two or three years on the land before he gets a self-sufficient crop. A good compromise, from his point of view, is for the agency to employ him for wages to do the preparatory work, so that when he eventually gets his farm, he starts with some accumulated savings. On the other hand, the more the agency does for the settler, the greater is the financial cost of settlement, and the smaller is the number of new areas which it can afford to open up. Moreover, we want to be able to rely on the spirit of "Community Development" as much as we can, to get the settlers to give their own free labour for communal works of general advantage (though the community spirit may not be very strong in the initial stages of creating a new community). In practice it is necessary to balance the advantage of getting and holding settlers against the disadvantage of cost. In those areas where there will be plenty of settlers even if the agency does little more than provide roads; the emphasis should be on opening up as much land as possible, at low initial cost; whereas in other countries, where the people are reluctant to move from their villages despite congestion, it is necessary to tempt them by making the new settlements very attractive.

Settlers' capital. What we have just discussed is in effect how much fixed capital the agency should sink in the settler. Much the same considerations apply to working capital. The settler needs tools, seeds, fertilisers, food until the first harvest, livestock, and so on. Many settlements have failed not because of lack of fixed capital—for the settler can rig up a temporary hut, or cut a track to the main road—but because the settler did not have enough working capital to cultivate the land economically. This is why the settlers' own capital is so important; why recruits who have capital are preferable to those who have not (*ceteris paribus*); and why it is useful to have the recruits work for wages before taking over their farms, whether working for other settlers, or working for the agency on preparing the land, or on a demonstration or experimental farm (if the agency runs one). Nevertheless, it is most unlikely that settlers will have all the capital they need, and the difference must be provided by or through the agency, since there is no security to offer to other lenders (neither the land nor the house can be mortgaged, at any rate at the beginning).

On the other hand, the settlement agency is bound to be short of money, and simply cannot afford to supply the settler with all the capital he is likely to require. I would say that the absolute minimum is to ensure what is necessary to make production economic—main roads, water, seeds, fertilisers, tools, livestock—these the settler must have if he is to make a success of the settlement. As for the rest—housing, clearing the land, schools, hospitals, side roads—experience shows that he can make do with rudimentary facilities for a start, which can be improved later; as the returns of farming begin to come in. If the agency is short of money, it should not bother to provide the latter unless it has difficulty in attracting settlers. But in any case it should assure itself that the former are available to every settler, either from his own resources, or from the loans it makes to him. I have the distinct impression that many settlement agencies fall down on their minimum obligations in the sphere of providing working capital.

Group activities. It is now necessary to enquire whether people should be settled on large units, or whether each settler should have his own farm; and in the latter event, what facilities should be organised on a communal basis. This question has to be faced because of the economies of large scale organisation.

The large plantation has well known economic advantages over the family size unit (employing no labour at all); its disadvantages are as a social unit. Large organisations have to be administered on a hierarchical basis, and this gives rise to conflicts and tension between the few who command and the many who have to obey. These tensions are at their greatest if the plantation is owned by private capitalists, but they are not much less if it is owned by the state, or owned by the workers themselves collectively. It used to be thought, in the nineteenth century, that government ownership would abolish exploitation (real or imagined) and unrest, but this myth is now thoroughly exploded. For instance, when the Government of Puerto Rico bought out several large American sugar plantations, there was no noticeable improvement in industrial relations. The myth that all would be well if the workers owned the means of production collectively is even older, but it has never—except temporarily in the peculiar conditions of Palestine—proved possible for a group of workers (say 100 or more) to run a large organisation collectively (I am not referring to co-operatives with a dozen or two members, which are relatively easy to work, though not by any means always so) and demo-cratically (by which I rule out collectives in the U.S.S.R.), without coming to grief either through internal dissension and lack of discipline, or else through capital consumption—and there have been many attempts at this in the history of the world. There is still colonisation going on in large units, whether in private plantations, or in government plantations (of which there are interesting examples in British West Africa) or in collectives. But most of the under-developed countries have now turned their backs upon the large unit. Their ideal in colonisation is the family size farm, or something rather like it. They may establish a plantation for pioneering purposes, to discover what crops or agricultural methods are appropriate, or to introduce a new crop or new methods to surround-ing peasants, but this is a special function.

If the family size farm is to be economic, some central agency must organise on its behalf all those matters which are best done on a larger scale—mechanical operations, irrigation, pure seed farms, research, technical advice, processing the crop, marketing the crop, credit, purchasing supplies, and so on. These may be done by private firms, by co-operative action, by the land settlement agency, or by some other government agency. I do not want to raise here the question who should do these things, which is a subsidiary question well covered in the literature. Rather I would like to emphasize that if small scale farming is to be efficient, it is absolutely necessary to have a framework of centrally organised services doing each of these things on a large scale. If one examines small scale farming in under-developed countries, what sticks out a mile is the inadequacy of this framework, especially in the spheres of water, seed farms, research, extension and credit.

The other question I would like to raise is whether the settler should be under the control of a central agency in these matters, and compelled to follow their advice, or whether he should be free to use or reject their services as he wills. The classical example of control is the well known Gezira* scheme, where the farmer's land is ploughed for him, and where he has to plant the seed he is given in the rotations he is told, to fertilise and cultivate as recommended, and to hand over the crop for processing and marketing—for all of which operations he has of course to foot the bill. The case for compulsion is that it ensures ever-increasing efficiency, whereas if the service were voluntary many farmers would plant inferior seeds and cultivate or market in inferior ways. Compulsion combines the advantages of the plantation with the advantages of family size; on the other hand it does this only by partly reducing the status of the settler from that of independent farmer towards that of labourer acting under orders. Despite the success of the Gezira scheme, it has not often been imitated. As far as I know, the imitations can be counted on one's fingers, and none of them is so clearly successful. Probably the best answer is to apply compulsion in those cases where the advantages of plantation type are known to be considerable—of which sugar cane is probably the most outstanding example at present—but not to use it where the advantages are not so clear—as in rice, or cotton, or rubber.

Some compulsions are probably desirable in any case, even without going the whole hog of Gezira. For example, in rice cultivation, control of movement of water on and off the land may make it desirable for the irrigation authority to lay down a planting calendar to which all settlers must adhere. Or, in the case of cotton, it may be desirable, in the interest

---

* EDITOR'S NOTE: The Gezira scheme is the outstanding settlement project in Africa. About one million acres of land are irrigated. A standard reference is Arthur Gaitskell, *Gezira: A Story of Development in the Sudan*, Faber & Faber, Ltd., London, 1959.

of preventing hybridisation, to insist on all farmers planting only the pure lines of seed provided by the agency. Or there may be compulsory measures in the interest of soil conservation; compulsory crop rotations in the interest of soil fertility; or compulsory disease controls, to prevent the spread of plant or cattle epidemics. Compulsory marketing through designated agencies has also become very popular, for many reasons, good and bad. All these compulsions represent a compromise designed to combine the social advantages of small scale operation with the economic advantages of large scale control. My own belief is that it is a good compromise, and that land settlement agencies do not make sufficient use of such compulsions.

Acreage per settler. Two principles determine how much land the settler should have: (*a*) it must be enough to make a living; (*b*) it must not be more than he can cultivate. Most settlement agencies make the mistake of thinking that the latter is more important than the former; accordingly they do not give the settler enough land on which to make a living, and so after a while he quits.

In fact the latter is no principle at all. The amount of land a family can cultivate depends on the equipment it has; perhaps three arable acres, if it has only a hoe; 10 to 15 acres with a plough and draught animals; 50 acres and upwards with a tractor. It is no use giving the settler less land than he needs in order to make a living. One must first determine what this area is, and then adjust the equipment accordingly.

By "to make a living" I mean to be able to earn as much on the land as he could earn if he went to town and did the sort of work which men of his education and ability can get. In these days this sets rather a high standard. For, in the under-developed countries, wages in the towns are tending to rise continually, through the pressure of trade unions, or of inflation. Let me give an example. An intelligent wage earning family in a Nigerian town could earn at least £60 a year. If the alternative is to grow sorghum, yielding 10 cwt. an acre at £15 a ton, it needs to have 8 acres under cultivation (not allowing for fallows or for rent or other costs) to get the same income. It is not necessary to have quite the same income—a differential of 30 per cent or more between town and rural incomes seems to be acceptable. All the same, wherever one makes this calculation, the conclusion seems to be that in the under-developed countries the family needs around a dozen acres of arable land. There are many examples of land settlement schemes, especially in Africa, where the settler is getting twelve acres or more of arable land, but there is also a marked tendency elsewhere to give the settlers only about five acres of arable land per family or even less (e.g. the West Indies, Malaya, Ceylon, Indonesia).

I am fully aware of the complications in this kind of calculation: the different sizes of families, the different yields of different crops, the need to have some non-arable land, complications of shifting cultivation, non-availability in some areas of sufficient draught animals and so on. I do not stick to any particular figures. But I do stick to my impression that in some of these schemes one of the causes of failure is that the settler is not given enough land to keep him from drifting into other employments. I admit that there are important exceptions. Market gardening can be extremely profitable on as little as two acres—but this is irrelevant to the colonisation schemes we are discussing, which are seldom near to big towns. More important is the fact that at current prices five acres in sugar cane, in rice, in cotton or in cocoa may yield a pretty large income by local standards (how long these prices will last no one knows). I admit also the political difficulty of settling a few people on twelve acres when most of their compatriots have to make do with five or less; as well as the financial difficulty of doing this if it means equipping the farmers with ploughs and animals or arranging for mechanical assistance, in countries where their compatriots are still at the stage of the hoe. I admit that it may be politically or financially impracticable to give the settler more than five acres, and that it may also in some cases be unnecessary. All I am saying is that if he cannot make a living on five acres, it is a waste of effort to try to establish him on an acreage which will not be large enough to hold him.

In those countries where settlement is associated with mechanical cultivation by a central agency, the settler gets around 30 to 50 acres (e.g. Sudan, Nigeria). Mechanical cultivation, however, belongs to countries where land is abundant relatively to labour. In countries where there is already surplus labour in the countryside its introduction is justified only in those marginal cases where it makes possible increased yields *per acre*. Mechanised land settlements have a future in Africa, or in parts of Latin America or the Middle East, but not much future in the West Indies or in South East Asia (except Burma and Siam).

Tenure. There has been a tremendous battle of words over the relative merits of freehold and leasehold tenures in land settlements. Since these tenures are not absolutes, but overlap widely, it does not matter, I suggest, what name the tenure is given, provided that certain principles are observed. On the one hand the settler must have security of tenure, and must be free to pass the farm to his heirs. These are characteristics of a freehold system. On the other hand, tenure must be subject to certain restrictions. He must live on the farm and cultivate it. He must not subdivide it between his heirs. He must not mortgage the farm. He cannot sell except to approved purchasers--or may even not be allowed to sell at all, in which case he must be guaranteed compensation for improvements if he surrenders his holding to the agency. He may also be subjected to a number of the compulsions referred to [in "Preparing the Site"] relating to what, when, or how to plant, to soil conservation, to rotations, to disease control, or to the sale of his crop. These restraints can be called covenants, if we choose to refer to the system as freehold tenure, or clauses if we prefer to call it a leasehold contract. It is the thing, and not its name that matters.

Difficult problems arise in connection with the rent, or whatever name we give to the annual payment which the settler must make to recoup the agency for the investment it has made on his behalf. First there is the question whether this should be a fixed annual sum, or whether it should be a proportion of the harvest. Like most other economists, I do not like proportional rents because of their disincentive effects. On the C.D.C.'s settlement in Nigeria,* the farmers were being asked to pay two-thirds of their crop to the company, and though this was a very fair proportion in terms of the company's costs as well as in terms of what was earned by the farmer, there was evidence of its disincentive effect. In the United Kingdom, where people like both work and money, it may not make much difference if the Chancellor takes two-thirds of marginal income (a much disputed point), but in some under-developed countries where the preference for leisure is high and the opportunities for spending income are restricted, proportional rents may damage incentive. On the other hand, proportional rents are easier on the farmer in circumstances where income fluctuates widely from year to year. Probably the best compromise is a combination: a basic rent fixed in money or in kind plus a small proportion of the crop (say ten per cent), plus separate charges for specific services (mechanical ploughing, marketing, seeds, fertilisers, etc.).

The next question is how large the annual payment should be, and, in particular, should it be large enough to reimburse the agency completely for its investment? Some of these settlement schemes are frightfully expensive, especially where they involve great expenditure on irrigation or on drainage. Costs in Ceylon are running out at well over £1,000 per settler, which is a frightful sum for five acres of irrigated and three acres of dry land. Translated into a 30 year annuity at 5 per cent it would work out as an annual charge of over £12 per irrigated acre, a charge which a yield of perhaps 12 cwt. of rice per acre can bear only for so long as rice maintains its currently inflated price.

Clearly we cannot say that the annual charge must equal the cost. It must be determined, rather, in relation to yields on the one hand, and to what the farmer could earn in alternative occupations on the other. Obviously this itself depends on the number of acres allocated to the settler, since the amount of rent he can afford to pay per acre increases as the number of acres increases, and this is a part of the case for giving the settler more land rather than less. Where land can be brought

* See editor's note on page 300.

into cultivation cheaply, the cost may well be less than the rent which the farmer can bear. But where land settlement is expensive the cost per acre is almost always much greater than the farmer could afford to pay, unless it is feasible to grow crops with extraordinarily high money yields per acre. In these circumstances the question that arises is not whether to fix the charge at a level that covers the cost, but whether to undertake settlements which will cost more than the farmers will be able to pay. The answer to this question is an exercise in the theory of surplus resources. If labour is abundant and unemployed, there is little real cost in employing people to build irrigation systems, and this is eminently worth doing even if the cultivable land which results therefrom cannot be sold or rented at a remunerative price. In all such cases one has to peer behind the veil of money, and ask what are the real costs, and what addition to real national income results. When the veil is replaced the Minister of Finance may be extremely embarrassed to find that what is good economic sense is very difficult in financial terms. This is a very important problem in under-developed countries; they have idle resources, especially labour which commonsense urges them to use for capital formation, but which cannot be so used without the embarrassment of budget deficits, or balance of payment deficits or inflation at home. This is not the place to elaborate this enormous practical problem, and its possible solutions. Its relevance to my present theme is merely the fact that much land settlement has to be subsidised, and deserves to be subsidised, and that this will be a brake on the rate of colonisation unless Ministers of Finance are extraordinarily clever, not only as economists, but even more so as politicians.

Conclusion. I hope I have said enough to stimulate an evening's discussion. My final plea is that some agricultural economists should do a lot more empirical research into this subject, not only because of its intrinsic interest, but also because of its current practical importance in the under-developed world. At present, the literature is very fragmentary, and scattered in out of the way places. If I succeed in stimulating one or two of my listeners to work and publish in this field, I shall feel amply rewarded.

DISCUSSION ON PROFESSOR LEWIS' PAPER

Andrew W. Ashby:

I would like to thank Professor Lewis very much indeed for this interesting paper on land settlement. In many countries of the world land settlement is an important issue at the moment, and I would agree with Professor Lewis that there is a great need for the exchange of experiences and ideas on this subject. We at the Institute of Agrarian Affairs at Oxford are trying to disseminate in our publications experiences about land settlement in different countries and we welcome very much indeed this contribution on the subject.

I would like to take issue with Professor Lewis on one aspect of his paper—the size of holdings. I suspect that my issue is somewhat more apparent than real but I don't think that the size of holdings in itself is an important consideration. I agree with him that the main thing is the standard of living which the settlers can obtain from their holdings. Obviously size plays a very important part in determining this standard of living, but it is not the sole determining factor, another very important one being prices, particularly product prices. One of the great problems in land settlement is to determine the price relationships which are going to exist, both in the present and in the future, because the acreage which a settler should have in order to obtain a satisfactory living depends on the level of prices, both present and future. Too often price forecasts seem to be based on existing price levels and this results in either windfall profits or great hardships to the settlers when prices change.

The other point I wish to raise is that Professor Lewis didn't seem to take note, or very much note, of one of the most important items of equipment of the settler, namely the size of his family. It seems to me that the size of the family is most important in determining the area which should be allocated to individual settlers. Too much settlement policy seems to be based on the fact that the settler is a married man with young children who do not work on the holding. When these young children grow up and start working, obviously a larger holding is required to provide the family with a satisfactory standard of living. If these children marry and still desire to have a share in the income of the holding, the available income is distributed amongst many more heads and is going to result in a level of poverty amongst the people sharing it. On the other hand, should those young people leave the holding the settler will by then be older and less capable of dealing with the size of holding that he was able to manage as a young man and obviously his income will be affected. In too many parts of the world settlement policy seems to be based on a fixed size of holding determined according to estimates of what a man can work, without any assistance from his children, and no provision is made for varying sizes of settlers' families, particularly with regard to their working potential over time.

19. Trade Fluctuations and Buffer Policies of Low-income Countries*

RAGNAR NURKSE

INSTABILITY OF EXPORT EARNINGS: CAUSES AND EFFECTS

Agricultural production suffers from a good deal of natural instability due to weather, pests and plant diseases. As if this were not enough to relieve the monotony of rural life, the notorious cyclical variations in export proceeds are superimposed on the random changes in output. If movements on the supply side were the dominant factor in the export trade of primary producing countries, then export prices and quantities would tend to fluctuate inversely. Actually, prices and quantities accentuate—instead of mutually offsetting—each other in their effect on the export proceeds of primary producing countries. This fact is brought out clearly in a recent United Nations study.[1] Based on the experience of the first half of the present century (1901–1951), this study finds that, on the whole, price and quantity changes contribute about equally to the cyclical ups and downs in export proceeds realised for the leading primary commodities that enter into international trade. Indeed, the cyclical variability of export quantities is, rather surprisingly, somewhat greater than that of export prices: the average fluctuation *per annum* turns out to be 17% for the quantities and 14% for the prices of the 18 major products.[2]

The parallel movement of export prices and export quantities reflects unmistakably the dominant role of demand conditions. It furnishes conclusive proof—if proof were needed—that the export fluctuations of primary producing countries originate in the world's industrial centers. More specifically, they seem to originate in the cyclical swings of investment in fixed capital. That is the way in which economic progress has taken place and is taking place in the advanced industrial countries. The effects of the industrial investment cycle on the demand for primary

* From *KYKLOS*, vol. 11, fasc. 2, pp. 141–154, 1958. Reprinted by permission of *KYKLOS*. The author was late professor of economics at Columbia University.
[1] *Instability in Export Markets of Underdeveloped Countries*, New York 1952.
[2] See Tables 1 and 2 in the study just cited. For the sake of greater comparability the average annual percentage change in prices during cyclical upswings and downswings has been computed for the same 18 commodities as that for the quantities.

products are, as we all know, magnified by inventory changes arising from speculative activities or simply from the normal desire to keep stocks adjusted to the volume of trade and production. Hence the characteristic cyclical variability of the demand for primary commodities.

The effects on undeveloped countries are serious, partly because of the peculiarly important role which external trade plays in their economic life. If we regard Western Europe, the United States, Canada and Japan as the predominantly industrial area (A) and all other countries outside the communist orbit as "underdeveloped" (B), we can divide the trade of all non-communist countries into the following four classes of exports and observe the percentage share of each of these classes in the total:[3]

The 20 countries in Group A have a total population of about 500 million. The more than 100 countries (i.e., customs units, including dependent territories) in Group B have a population of over 1000 million. Yet the intra-trade of A is four times larger than that of B. Why do underdeveloped countries trade so little with each other? Why does so little of the rubber, tin and coffee they produce go to other countries in Group B? Mainly because these countries are poor. Low productivity and low purchasing power create a relative vacuum in their internal economy. That is why their exports to the industrial world (B to A in the table below), which are about two and a half times as large as their exports to each other, are so important to them. And that is where the fluctuations we are discussing take place.

The asymmetry in trade relations between A and B compared with the volume of intra-trade within each group is significant. What may be a mere ripple for A may seem like a tidal wave for B.

The instability of export markets for primary commodities makes any steady development policy difficult; discourages investment in primary production itself; generally limits the "economic horizon"; and destroys the sense of continuity so necessary in private as well as public planning. "People have learned out of the past that wealth comes quickly in Brazil through a boom, and that a sudden turn of events may bring disaster."[4]

[3] Based on figures for 1955 given in GATT, *International Trade 1955*, Geneva 1956. These figures exclude trade within the Soviet orbit. Again for the sake of comparability I have adjusted them further so as to exclude trade between Soviet and non-Soviet countries as well.

Exports of A countries to each other........	40%
Exports of B countries to each other.........	10%
Exports from A to B.....................	25%
Exports from B to A.....................	25%
Total exports.............................	100%

[4] *Economic Growth: Brazil, India, Japan,* edited by Simon Kuznets and others, Durham 1955, Duke University Press, p. 408.

The violent fluctuations of the export trade may well be a major cause of the speculative attitude and the "get-rich-quick" mentality so widespread among businessmen in underdeveloped countries. Through the cyclical instability of foreign trade it may be that dynamic growth in the advanced countries has tended in this way to impede the progress of the poorer countries.

There are two fundamental remedies, one on the side of the industrial, the other on the side of primary producing countries. The first is to control the business cycle. There is no doubt that something has been achieved in that direction. Another great depression will not be allowed to happen. Yet it is unlikely that upswings and setbacks strong enough to cause serious trouble in international commodity markets can be avoided altogether.

The other basic remedy is for the underdeveloped countries to make themselves less vulnerable to such fluctuations. This means filling the vacuum in their domestic economies through a diversified growth of mutually supporting activities catering largely for the home market. It means, in a word, industrialization. Diversification of exports alone may help, since many countries are dependent on a too limited range of export commodities, but it does not go to the root of the problem. Industrialization is the "structural" solution as Professor Eugenio Gudin calls it in his admirable discussion of this problem in his *Principles of Monetary Economics*.[5] It may come; but it will take time. Let us consider the palliatives that might be applied right away.

INTERNATIONAL MEASURES: BUFFER STOCKS

The export markets of primary products could be stabilised by means of buffer stock agencies. These would buy or sell commodities as soon as their world market prices fell to a predetermined minimum or rose to a certain maximum level. Between these official buying and selling points, which could be set some distance apart, prices would be free to vary. Both the support and the ceiling prices could be adjusted from time to time in the light of experience, to take account of long-term changes in demand or supply conditions. The adjustment could be made perhaps to some extent (depending on the distance between floor and ceiling) automatically on the basis of a moving average of prices recorded in the past eight or ten years, even though it is clear that the operation of a buffer stock agency itself would limit the actual range of price variation.

But this is not a device that any single producing country can adopt. Even if the major producing countries adopted it for a given commodity

[5] *Principios de Economía Monetaria*, Vol. II, Chap. x, Rio de Janeiro 1952.

by joint action, difficulties are bound to arise from the natural producer interest in maintaining the buying and selling prices of the buffer stock agency at too high a level. However, the chief practical obstacle which is usually mentioned is that primary producing countries do not possess the financial resources necessary for operating schemes of this sort.

Such schemes would therefore have to be organised on an international basis. In 1951 a United Nations committee of experts, in a report on *Measures for International Economic Stability* (known as the "Angell Report," after the committee's chairman), came out strongly in favor of international commodity agreements, expressed some optimism about their practical chances of success and called upon the International Bank for Reconstruction and Development to finance buffer stocks of primary products. It emphasized the interest which importing countries have in promoting such arrangements. For an importing country a buffer stock can indeed serve the purpose of cheapening the average cost of imported commodities by making purchases in times of recession and releasing reserve stocks in boom periods. As things are, the importing countries tend to buy most when prices are high and stop buying when they are low—a short-sighted and uneconomic procedure even from their own national point of view.

And yet the buffer stock idea, attractive as it is to both sides of the world market for primary commodities, has made no progress at all in its practical execution. The United States has, on the whole, opposed it, even though occasional pronouncements in favor of it have been made in the Paley Commission Report and elsewhere. A new committee of experts set up by the United Nations in 1953, in its report on *Commodity Trade and Economic Development,* though it made some ambitious theoretical investigations, took on the whole a cautious line in regard to international commodity agreements. It pointed to "the tendency of such measures to break down as soon as they fail to serve the immediate national interest of the members" (p. 43); and it noted that the suggestion that the International Bank should concern itself with the financing of buffer stocks "has not been favorably received by that institution" (p. 48).

Is there anything wrong with the buffer stock principle itself? It could be argued that the accumulation of idle commodity stocks would be a wasteful use of the world's capital funds—at a time when these are needed for more urgent development purposes. We may concede that capital investment in buffer stocks of primary products is a wasteful and unproductive investment if considered in isolation. But of course the investment should not be looked upon in isolation, simply as a stock of unused goods. If it achieves greater stability in international commodity markets it might well yield substantial dividends in terms of long-term development in primary producing countries. Besides, it should be noted that buffer stocks would not necessarily result in any net increase in the average holding of stocks of primary commodities in the world. The point is that stocks exist in any case, but under present conditions their behavior is largely such as to accentuate the cyclical swing of prices and incomes of primary producers. International commodity arrangements need not at all add to the world's total burden of carrying inventories, but would seek mainly to impose a steadying pattern on the movement of stocks of primary products.

It is possible that the practical application of the buffer stock principle on an international scale would encounter insuperable administrative and political difficulties. There is one point, however, that may suffice to explain why the buffer stock idea, despite extensive international discussion, has not materialised in any concrete form during the period since the war. The point is simply that buffer stocks can only be started in times of recession, not in boom periods. On the whole, the last ten years have not been favorable to the accumulation of such stocks. Any attempt in this direction would have accentuated the existing inflationary pressures, as did the accumulation of strategic reserves by governments after June 1950. A state of inflationary pressure and full employment is obviously not suitable for the initial setting up of buffer stocks, and perhaps this is a reason why we have not had any since the Second World War.

NATIONAL MEASURES: BUFFER FUNDS

A favorite national device consists in taxing exports of primary commodities in good times and subsidising them in bad times. The purpose of this policy is not to reduce the variations in world market prices, but to soften their impact on the domestic economy by steadying the disposable income realised by primary producers. This can be done in one of three ways. (1) A central marketing agency can be established, which guarantees a certain price to domestic producers and sells the products abroad at whatever price they may fetch in the export markets. The domestic price paid to producers could conceivably be fixed in such a way that the scheme would amount to a tax in good and a subsidy in bad years. (2) A scheme of essentially the same kind may operate expressly in the form of variable export taxes and export subsidies. (3) An exchange control agency can do the same thing by lowering and raising the official buying rates at which it takes over the foreign exchange proceeds of exporters. If its selling rates of foreign exchange remain constant the agency can operate so as to make a profit in periods of high export prices abroad and a loss at other times.

The leading examples of method (1) are today the West African Marketing Boards for cocoa, groundnuts, palm oil, etc. New Zealand started its scheme for dairy products in 1936. The policies pursued by the Perón regime in Argentina by rather similar means will be referred to below. Method (2) has been used widely by various countries in South-East Asia in recent years. The manipulation of exchange rates on which method (3) depends is a familiar practice in Latin America.

The administrative and political differences between the three leading methods may be very important, but for our purpose their common features are of central interest. They all tend to sever the connection between fluctuations in external prices and export proceeds, on the one hand, and the net prices and incomes received by producers, on the other hand. They interpose, as it were, a variable transmission mechanism that can, at least in theory, be used for cyclical stabilisation purposes in primary producing countries. They are national measures available to any single country, and are not dependent on international agreement. Above all, they can and should be operated in such a way that a "buffer fund" of foreign exchange is accumulated when export prices are high and is drawn upon when export prices are low. In contrast to a buffer stock of commodities, a buffer fund of this sort can best be started when world demand is booming.

Just as commodity inventories and cash holdings are to some extent alternative means of coping with uncertainty and instability in the business world generally, so buffer stocks and buffer funds are alternative methods of stabilisation policy for primary producing countries. They are substitutes for each other: the existence of buffer stocks would make foreign exchange reserves less necessary and vice versa. There are differences between them in regard to storage and other carrying charges (which may be negative for buffer funds), but there is one thing they have in common. When it is said that buffer stocks have to be financed and are therefore impracticable for such countries, we must remember that buffer funds, too, have to be "financed"—through abstinence in boom periods. The chief difference lies in the non-specific content of the buffer fund and in the consequent possibility for any individual country to adopt this device independently. The burden of financing is, however, a very real one, in view of pressing needs for imports of equipment as well as consumer goods. In what follows it will be assumed that countries are willing to carry the burden involved—in terms of imports forgone—in operating a buffer fund of gold or foreign exchange.

Under a system of this kind the deflationary effects of a budget surplus—a surplus realised by a separate agency if not by the government itself—tend to offset the inflationary effects of the balance of payments surplus in booms. The reverse occurs in slumps. This procedure can be regarded as a way in which the principle of "functional finance" is implemented in a country depending on exports of primary products. In substance, forced saving is imposed on the country in export booms, so as to permit dissaving in export slumps.

Could we not trust the individual producer spontaneously to lay aside part of his boom-time cash receipts for use in hard times? Producers should recognise that the swollen earnings from an export boom should not all be treated as currently spendable income, but should be kept in reserve against the inevitable reversal of their fortunes. However, the simple answer is that producers, especially in low-income countries, do not in fact behave like this. The reason may be inability to take long enough views, an imperfect financial system, or simply the poverty of individuals. In any case the argument is that the proper treatment of producers' earnings must be enforced by government action or by some other central organisation.

Nevertheless, the whole principle of variable export taxation and subsidisation—whatever administrative form it may take—is open to objections. This note will concentrate on one major point. The question is this: Can it be right to tax the primary producers when their products command a good price abroad and to subsidise them when the reverse is the case? If supply for export is at all responsive to the tax or subsidy, does this not, in the first place, reduce the country's foreign exchange earnings on the average and, secondly, accentuate the cyclical swing of prices on the world market? Should a country not follow the opposite course, namely, let the export volume increase to the utmost when prices abroad are favorable and let it decline when export prices become less attractive?

The answer depends largely on whether in fact the export supply of primary products is elastic or inelastic with respect to price. If it is completely inelastic, if the quantity supplied for export is not at all influenced by the unit price received—then the question does not arise, and the policy under discussion will have at least in this respect no bad effects. If supply is "perversely" elastic, as is sometimes said to be the case, so that an *increase* in price would actually lead to a *reduction* in supply and vice versa, then the most effective policy would be in boom periods to tax exports so heavily as to cut down the net price received by the farmers, and in slumps to subsidise them so as to increase it. In that case the quantities supplied for export would move up in booms and down in slumps, which would be the right pattern from the producing country's national viewpoint as well as for the stabilisation of the world market.

In actual fact the supply of primary products exported is generally—though perhaps not invariably—rather elastic with respect to price. This is shown by the United Nations study already cited, *Instability in Export Markets of Underdeveloped Countries*. The experience of the last half-century, as we have noted, reveals a substantial positive correla-

tion between price changes and export quantities of the 18 leading primary commodities in world trade. The fact that supply of primary
products does respond to prices in the normal way is obviously of
crucial importance in judging the policy now under discussion. This
policy, by stabilising the prices received by producers, interferes with
the incentive to produce more when export prices are high, and serves
perversely to keep up production for export when export prices are low.
This is obviously not a pattern that maximises the producing country's
export proceeds over the business cycle or that helps to stabilise the
international markets for primary commodities.

The West African marketing boards have been the subject of some
interesting discussion in recent years. During the postwar boom these
boards have made big "profits" and accumulated enormous reserve
funds. P. T. Bauer and F. W. Paish, in two long articles on "The Reduction of Fluctuations in the Incomes of Primary Producers,"[6] have
been greatly concerned with the restrictive effect of such policies on the
volume of output for export, and have advocated a moving average
formula to make sure that the price paid by the marketing boards to the
producers is gradually adjusted to keep it in touch with world market
trends.

But even these authors do not, in the last analysis, question the
principle of the guaranteed price scheme. We may agree that such
a scheme can be beneficial by reducing the risk and uncertainty of day-
to-day price variations and by permitting the farmer to concentrate
his attention on productive rather than speculative pursuits: Yet the
initial doubts which Messrs. Bauer and Paish themselves express are
not removed by the formula which they favor. When they object to
marketing boards as instruments of taxation and compulsory saving
their argument is directed against the *persistent* use of such agencies
for these purposes. They want to make sure that the schemes confine
themselves to the cyclical stabilisation of primary producers' income
and that they do not trespass on wider grounds. If we abstract from less
essential complications, the Bauer-Paish formula would require the
fixed domestic price to be adjusted every year so as to make it equal
to the average export price realised in a certain number of years past
(though there is a suggestion of weighting the latest year more heavily
than the earlier years in the moving average). Taxation and compulsory
saving in some years would still be part of the scheme, but would be
more likely, under such a formula, to be offset by subsidisation and
dissaving in other years. The scheme would confine the alternate taxation and subsidisation—or saving and dissaving—strictly to primary
producers of export commodities. That is its merit in the eyes of its
authors. In my own view, that is precisely its basic drawback, because

[6] *Economic Journal,* December 1952 and December 1954.

it will tend, as already explained, alternately to limit and to support the volume of export production at just the wrong times.

Let us consider, by way of contrast, a policy under which the domestic price of the export crop is left free to follow the world market, at least from year to year, if not from day to day. Suppose, however, that taxation *generally* (through excise revenues, income taxes, import as well as export duties) were increased in the country in export booms and reduced in slumps. In this way a budget surplus could be achieved in boom periods, checking both the expansion of incomes and the increase in imports, so as to accumulate the essential buffer fund of foreign exchange available for expenditure in depression years. The crucial point is that in this case it would be done without interfering with incentives to shift resources into or away from production for export in response to varying market conditions. In the national income accounts this policy would aim at stabilising aggregate disposable income and not solely the disposable income arising from export production. Surely the use of general fiscal policy in this countercyclical fashion is better than the narrow form of taxation (positive or negative) that fastens itself exclusively on the price of the export commodity. Price movements have important incentive effects which no underdeveloped country can afford to eliminate from its commercial and development policies.

In reality, it must be conceded that in many countries the practical possibilities of conducting a general countercyclical fiscal policy are extremely limited. Even though other sources of taxation exist, it may be that operating on the prices of export products is the simplest and easiest form of countercyclical fiscal policy. We can only plead for a recognition of the undesirable incentive effects of export taxation and subsidisation. For the accumulation of a buffer fund of foreign exchange it can be harmful to rely entirely on taxing export products through marketing boards, differential exchange rates or outright export duties. In practice, the best that governments could aim at is probably a compromise, involving in boom periods some taxation of exports, yet allowing a part of the increase in export prices to benefit producers' receipts, and endeavoring through other fiscal methods (e.g., higher income, property, excise or even import taxes) to keep total disposable incomes, and consequently the demand for imports, in check.

Aside from such administrative considerations, exclusive reliance on export taxation and subsidisation during the business cycle can only be defended on the ground that the cyclical shifts of effort and resources into and away from export production in response to external price changes would—even if stability of total disposable income is achieved—upset the stability of the domestic economy by demanding too much structural adaptation in the short run. A policy of stabilising the net domestic price realised by producers of export crops can be regarded as a deliberate attempt to restrain such shifts, so as to avoid disturbing the country's economic life. This would be a case of choosing a lower average real income for the sake of greater stability. The economist cannot quarrel with such a choice—so long as the choice is made with open eyes, with full awareness of the economic advantage of exporting more when export prices are high and less when export prices are low.

TAXING EXPORTS TO FINANCE DEVELOPMENT

In conclusion let us take a look outside the cyclical problem with which this note is mainly concerned. It is of some interest to consider the taxation of exports of primary products not as a cyclical but as a permanent policy designed to finance industrial development in the domestic economy. The considerations of incentive which we stressed in the cyclical context arise in this case also.

It is particularly instructive for this purpose to examine the contrast between Argentina's policy after the Second World War and the policy followed by Japan in the latter part of the 19th century.

Argentina's policy of exporting primary commodities through the medium of a government monopoly is too well known to require description. Since prices received by farmers at home were kept far below the prices obtained abroad, the system was equivalent to heavy taxation, year in year out, of the exports of primary products. The main object was to finance industrialization. The results are equally well known. Supplies available for export dried up. Serious damage was thus inflicted on the country's major source of foreign exchange, at a time of favorable export markets. Correspondingly, Argentina's import capacity was severely weakened. In 1950–1952 her imports of capital goods were 37% below the level of 1947–1949, and even below the prewar level of 1937–1939.[7]

If world demand for Argentine exports had been inelastic, the taxation of export production and the decline in export volume would have led to an increase in export proceeds. But Argentina is not the only seller of the products she exports. Argentina alone is evidently faced with rather elastic external demand. Even if a country were the sole exporter of a commodity such as rubber or coffee, world demand for its exports can be inelastic only over a certain range of price changes. If it were inelastic over the whole range this would mean that the world would be willing to spend all of its income on rubber or coffee. This the world is not prepared to do. Demand can be inelastic over only a limited range; sooner or later it will turn elastic as supply is restricted

[7] United Nations, *Processes and Problems of Industrialization in Underdeveloped Countries*, New York 1955, p. 113.

and price increased. The exploitation of a monopoly position by a single country or by a group of countries acting in combination is therefore always a tricky business; the scope for such action is usually rather limited.[8] Within any such range, a reduced quantity of export shipments would extract from the world market an increased amount of foreign exchange. *If* such possibilities exist, then export taxation can be an effective means of discouraging export production and at the same time appropriating for public purposes the increase in export proceeds. In that case the argument for taxing exports is one that applies continuously, regardless of cyclical changes, and is not particularly relevant to the "buffer fund" model discussed earlier. But, to repeat, such possibilities are nearly always very limited. They certainly did not exist for Argentina in any marked degree in the years after 1945. In these circumstances the ruthless taxation of Argentine exports of agricultural products killed the goose that laid the golden eggs which were expected to pay for the program of industrialisation.

Now let us look at Japan. World market conditions for Japanese exports of raw silk were highly favorable after 1867, when the drive for industrialisation was started. The Japanese government, however, did not tax exports of silk; it taxed farmers on a broader basis, mainly through the famous land tax, which was reassessed and tightened up in the 1870's. In this way it left intact the incentive to produce silk for export at a time of favorable export markets, while yet, in effect, intercepting the foreign exchange proceeds of these exports for use in industrial development.

In the domestic income flow the land tax was a means of skimming off the extra income earned by agriculturists from silk produced for export; it was a means of compulsory saving. In the foreign exchange accounts it was a means of releasing a growing portion of the country's export proceeds for imports of capital goods, which, as we know, greatly increased in volume. Without the necessary domestic "abstinence," the foreign exchange proceeds would not have been available for investment in imported equipment. The domestic income flow and the foreign exchange accounts are so often treated as two independent things that their interrelations, as illustrated in this case, can hardly be overemphasised.

For our present theme, however, the main point of the Japanese example is that taxation was imposed, not on exports as such, but on a basis separate from export prices or export proceeds. This allowed the price incentive to function so as to promote export supplies in full response to a favorable trend of export prices.

[8] As the "optimum tariff" argument suggests, a country in such a position would ideally restrict export supplies to a point where it would actually operate on the elastic portion of the demand schedule which it faces in the world market.

Essentially the same point, it seems to me, is applicable to the cyclical problem of income stabilisation in countries highly dependent on exports of primary commodities. In the context of cyclical stabilisation the object is not so much the financing of capital-goods imports as the accumulation of a buffer reserve of foreign exchange which will permit the country to live beyond its foreign exchange earnings in bad times. Here too it seems desirable to secure the necessary internal saving in boom periods in such a way as to leave some—if not full—scope for export price changes to operate as incentives to increased supply. Naturally the force of this argument will vary from country to country and perhaps still more from product to product. If the United Nations study of 1952, however, is correct in suggesting a high correlation between cyclical changes in export prices and quantities, it seems plausible to conclude that the supply of primary products for export is rather sensitive to price changes. If this is so, the argument may well be of fairly general relevance to the export policies of underdeveloped countries today.

20. International Commodity Arrangements*

GERDA BLAU

The main purpose of this paper is to consider the scope and limitations of international commodity arrangements as instruments for promoting economic stability and growth, particularly from the point of view of the less developed countries. In the closing years of the war and in the immediate postwar years very high hopes were entertained of the creation of a widespread network of individual commodity agreements as part of a new international economic order. Since then, there have been a large number of resolutions by the United Nations,

* The views expressed in this paper are the personal views of the author and do not commit the organization to which she belongs. Presented to the International Congress for Economic Development, September, 1962, and reproduced in the *Monthly Bulletin of Agricultural Economics and Statistics*, vol. 12, no. 9, pp. 1–9, September, 1963. Reprinted by permission of the International Economic Association and the author. The author is director, Commodities Division, Food and Agriculture Organization, Rome.

and Specialized Agencies, and other intergovernmental organs urging the negotiation of commodity agreements; there has also been a great deal of preparatory work and discussion concerning individual commodities. Yet, in the seventeen years since the end of the war, international agreements have been concluded for only five commodities—wheat, sugar, coffee, tin, and olive oil. Of these, the only two functioning at present as agreements which qualify as producer-consumer agreements and contain some operative provisions designed to influence world trade, are those for wheat and tin.[1] The total value of world trade in the five commodities for which agreements have been concluded in one form or another accounts for about 10 percent of world trade in primary products. The proportion of trade actually covered by agreement provisions is considerably less.

In recent years, there has been a growing sense of disappointment, particularly on the part of the primary producing countries, with the limited results attained so far. Increasing attention has been paid to other techniques which could serve either as a substitute for, or as a complement to, the working of international commodity agreements. At the same time, efforts continue to be made by governments to overcome the obstacles that have hitherto frustrated the conclusion of more effective commodity agreements on standard lines and also to explore the possibilities of new types of agreements of a more comprehensive kind.

OBJECTIVES OF COMMODITY AGREEMENTS

International commodity agreements can, in principle, be devised to serve one of five objectives or a combination of them:

1. They can attempt to raise, or uphold, export earnings by means of arrangements among producers, restricting production or exports or both (the prewar commodity agreements concluded in the 1930s were mainly of this type and their experiences have illustrated some of the

---

[1] The International Sugar Agreement continues formally in force until the end of 1963 but its operative provisions have ceased to function as from the beginning of 1962, owing to the failure of governments to reach agreement on the reformulation of quotas. For coffee, there has been a succession of one-year producers' agreements by which the governments concerned agreed to limit exports. A new coffee quota agreement on more comprehensive lines, providing for the participation of importing countries and intended to run for a period of five years, is at the stage of negotiation. The olive oil agreement, although negotiated in accordance with the rules of the Havana Charter, provides only for a series of coordinated national measures without attempting to regulate international trade (which in the case of olive oil merely accounts for about 5 percent of world production and consumption). Good progress has been made in recent months with preparatory work on an international agreement for cocoa.

difficulties of effective operation of such arrangements in the forms then applied).

2. They can attempt to promote economic stability, both in the producing and in the consuming countries, by preventing undue fluctuations of prices and quantities traded but without interfering with long-term trends.

3. They can endeavour to mitigate the problems and hardships of such long-term adjustments as may be required in cases of persistent disequilibrium between production and consumption, particularly under conditions of inelastic supply and demand.

4. They can try to counteract the shrinkage of markets to primary producers which results from protectionist measures or preferential arrangements in importing countries.

5. They can be used as instruments for intergovernmental commodity programing by governments on more comprehensive lines, taking account of trade on both commercial and concessional terms, of national policies relating to production, prices, and stocks, and of the close links between problems of commodity trade, aid, and development programs.

One of the chief difficulties in the actual negotiation of international commodity agreements has been that the participating governments have not always been fully conscious of which of these five objectives they were mainly aiming at; nor were they fully conscious of the extent to which any of these objectives could be successfully attained by one or the other of the standard types of agreement-techniques. The primary exporting countries have been naturally interested not just in the stability of prices but in securing reasonable returns in terms of the manufactured goods which they are buying—in much the same manner in which the primary producers of the developed countries are mainly interested in obtaining some degree of parity of purchasing power in relation to the rest of the economy. The importing countries, on the other hand, have been mainly interested in securing more stable conditions of trade and have been prepared to consider any measures influencing the levels of exporters' returns, over an average of years, only insofar as such measures formed part of a process of orderly adjustment of production to the changing conditions of the world markets. Hence the emphasis in Chapter VI of the Havana Charter (which was intended, and still serves, as a code of guiding principles governing international commodity negotiations) that no interested government should be excluded from negotiations, and further that "participating countries which are mainly interested in imports of the commodity concerned shall, in decisions on substantive matters, have together a number of votes equal to that of those mainly interested in obtaining export markets for the commodity." The two main objectives of international commodity agreements, as envisaged in Chapter VI of the Havana Charter, are to prevent or moderate pronounced fluctuations in prices but without interfering with long-term trends, and to provide a framework for facilitating adjustments between production and consumption, having regard in both cases to the desirability of securing long-term equilibrium between the forces of supply and demand. In other words, the main objectives are those stated under (2) and (3) above.

BALANCE OF BARGAINING POWER

The provisions of the Havana Charter which prescribe that producers and consumers should have equal weight in shaping the provisions of an international agreement are obviously important and commendable from the point of view of international ethics. At the same time, they have undoubtedly made the negotiation of individual commodity agreements more difficult than during the interwar period of largely unilateral approaches by producers or by their governments. For these provisions of the Charter imply that an agreement is negotiable only as regards matters on which there is an identity of interest of both parties, or on points on which a "bargaining balance" can be reached—i.e., where the advantages of adhering to the agreement are assumed to balance its disadvantages, from the point of view of each participant.

Indeed, it is only in regard to the moderation or elimination of price fluctuations that there is a clear identity of interests between the exporting and the importing countries—though even here the interests of the exporting countries (which in typical cases derive the great bulk of their foreign income from the sale of one or a few primary commodities) are very much greater than those of the importers whose economies are not greatly affected by changes in the price of any one of these commodities.

The postulate of non-interference with long-term trends implies that prices resulting from an agreement should not differ, on the average over a number of years, from what they would have been in the absence of an agreement. Since the future is unknown, this "neutral price" can be definitely ascertained only *ex post*, whereas the technical solution of the problem presupposes that it is known *ex ante*. In the absence of such pre-knowledge, any commodity agreement necessarily partakes the character of a speculative deal—a deal which can be justified as a form of insurance against the risk of undue losses resulting from large and unexpected price variations. The fact that the conclusion of price-stabilizing commodity agreements has proved so difficult in practice appears to indicate that neither exporters nor importers were really prepared to pay a substantial premium for this kind of insurance. Moreover, for a number of commodities it is difficult, or impossible, to speak of a representative world price. And as to the interests of exporters, their *main* concern, of course, has been with prospects for their total export proceeds (depending on volume as well as price) and with the average level of export proceeds over a number of years, measured in terms of import purchasing power, not merely with short-term fluctuations in money terms.

Added to this is the fact that in recent years (since 1954) the primary exporting countries have been faced with a slow deterioration in their terms of trade resulting from an unfavourable trend of commodity prices in relation to the prices of manufactures. The impact of cyclical changes has become relatively less important. Yet, for a solution of the trend problem the types of commodity agreements which have been the subject of international discussion and negotiation in the 1950s are not, in themselves, a sufficient instrument. Nor do these agreement-techniques take sufficient account of the need for improved co-ordination of national policies in developed countries.

THREE STANDARD TYPES OF AGREEMENTS

Three types of agreements have been negotiated and their subsequent history illustrates the same fundamental difficulties.

The first of these is the *multilateral contract agreement*. The main feature of such an agreement is that it contains an obligation on importers or exporters to buy or sell certain guaranteed quantities. These guarantees have to be implemented at a stipulated maximum price, or stipulated minimum price, whenever the free-market price reaches or exceeds these limits. To be reasonably effective, such a multilateral contract agreement should cover a high proportion (say two-thirds) of the total trade of the participants and the spread of prices between the floor and the ceiling should not be too wide. It would then protect the real national income of both the importing and the exporting participants from the major ill consequences of fluctuations in the world price, while preserving the free-market price as a mechanism of adjustment for securing a balance between world production and consumption.

The only case of a multilateral contract agreement is the International Wheat Agreement. The original Agreement of 1949 provided for guaranteed quantities which covered about two-thirds of world trade; the maximum price was $1.80 per bushel and the minimum price was stipulated to fall progressively from $1.50 in the first year covered by the agreement to $1.20 in the fourth and final year. During the four-year period world prices were running continuously above the stipulated maximum; importing participants availed themselves of their right to buy the agreed quantities at the stipulated maximum price, so that no less than 95 percent of the guarantees were effective. As it turned out, therefore, the 1949 Agreement operated entirely in the interests of the importers. When the Agreement came up for re-negotiation in 1953, the major exporters were successful in securing a rise in the stipulated maximum price to $2.05, and of the stipulated minimum price to $1.55, throughout the subsequent three-year period. This was achieved at the expense of the withdrawal of the United Kingdom, whose representatives expected—correctly as it turned out—a decline in world prices. During the period covered by the second agreement, some other importers also withdrew. As a result, the proportion of world trade covered under the second agreement dropped to 25 percent, as against 60 percent in the case of the first. When the agreement was re-negotiated for the third time in 1959, the idea of guaranteed quantities was abandoned and was replaced by a simple undertaking of member-importing countries to purchase a minimum percentage of their commercial requirements from member-exporting countries, as long as prices move within a stipulated range, but without any obligation to buy guaranteed quantities at the minimum price. The exporters retain the obligation to sell at the maximum price, if called upon to do so by importing countries, an amount equal to the annual average of importers' purchases over the previous four years (minus transactions already made within the agreement year).[2] This new type of agreement has made it possible to bring in the great bulk of commercial world trade, but only at the expense of eliminating some of the former operative provisions concerning rights and obligations, particularly those relating to purchases of stipulated guaranteed quantities at specified minimum price levels. In any case, during the period covered by the four agreements the significance of the world price of wheat as a mechanism of adjustment has been progressively undermined, partly because it has more and more been set by the two largest exporters and partly because, faced with growing surplus supplies, the exporters have been disposing of an increasing proportion of their supplies under special arrangements on concessional terms.[3]

The second type of agreement, on which particularly high hopes had been set in the early postwar years, consists of the institution of an *international buffer stock*, which stabilizes prices by an obligation to buy whenever the world price falls below a certain minimum and to sell when the price rises above a certain maximum (combined perhaps with a discretionary right to buy or sell between these limits). The well-known problem of a buffer stock scheme of providing adequate finance to enable the authority to carry out its functions is closely related to the difficulty of successfully forecasting the future relationship

---

[2] The latest agreement, which started operating in 1962, is similar in character to the 1959 agreement. The minimum and maximum prices have been raised to $1.62½ and $2.02½ per bushel. The U.S.S.R. is a member of the current wheat agreement.

[3] This point will be further considered on pages 331–332.

between supply and demand, and of securing international agreement on a range of prices at levels consistent with the prospective movement of the long-term world price which secures a balance of supply and demand. Unless the trend of this long-term world price is stable or rising, a buffer stock is not likely to be successful in ironing out the fluctuations from the trend for more than a limited period of time. The reason is that with a falling trend the necessary downward adjustment of the operating range of prices cannot be secured with sufficient promptitude, even if the experts were successful in distinguishing between what is a fluctuation and what is a trend. With a rising trend the same difficulty arises, but since this does not impair the finances of the buffer-stock authority (on the contrary, it tends to strengthen them), it does not prevent it from resuming operations subsequently, once agreement has been secured on the revision of the operating range of prices.

The only buffer stock scheme covered by an international agreement is the International Tin Agreement, which, however, provides for contingent export control as well as for a buffer stock. As it has turned out, this is one of the few commodities for which in recent years the relationship between world consumption and production has been favourable to producers. Nevertheless, the scheme ran into difficulties less than two years after its inception in 1956, when the tin price fell heavily and the manager of the buffer stock used up all his cash resources (including some supplementary resources) in the purchase of tin without succeeding in stabilizing the price. Subsequently, the world price was held up by the export controls provided in the agreement. Over the first full year of control, the over-all reduction of exports by participating countries was no less than 41 percent and over the second full year it was 36 percent. Despite this, and on account of considerable supplies from the U.S.S.R., the price collapsed temporarily in the last quarter of 1958 but recovered rapidly in the subsequent year, aided by an arrangement with the U.S.S.R. about exports.

The third type of agreement is an *export-restriction agreement,* which makes provision for the limitation of exports insofar as this is necessary in order to secure some degree of stability of prices. The Havana Charter laid down specific conditions with which the operation of such an agreement should comply, designed mainly to protect the interests of consumers and to prevent the imposition of too rigid a pattern of production. Unlike the two types of agreements already considered, the effectiveness of an export-restriction agreement depends to a very large degree on the comprehensiveness of the agreement, i.e., on the extent to which it brings under control all important sources of export, actual and potential; on the extent to which substitutes are available; and on the importance of international trade of the commodity in relation to world production and consumption. Moreover, to be effective, an export-restriction scheme logically requires the regulation of output by *individual producers* and not only of exports by the countries as a whole. Failure to secure world-wide participation in a quota arrangement on the part of exporting countries is less serious in so far as importing countries are brought in as participants and undertake to discriminate (in one way or another) against non-participating exporters. At the same time, the very features likely to strengthen the effectiveness of a quota-restriction agreement as an instrument for raising or upholding export earnings in the short run—such as comprehensiveness of membership, stringent quota provisions, and strict adherence on the part of both exporters and importers—are also those likely to endanger the long-term prospects for the industry as a whole, by impeding change, sheltering high-cost producers, and by generating centrifugal forces which may eventually lead to the collapse of the whole arrangement. Great care must be taken, therefore, to set quotas realistically, so as to allow for sufficient flexibility and to encourage efficiency and desirable structural adjustments in the primary exporting countries, as well as expanding markets in importing countries.

Apart from the International Tin Agreement, to which reference has already been made in connection with its buffer stock features, the only postwar instance of an operating agreement of this kind is the International Sugar Agreement.[4] The agreement, in the form negotiated in 1953, relied on a system of export quotas for the so-called "free-market" sector which accounts for less than one-half of world sugar trade and provides the balance of requirements not covered by special trading arrangements. It differed from the export-quota agreements concluded before the war, in that it contained automatic provisions for an increase in the quotas whenever the world price exceeded a certain maximum for 30 consecutive days and for a decrease in the quotas when it similarly fell below a certain minimum; and in that it imposed an obligation on importing countries to procure a certain part of their supplies from participating exporters. The exporting countries agreed to regulate their production so as to avoid the accumulation of stocks in excess of 20 percent of their annual output. The initial export quotas, fixed each year in the light of estimated requirements, were adjusted thereafter on the basis of price movements with the object of maintaining the price within the range of 3.25 to 4.35 cents. Prices remained fairly stable, near the minimum of the range, until 1956, when a short European crop and comparatively low levels of reserves coincided with the strong stimulation

---

[4] The new draft agreements for coffee and cocoa are also based on export quotas (for traditional markets), supplemented in the case of the draft coffee agreement by some provisions for the regulation of output.

of demand caused by the Suez crisis. With prices running well above the maximum of 4.00 cents, all quotas and limitations became inoperative until late 1957, when prices again moved within the range. In the following year, the original provisions were amended to allow for automatic and discretionary quota adjustments at various points within the initial price range. In more recent years, the efficiency of the agreement has been impaired by the drastic changes in the pattern of trade following the cessation of arrangements between the United States and Cuba. Since January 1962, all operative provisions have been suspended owing to the inability of participating governments to agree on the distribution of quotas.

What the record of operations of these three types of agreements has shown is that it is extremely difficult to deal with the problem of price stability in isolation and to conclude agreements which suceed in stabilizing prices but without interfering with what the trend of prices would have been in the absence of such agreements.[5] The problems of trend and fluctuations, while they do logically call for different kinds of remedies, cannot, in fact, easily be separated and treated apart from each other outside the world of economic textbooks. The agreements operated in postwar years have succeeded in serving some limited objectives, but they have not proved capable of dealing with the two main sets of commodity problems which call for action: the need for some assurances, particularly to low-income exporting countries, of fairly stable and remunerative average levels of export proceeds for a number of years ahead, say for the five-year periods normally covered by national development plans; and the need for improved international co-ordination of *national* policies of the developed countries.

DIFFERENT CATEGORIES OF COMMODITIES

Before we can consider further the implications for postwar experience, it is necessary to look at the problem in more concrete terms, in the light of the main features of the actual patterns of world com-

[5] It would, of course, be an exaggeration to say that the difficulty of securing agreement over prices or quotas was the sole, or even the main, factor responsible for the failure to reach agreement in the case of a number of commodities where a great deal of preparatory work was done to consider possible forms of regulation and where there was a clear desire on behalf of both exporting and importing countries to reach an agreement of some kind—as, for example, in the case of cotton, rubber, and rice. There are serious technical difficulties connected with grading, standardization, storage qualities, and limitations imposed on the effectiveness of controls due to competition from synthetic materials or other close substitutes. Account must also be taken of the structure of the market which, in the case of rice, for instance, is characterized by a network of bilateral trading arrangements that could not easily be dispensed with. All these factors add to the difficulties of formulating obligations capable of clear interpretation.

modity trade. One of the reasons for the comparative lack of success so far has been that in many of the intergovernmental discussions of commodity questions the problem has been approached in a generalized way without sufficient regard to the basic differences between different groups of commodities. Indeed it is one of the merits of more recent intergovernmental consultations, particularly those connected with the Common Market, that they have drawn attention to (though they have far from solved) the different types of problems which need to be considered for different categories of products.

COMMODITY EXPORTS OF THE DEVELOPED COUNTRIES

It is not always realized that no less than one-half of the total value of world commercial exports of primary products[6] both originates in, and is absorbed by, the developed countries of North America, Western Europe, Oceania, and Japan. The bulk of such trade consists of temperate-zone agricultural products, mainly foodstuffs. The pattern of trade in this group of commodities is very largely influenced by the domestic agricultural stabilization and support policies of virtually all the importing countries and of the United States (which, of course, is the largest exporter). The funds required for the support of agriculture are drawn from the non-agricultural sectors of the countries concerned. This is a very important difference from the situation prevailing in underdeveloped countries, where virtually all incomes are low and where agriculture accounts for the dominant part of the national income. In such countries there are no resources available for the price support of agricultural export commodities. Indeed, the export-producing sectors of these economies are often called upon to provide economic assistance for programs to raise productivity in the even poorer agricultural subsistence sectors and for purposes of development and diversification generally.

The existence of an extended network of domestic agricultural policies in the developed countries has important consequences. A network of such measures provides an effective barrier against any sudden large-scale contraction of agricultural incomes such as occurred in the Great Depression of the early 1930s. At the same time, the existence of independent national policies of price and output regulation has created a situation in which the patterns of production for some of the most important commodities (such as wheat) have been completely divorced from world supply and demand relationships, resulting in large and growing surplus stocks in some of the exporting countries. These policies have led to the introduction of export subsidies, or of two-price systems

---

[6] Excluding petroleum and the exports of the centrally-planned economies.

on behalf of the exporters, and of varying forms of import regulation on behalf of the importers.

The emergence of structural surpluses—a consequence of remarkable technological progress and not only of the national policies—has resulted in new forms of trade flows, on concessional terms, from the developed mainly to the underdeveloped countries.[7] It has not been found possible up till now to bring such concessional trade within the operative provisions of the International Wheat Agreement (which is the sole international agreement in operation for a predominantly temperate-zone staple commodity). However, a beginning has been made in evolving a new code of international ethics through the acceptance, by most of the governments concerned, of a flexible set of principles[8] which encourages constructive uses of surplus supplies, mainly in low-income food-deficit countries, and at the same time provides some safeguards for the interests of commercial exporters. It has also been found possible to secure the acceptance by a large number of governments of a set of principles concerning national price stabilization and support policies,[9] which reflects the highest common denominator of international understanding attainable so far from governments with differing and partly conflicting policies. These attempts to arrive at sets of agreed principles, which are formally accepted by governments but which do not imply any contractual obligations and carry no sanctions, are nevertheless of importance, particularly in view of the fact that governments have been generally reluctant until now to accept contractual obligations that interfere with their sovereign rights in shaping domestic policies.

Thus, while the domestic agricultural policies of the developed countries have lessened their incentives, as compared with the early 1930s, to insure against violent price changes by means of international agreements, their incentives to secure access to markets have been increased as a result, and the promotion of the latter objectives requires commodity agreements of a different character. The current discussions on the Common Agricultural Policy and related negotiations with the United Kingdom and other Commonwealth and third trading partners, though still in a preliminary stage, show an increased willingness, in the case of temperate zone foodstuffs, to work for international agreements of a much more comprehensive type. Such agreements would comprise trade both on commercial and on concessional terms and also some guarantees

---

[7] So far mainly from North America to the food-deficit regions of Asia and also to a number of Latin American and African countries.

[8] *FAO Principles of Surplus Disposal and Guiding Lines.* FAO document C 55/22, Appendixes A and B. Rome, July 1955. The main features of these principles have also been incorporated, since 1959, in the consultative provisions of the International Wheat Agreement.

[9] *National Agricultural Price Stabilization and Support Policies: Guiding Principles Recommended by FAO.* FAO, Rome, 1961.

of access to the European consuming markets, as well as policies concerning prices, production, and stocks in the participating countries.

COMMODITY PROBLEMS OF UNDERDEVELOPED COUNTRIES

With regard to the other half of world commodity trade, which originates from the underdeveloped countries, the nature of the problems is quite different. This trade consists primarily of tropical agricultural products (though it also includes some temperate-zone agricultural exports from semideveloped countries of Latin America) and, to a lesser extent, of minerals. About three-quarters of this trade is absorbed by the developed countries, mainly those of North America and Western Europe, which thus take about 85 percent of the world imports on commercial terms of all primary products.[10] In the case of these tropical export products and minerals, in contrast to temperate zone foodstuffs, the problem of the narrowing of markets due to protectionist measures by the importing countries exists only in a few cases (notably sugar),[11] though analogous problems arise on account of preferential arrangements which may now become more important owing to the European Common Market. On the other hand, the markets for exports of raw materials from the underdeveloped countries (with some exceptions, such as petroleum) are affected by other causes: the growing use of synthetic materials of various kinds, the reduction of the amounts of raw materials required per unit of finished product, and a shift in the pattern of industrial production which has caused a decline in the relative importance of industries heavily dependent on imported materials. Added to this there is growing evidence of a structural overproduction for a large number of tropical products, owing to an increase of yields resulting from the important technological improvements of recent years, as well as the large increases in plantings (due to the high

[10] The only commodity which is mainly traded *among* underdeveloped countries is rice. This accounts for a large part of their share of world imports of primary products (although not more than 4 percent of world rice production enters into international trade). Mention should also be made of the as yet quantitatively unimportant, but expanding, flow of trade from the underdeveloped countries to the U.S.S.R. and other centrally-planned economies, which might become a balancing factor of growing importance in the world trade of primary products. (Continental China exercises a rather special role as an unpredictable, but occasionally important, exporter or importer of a range of primary products from the underdeveloped countries. She has become, at least for the time being, a major importer of wheat but these imports are drawn mainly from *developed* countries.)

[11] For this reason, the primary exporting countries have relatively little to gain from the usual kind of multilateral negotiation for the reciprocal reduction of tariffs and quantitative restrictions. Indeed, they may tend to lose, since their own exports are not predominantly hampered by trade restrictions, while the concessions made in return may handicap them in developing new industries.

prices of the early 1950s) which are only now coming into production. Moreover, the very spread of "development consciousness" of the underdeveloped countries has meant that increases in production have been encouraged, even of commodities whose world prospects have been known to be unfavourable, so long as they have offered a promise of increased export earnings for the particular country concerned. Available projections of the main tropical products for the period up to 1970[12] indicate a growing excess of world production over world consumption, even on the most optimistic assumptions concerning the growth of demand in the high-income countries. There is scope for some increases in the relatively less prosperous areas, where the income elasticities of demand are still relatively high, and in countries where consumption is now held down by high internal revenue duties[13] but, by and large, unless present trends are rapidly reversed, it is unlikely that the growth of consumption can keep pace with the projected increases in production.

The only long-term remedy is the economic development of the underdeveloped countries themselves. This would allow a diversification of their domestic production. They would then become less dependent on a few basic commodities for their export earnings and less dependent also on imports to cover their essential needs. On the other hand, the prospects of their economic development are greatly dependent on their ability to maintain and increase their foreign receipts, both through trade and aid. The developed countries of the world are beginning to recognize the fact that the "commodity problem" of the underdeveloped countries is not something separate from their development problem, but that the two are intricately involved with each other. This should open the way to a new approach to international commodity arrangements—not from the narrow viewpoint of improving the functioning of particular markets, but as part of a comprehensive approach to international programing, including assistance in the form of both trade and aid for the underdeveloped areas. The provisions of the Treaty of Rome provide evidence of a certain awareness of this in that the various aspects of economic aid to underdeveloped regions—stable prices and markets, financial assistance, long-term planning of production structures —are considered together. Unfortunately, they single out a narrow group of countries—the overseas associated members of the Common Market—for such comprehensive treatment. Nonetheless, if their envisaged programs do materialize, the need to extend the same treatment

[12] *Agricultural Commodities—Projections for 1970,* Special Supplement to the *FAO Commodity Review 1962.* FAO, Rome, 1962.

[13] The Commission of the European Economic Community has recommended to the members of the Common Market—the main group of countries which impose heavy revenue duties on these products—to abolish them within the next few years.

to the other underdeveloped areas of Asia, Africa, and Latin America will become the more obvious.

If one may hazard a guess as to the directions in which the thinking of the advanced countries anxious to assist the development of the poor areas of the world is likely to develop in the future, it will be in the direction of such a joint comprehensive program. Such a program could provide the latter not only with aid but also with longer-term contracts or other forms of market assurance for their exports. This alone would give to the underdeveloped countries a sufficiently firm basis for the elaboration of development programs geared to a definite knowledge of the external conditions with which they will be individually confronted.

It is obvious that it will take years, in the best of circumstances, before the governments of both the developed and the underdeveloped countries are prepared to face up to the need for such comprehensive long-term planning on an international scale, and before they are ready to accept its obligations. It will take further years before such a joint comprehensive program, related to both trade and aid, can be set to work effectively. In the meantime, the position of the underdeveloped countries is deteriorating and their needs are pressing. The export proceeds from the sale of primary commodities (excluding petroleum) have shown very little rise from the (pre-Korean) year of 1950 to 1957, and have been falling since that time. Their future prospects in the light of current production and consumption trends are unfavorable and their financial reserves are already under considerable strain. The question is what can be done *now* to alleviate the situation until such time as more comprehensive measures can be put into force.

There is, of course, a great deal which the underdeveloped countries could do on their own to improve their position—as, for example, through increased efforts to raise productivity levels in their subsistence sectors, aided by land reform; the elimination of waste both in their public expenditures and in their personal consumption; fiscal reforms and the introduction of improved marketing techniques, such as marketing boards, which could serve as a means of syphoning off revenue from the exporters as well as the purpose of stabilizing producers' prices. Further consideration of these problems would, however, go beyond the scope of this paper, which is primarily concerned with international policies.

COMPENSATORY FINANCING

The pressing need of underdeveloped countries is for more resources, particularly of foreign exchange, to sustain their development programs. The flow of economic aid has increased fairly rapidly in recent years, but it must be remembered that it still constitutes only a small fraction of the total foreign receipts of the underdeveloped countries, and the rise in aid has failed to compensate for the deterioration in their terms of trade in recent years. The first objective must be seen in a reversal of the adverse *trend* of export earnings, aided where necessary by policies of structural adjustment in both exporting and importing countries. In addition, however, the underdeveloped countries also urgently require assistance for replenishing their liquid reserves and for moderating the impact of fluctuations in their current export receipts. This second objective could be assisted by more liberal lending policies of the International Monetary Fund and it could be supported further by the adoption of proposals contained in the recent United Nations experts' report on compensatory financing.[14]

The United Nations experts put forward a scheme for the creation of a central fund, called the Development Insurance Fund, into which all member countries would pay contributions and against which members would make financial claims which would be paid automatically in stated circumstances. Such claims would be based on the decline of export proceeds in a particular year as against the average of the three preceding years, and would cover a proportion, say 50 percent, of the shortfall thus defined in excess of a minimum shortfall of 5 percent for which no compensation is payable. Two alternative types were envisaged and the experts thought that there would be some merit in adopting a scheme which made use of a combination of both. Under the first type of scheme, the compensatory payments are in the nature of a cash settlement, which does not have to be repaid in the future. Under the second type of scheme, the payments take on the character of a contingent loan, which must be repaid if the export proceeds of the subsequent five years are high enough to allow it (i.e., out of the excess of export receipts over the three-year base period) but not otherwise. As regards the contributions, the experts recommend that countries should contribute a percentage of their national income (possibly graduated in relation to per caput income), while low-income primary producing countries should contribute a fixed percentage of their export receipts. The experts estimate that the annual gross claims on the basis of a 50 percent compensation and a 5 percent minimum reduction would have amounted to $383 million per year on the average for the years 1953–1959 for the underdeveloped countries, whereas the claims of the high-income countries would have averaged $85 million on the same basis. The necessary contributions, on the other hand, assessed on all countries' export proceeds at a standard rate, would have amounted to $326 million annually from the high-income countries and $142 million from the low-income countries; thus involving an annual net transfer of $241 million

[14] *International Compensation for Fluctuations in Commodity Trade.* New York, United Nations, 1961. The Committee of Experts consisted of I. H. Abdel-Rahman, Antonio Carrillo-Flores, Sir John G. Crawford (Chairman), Albert G. Hart, S. Posthuma, and M. L. Qureshi.

from the high-income countries to the low-income countries, on the assumption that all benefits took the form of cash settlements. The merit of this scheme is that it gives a certain insurance against hardship to the beneficiaries in return for their contributions—in much the same way as that in which citizens of the modern state receive benefits in exchange for contributions in cases of sickness, unemployment, etc. And just as in the case of compensatory social insurance schemes, where part of the cost is borne by the state out of general taxation, the contributions are not levied on a full actuarial basis. The adoption of such a scheme would give partial protection to underdeveloped countries against the effects of both cyclical fluctuations and also (though to a much lesser extent) against an unfavorable trend of commodity prices, not only in relation to any particular commodity but to commodities in general. In this way it would secure some of the same objectives, as far as the stabilization of foreign income is concerned, as a network of commodity agreements. On the other hand, it should be emphasized that the experts' proposals, even if adopted in full, could do little more than the standard types of commodity agreements adopted so far as protection against unfavorable price trends; and, as we have repeatedly stated, it is unfavorable price trends rather than fluctuations which are likely progressively to constitute the dominant problem for underdeveloped countries in the coming decade.[15] Moreover, methods of international compensation, based on formulas of a fully automatic character and containing at the same time a built-in element of aid, or net transfers from the high-income to the low-income countries, have not received much practical support so far on the part of the high-income countries.

[15] Following the publication of the UN experts' report in 1961, the Organization of American States (OAS) published a proposal for the establishment of an international fund for the stabilization of export receipts. This was evidently influenced by the ideas of the United Nations experts. Like the UN Report, the OAS proposal assumes that compensatory finance should be available to cover a proportion (two-thirds up to a maximum of 20 percent of previous exports) of any shortfall of actual export proceeds, below their average in the previous three years. Like the UN Report, the OAS proposal also envisages that the high-income countries make a larger contribution to the fund than the low-income countries. The OAS scheme departs, however, from the recommendations of the UN experts in three respects. In the first place, compensatory finance will be available only to low-income countries and not to all countries, as under the UN scheme—the arrangement would thus no longer retain the character of a universal insurance scheme. In the second place, it envisages that the fund be financed by a single once-for-all payment, of which $600 million would be contributed by the low-income countries and $1,200 million by the high-income countries. In the third place—and this is the most important difference—the compensation payments envisaged under the OAS proposals are in the nature of loans which have to be repaid in a maximum of five years irrespective of the levels of export proceeds of the borrowing countries. The UN experts, on the other hand, recommend that the compensatory payments should either be outright cash settlements, or else contingent loans, which would have to be repaid only if the recipients' export earnings rose sufficiently within a specific period.

THE ROLE OF COMMODITY AGREEMENTS

The adoption of such a compensatory finance scheme would not, of course, obviate the need for individual commodity agreements. As the United Nations experts themselves emphasize, compensatory finance is complementary to commodity agreements and not an alternative to them. But we must be clear as to the objectives which individual commodity agreements should serve. In particular, it must be recognized that commodity agreements cannot be successful in stabilizing prices and in securing reasonable terms of trade unless they also succeed in bringing world production and consumption into balance. This naturally cannot be a matter of international agreements alone but requires a close co-ordination between international arrangements and national policies. The main objective of commodity agreements should, therefore, be looked upon as an orderly method through which patterns of production and trade can best be adjusted to the requirements of world demand over a longer period. From this point of view, quota arrangements or the multilateral contract can offer some of the elements required, for a limited range of commodities, provided that, unlike the existing agreements, they include provisions for the co-ordination of national policies of all countries concerned, and for the joint programing and adjustments, as required, of production patterns in both exporting and importing countries. As far as possible, they should also provide for co-ordinated measures influencing consumption, internal price levels, and related commercial and fiscal policies, not only for measures relating directly to the regulation of exports and imports.

Such co-ordination, while it could be assisted, on certain conditions, by export-restriction and multilateral contract agreements, calls in addition for a commodity-by-commodity approach of a broader kind. It is relevant here to mention that in the postwar period, in addition to commodity *agreements* which contain binding obligations between the contracting parties, international commodity *consultations* have proved of very real benefit in the actual solution of commodity problems, even when they did not eventuate in any formalized agreement. At one time commodity study groups were regarded as no more than an essential preliminary mechanism in arriving at international agreements, the tasks of which were accomplished once negotiations for a definite agreement had been opened. Experience with the Wheat Agreement and the Sugar Agreement has shown, however, that the continuing organs which were set up in connection with these agreements—the International Wheat Council and the International Sugar Council—by constituting a forum for consultations and for comprehensive annual reviews of the situation and prospects of the world market and of the plans and programs of individual countries, have provided very valuable services to participating governments, quite apart from their operational functions.

In addition, the study groups which have been set up for a wide range of commodities—grains, rice, cocoa, coffee, cotton, wool, rubber, coconut, citrus fruit, nonferrous metals—have already provided a widespread network of consultative machinery, which has undoubtedly assisted the co-ordination of national policies through the intense and mutual study of common problems. There can be no doubt that with increasing emphasis on the importance of commodity export earnings for the viability of underdeveloped countries, consultations, quite apart from more formal and mechanised arrangements, will have a major role to fill.

NEED FOR A CONCERTED ATTACK

The conclusions to be drawn from this analysis are not of the spectacular kind. There is no single panacea, no magic waving of the wand which would enable us to solve the world commodity problem in all its complexity. Indeed, an attack on any single front can reach only a limited objective. But it has perhaps been shown in this paper that there are a number of ways in which a genuine effort is likely to produce some useful results. What is needed is a concerted attack on a number of fronts—long-term lending and aid as part of a comprehensive development program; compensatory finance; international agreements for the regulation of production, for co-ordinated planning in the creation of new capacity, and for the provision of guarantees of access to markets; long-term purchase agreements, conditional and unconditional; continuing consultations between governments, both commodity by commodity and in close link with wider discussions on trade, aid, and development planning, including also confrontations of plans of individual countries—all of which should be pursued simultaneously and with vigor.

21. Development through Food Grants and Concessional Sales*

LAWRENCE W. WITT

INTRODUCTION

International capital transfers through public aid play an important role in financing development programs in less developed nations. A

* An original contribution. The author is professor of agricultural economics, Michigan State University.

1962 report states that "in the past three years aid amounted to 25–30 per cent of investment in the less-developed countries of the non-communist world and to about 20 per cent of their export earnings."[1] The United States has been a major contributor of aid to the less developed nations; the combination of a relatively large per cent of GNP and the sheer magnitude of the United States economy makes the absolute amount of aid large compared to any country. Substantial amounts of farm products have been shipped abroad under special government programs, to add 25 to 30 per cent to United States economic aid. Such shipments, now mostly under Public Law 480 (a United States law authorizing the shipment of surplus farm products abroad under several noncommercial arrangements) total about $2 billion annually at Commodity Credit Corporation costs, or a little over $1.5 billion at imputed export market values.[2] The magnitude of this United States public aid in farm products calls for a better understanding of the circumstances under which such aid can contribute to development.

Concessional sales and grants (donations) are made under special agreements between the United States and each recipient country. These arrangements are outside the normal financing of international trade. Under the major provision of Public Law 480, the United States Government receives deposits of soft currency in the recipient country in exchange for shipments of farm products (primarily wheat and cotton, but also feed grains, rice, nonfat dry milk, and tobacco). Under other provisions, grants of food are made to governments as aid in times of disaster, for designated development projects, and for school lunch programs. Substantial donations are made to religious and international welfare agencies for direct feeding programs. Also, long-term dollar loans to purchase food are included.

The program's popularity with congressional and lay audiences and its likely continuance makes a careful evaluation necessary. It has been referred to as a marriage of convenience, since, in fact, the shipment of surpluses may make it appear less necessary to revamp domestic farm policies in the United States. Domestic policy and internal pressures indicate an increase in the amount and proportion of farm products in foreign aid.[3]

[1] P. N. Rosenstein-Rodan, "Determining the Need for and Planning the Use of External Resources," in *Organization, Planning and Programming for Economic Development*, Government Printing Office, Washington, D.C., 1962, p. 68.

[2] For a clarification of these figures, see E. L. Menzie, L. Witt, C. Eicher, and J. S. Hillman, "Policy for United States Agricultural Export Surplus Disposal," University of Arizona Agricultural Experiment Station Technical Bulletin 150, pp. 38–39, 1962. See also T. W. Schultz, "Value of U.S. Farm Surpluses to Underdeveloped Countries," *Journal of Farm Economics*, vol. 42, no. 5, pp. 1018–1030, December, 1960.

[3] See my article, "Trade and Agricultural Policy," in *The Annals*, pp. 1–7, September, 1960.

The importance of "food for development" or "surplus farm product disposals" (the term used depending upon the view of the speaker) has grown significantly, and not only in United States policy. The original "temporary" three-year program passed in 1954 totaled $1 billion, and was expected to dispose of current surpluses, after which the program would stop. Instead, annual surpluses became larger, an additional $800 million was authorized thirteen months after the Law was first passed, and within a year another $1.7 billion had been added. While still calling it a temporary program, Congress has budgeted the program through calendar year 1964, for shipments which may be made as late as 1965 and 1966. The average appropriation is now $1.8 billion annually.[4] Moreover, other nations are beginning to participate in comparable export programs. A new World Food Program has been inaugurated under United Nations auspices, as partial implementation of the FAO Freedom from Hunger campaign. Some forty nations have pledged food, services, or cash to this new program.[5] Furthermore, the plans of the European Economic Community (European Common Market) clearly call for disposal of agricultural surpluses through commodity aid to less developed nations.[6] Thus, there is reason to believe that increasing amounts of farm products will be available to the less developed nations during the decade of the sixties, though not necessarily a proportionately larger fraction of public foreign aid. It is, therefore, especially important to understand the accomplishments and limitations of the United States Public Law 480 program during its first ten years of operation.

A FEW TERMS DEFINED

Public Law 480 is also known as the Agricultural Trade Development and Assistance Act of 1954. It authorizes the United States Department of Agriculture to dispose of surplus farm products outside the usual market channels, both at home and abroad. It has been modified and amended a number of times. Public Law 480 also is referred to as the Food for Peace program.

Title I is one section of Public Law 480. It authorizes the sale of surpluses abroad in exchange for currency of the recipient nation. Under terms of the agreement, virtually all of this currency must be accumulated and spent within the recipient country.

---

[4] For a review of government foreign trade programs preceding and leading to Public Law 480, see Karl Fox, Vernon Ruttan, and Lawrence Witt, "Farming, Farmers and Markets for Farm Goods," Supplementary Paper 15, Committee for Economic Development, New York, pp. 155–179, November, 1962.

[5] For plans and concepts behind this program, see FAO, "Development Through Food," Rome, 1961.

[6] See *Agricultural Commodities and the European Common Market*, FAO Commodity Policy Studies, no. 13, Rome, 1962, esp. pp. 24 and 25.

Title II of Public Law 480, authorizes grants to foreign governments to assist in times of natural disasters—floods, droughts, earthquakes. A 1960 amendment provides that food may be donated as partial wages for labor-intensive economic development projects.

Title III has three subsections or programs. One provides for surplus disposal within the United States. A second authorizes donations to religious and international organizations to feed the needy overseas, primarily through schools, orphanages, and so forth. The third authorization is for barter programs—defined separately below.

Title IV authorizes long-term credit sales of surplus farm products to foreign governments, to be repaid in dollars, over a ten-year period. They are concessional sales since the interest charge is less than the usual rate.

Local currency refers to the pesos, rupees, or other currency paid to the United States Embassy for farm products received under Title I. It is similar to the counterpart funds developed in Europe through the Marshall Plan.

Additionality refers to the requirement of Public Law 480 that Title I imports should be *in addition* to a country's commercial imports.

Barter, under Title III, is a procedure by which the United States Department of Agriculture exchanges surplus farm products for materials used in United States foreign aid and other programs, or for storable, nonfarm products (such as minerals) which are stockpiled. The farm products are exported by the private trade; the products received may be of domestic origin but usually are of foreign origin.

THE RATIONALE FOR PUBLIC LAW 480

The political and economic forces which led to the development of Public Law 480 stem from the price support and surplus accumulation aspects of United States agricultural policies; but similar policies are found in most of Europe and in certain less developed countries. A concern for nutrition and a sense of humanitarianism are also involved.

The reconstruction of Europe after World War II required substantial amounts of food imports. As European agriculture recovered, United States farm exports declined and stocks accumulated in government hands, under the minimum price guarantees. Farm groups, and farm state congressmen, who held seniority positions in many committees, sought ways to offset the decline in exports and to postpone agricultural policy readjustments. An early step was the more liberal provision of food gifts to church-related organizations, CARE, and UNICEF, for local distribution to indigent people in other countries. Also several special bills were passed to donate or loan agricultural surpluses to nations suffering from natural disaster—India, Pakistan, and Afghanistan.

Meanwhile, as early as 1949, the FAO (UN Food and Agriculture Organization) gave special attention to certain commodities in world agricultural trade for which effective demand appeared inadequate. By 1953, the FAO was stressing that the foremost means of absorbing excess supplies were courageous policies for increasing consumption. Three methods of using surpluses were advanced—two old and one new. The old and familiar methods were improving nutrition, mostly through direct feeding, and meeting famine and near-famine conditions caused by crop failure. The new proposal was to use surpluses to aid economic development. The FAO staff was asked to undertake pilot field surveys in countries which were possible recipients of surplus farm products.

One such survey was made in Egypt in August, 1954. Another was made in India—a country with a large potential for using surpluses in economic development—under the leadership of M. Ezekiel. This study laid the theoretical groundwork for facilitating development through capital transfers of surplus farm products.[7] This FAO pilot study was published one year after Public Law 480 was passed, as Public Law 480 shipments—emphasizing disposal not development— were increasing in momentum, and as it was becoming evident that United States farm surpluses and Public Law 480 shipments were more than temporary phenomena. The FAO study has helped to legitimize food aid for economic development and has provided an additional justification for continuing the program. From the standpoint of the United States, Public Law 480 has two major objectives: reducing surpluses and assisting in economic development abroad; and several minor objectives; improving the health and nutrition of disadvantaged groups, advancing foreign policy interests, and changing market and diet patterns to benefit future commercial exports from the United States. An important step in fulfilling the major objectives would be surplus shipments tagged for economic development projects.

The views of many economists in government and academic positions towards the original Public Law 480 program were mostly negative,[8] along the following lines. Developing nations need to industralize; hence, their primary import needs are for machine tools and capital equipment, rather than for farm products. Many developing nations also need an improved agriculture for local production and export, but concessional sales of farm products would be detrimental to agricultural prices in the recipient country (and to prices received by other exporting nations);

---

[7] *Uses of Agricultural Surpluses to Finance Economic Development in Under-developed Countries: A Pilot Study in India,* FAO Commodity Policy Studies, no. 6, Rome, Italy, June, 1955. The supporting data for the FAO study are reported in V. M. Dandekar, *Use of Food Surpluses for Economic Development,* Gokale Institute of Politics and Development, Publication no. 33, Gokale, India, 1956.

[8] See, for example, Raymond Mikesell, "Agricultural Surpluses and Export Policy," The American Enterprise Association, Inc., Washington, February, 1958, and several articles by various authors in the *Journal of Farm Economics,* pp. 1108–1138, December, 1957.

hence, Public Law 480 was condemned as imposing the United States farm problem upon the rest of the world. Surely Public Law 480 would worsen United States foreign relations.

The FAO pilot study in India pointed out that commodity aid might lead to capital formation by using underemployed labor to build roads, schools, and other facilities. Since farm products constituted at least half of the consumption goods of such rural workers, the report suggested that as much as half of the cost of certain projects might be met by farm products, and a fourth or more from imported surplus agricultural commodities such as wheat, cotton, and dried skim milk.[9] A foreign exchange gap frequently occurs early in the development process, sometimes coinciding with a food gap since agricultural output is sluggish; Public Law 480 supplies can close up the food gap and the foreign exchange gap. These ideas stimulated a new defense or rationalization for Public Law 480; but because this seemed so much like a marriage of convenience, many observers remained suspicious. There is ground for skepticism since some defenders of the program overstate their case; at the same time, the attacks on the program often fail to recognize the possible benefits of the program.

The remainder of this paper will point out some of the difficulties and the possible contributions of farm products as external aid. It will be necessary to differentiate, also, between the intended program operations and the actual operations, since empirical evidence indicates that the programs in some countries are far more successful than they would have been with strict adherence to the established program. Adjustments by the recipient country, unintended so far as the sending nation is concerned, have added to the value of Public Law 480 imports.

THE MECHANICS OF NEGOTIATING AND EXECUTING PUBLIC LAW 480 CONTRACTS

Some clarification of Title I Public Law 480 operations is required before examining its impact upon receiving nations. A request for commodity aid is made by a prospective recipient country. The reasons for the request and the information which led to a formal request may have involved a variety of interactions between Embassy and technical assistance personnel of both countries. After evaluation and negotiation, an agreement is signed for an approximate amount of several commodities and estimated total export values. The agreement also designates uses for the local currency, the exchange rate applicable, sometimes the local price to be charged, arrangements if imports lead to exports, and other provisions.

[9] The commodity composition of Public Law 480 shipments is summarized in University of Arizona Experiment Station Technical Bulletin 150, p. 58.

Specific arrangements are made between exporters and importers. The exporter generally is a private United States export firm; the importer may be a private trader in the recipient country or a government agency charged with responsibility for importing certain commodities. In any case, financial and other arrangements must be made with both governments. The United States government pays dollars to the exporter as he ships designated quantities of commodities; thus, tax dollars pay for commodity exports. The receiving government collects local currency from the importer as the commodities are imported and sold in the local distribution system. These currencies are paid by the receiving government to the United States government—the United States Embassy in the receiving country. The way in which these local currency deposits are finally liquidated determines whether the farm products have been a loan, gift, or partial gift of the United States economy to the recipient economy.

All United States firms—farmers, market agencies, etc.—are paid dollars for Public Law 480 products just as in commercial sales transactions. In the importing country, importers, processors, and consumers purchase Public Law 480 products by paying for them in local currency just the same as if the commodity were locally produced and sold in the processing and retail marketing channels. Food aid under Title I, part of Title II, and Title IV, is not a gift to consumers, nor a gift by producers.[10] Title I wheat (or other commodity) is indistinguishable from other wheat, so far as the consumer is concerned; he pays the market price for his purchases. Therefore, the Title I sales agreement essentially is a government to government loan or grant. To the extent that a proportion of local currency is actually used by the United States Government, this amount is a prepayment in farm products of future United States expenditures in the recipient countries, expenditures which otherwise would have been paid in dollars. To understand the developmental impact of the program, and other effects, it is necessary to examine two items. One of these is the recipient country's use of the local currency designated for loan or grant within the country. The other is the change which has occurred in other economic activities *because* of the receipt of Public Law 480 commodities. We shall examine these issues in a review of specific country programs, and then attempt a general review and appraisal.

IMPACT OF PUBLIC LAW 480 ON RECIPIENT COUNTRIES

Most of the appraisals of Public Law 480 programs, until recently, can be roughly divided into two groups. One approach is qualitative

[10] Most Title II and all Title III shipments, however, are a gift to the final consumer.

and theoretical, either arriving at negative conclusions via international trade theory, or exploring the conceptual potential of food in development planning. The second approach, often used by those closely connected with the administration of the program, presents arguments for the program without adequate conceptual foundations.[11] However, there are now a number of empirical studies by local and/or international observers in specific countries.[12] These studies come to different conclusions, and indicate that Public Law 480 shipments have a wide range of possible impacts depending upon the policies of the recipient country, the effectiveness of the program administration in both the sending and the receiving country, and the relative strength and potential of the agricultural-food sectors of the recipient economy.

Let us turn now to some of the evidence and experience with Public Law 480 in specific countries.

Israel

Israel is the largest recipient of Public Law 480 commodities on a per capita basis—about $81 per person for the 1954–1961 period compared with about $25 for Yugoslavia, the second largest recipient nation. During the 1950s, Israel had a rapidly expanding economy. Population doubled, mainly because of immigration. Gifts from abroad made substantial contributions to capital formation. The balance of payments for the decade indicates that about a third of the total receipts were earned from exports, while nearly half came from grants and other unrequited transfers. Prior to Public Law 480, Israel was surfeited with shortages, rationing, careful husbandry of its foreign exchange, and other controls to keep inflationary forces in check. The situation was one in which food imports were easily absorbed.

The impact of Public Law 480 imports on internal agricultural production, surprisingly, was to stimulate rather than discourage agricultural production.[13] There were two reasons for this. First, Israeli authorities were willing to decontrol many food prices and to remove rationing controls, since additional imports were forthcoming in sufficient amounts to prevent serious inflation. Legal prices rose modestly while black

[11] An extended bibliography on Public Law 480 may be found in University of Arizona Experiment Station Technical Bulletin 150, pp. 104–111.

[12] A number of these studies—for Israel, Colombia, Japan, and Pakistan—are reported and evaluated in Lawrence Witt and Carl Eicher, "The Effects of United States Agricultural Surplus Disposal Programs on Recipient Countries," Michigan State Experiment Station Research Bulletin 2, 1964.

[13] See F. Ginor, "Analysis and Assessment of the Economic Effect of the U.S. Public Law 480 Title I Program in Israel," Bank of Israel, Tel-Aviv, October, 1961. See also A. E. Kahn, "Agricultural Aid and Economic Development: The Case of Israel," *Quarterly Journal of Economics*, vol. 76, pp. 568–591, November, 1962.

market prices fell precipitously; since nearly all local farm production was paid for at legal prices, the net result was more favorable farm prices. Second, imports of feed grain provided the basis for a substantial expansion in livestock production, particularly in poultry, both for domestic and export use. Grain supplies were no longer closely rationed; inventories increased and provided a secure base for larger livestock numbers.

Consumers were able to increase the quantity of food and variety of their diets because of Public Law 480 imports. While the Israeli government had followed a policy of making available ample supplies of bread, many other products were in short supply and were rationed before Public Law 480 contracts. Feed grain imports under Public Law 480 provided more dairy and poultry products domestically; imports of dried milk, fats and oils, and minor amounts of other products also added variety. It is estimated that consumption increased by four to five per cent for 1958–1960 over 1954, with a substantially greater increase for meat and eggs and decreases for cereals and fish.

Internal development programs were expanded by an increase in development loans, many of which utilized excess capacity in the building industry as well as unemployed workers. The government authorized additional development projects because the additional imports reduced the threat of internal inflation and enhanced the ability of the economy to absorb the additional purchasing power. The loans actually financed by Public Law 480 local currency did not draw heavily on imports; however, the Ginor report indicates that the true additional projects, in fact, did draw more heavily on imports.[14] This was made possible by changes in the import patterns, to which we now turn.

In theory, Public Law 480 sales are additional to "usual commercial imports from the United States"; since 1958, this provision applies to all commercial imports, except those from the Communist bloc. The Ginor report, however, indicates that Public Law 480 imports did substitute for commercial imports. It is estimated that only 31 per cent of the Public Law 480 Title I imports were additional.[15] To some extent, however, Public Law 480 imports from the United States substituted for imports no longer available from Turkey and Argentina. Public Law 480 imports also replaced imports from Bulgaria and the U.S.S.R. Thus, diversion of commercial trade is closer to 50 than to 70 per cent, since together these four countries provided about 15 per cent of imports in 1950–1954, barely 5 per cent in 1955–1960, and nothing in 1960. On the other hand, commercial imports of feed grains, soybeans, and certain other non-Public Law 480 farm products increased, partly as a result of the increased domestic demand, no longer held back by rationing,

[14] Ginor, *op. cit.*, pp. 48–49.
[15] *Ibid.*, pp. 93–95.

and partly because of additional development projects. Also, some exports of poultry products swelled the export earnings.

Whatever the reason, the reduction in commercial purchases of the thirteen Title I commodities, but mostly wheat and feed grains, made possible an increased commercial purchase of other imports; part of these provided the import component of the expanded Israeli development program. The rest went for a variety of purposes, including increased reserves of foreign currency.

This review of Public Law 480 in Israel indicates that the program made a significant contribution to Israeli development. In fact, Kahn concludes that for Israel Title I aid "has been almost as good as free dollars."[16] However, part of this favorable report is due to the *program in practice being different from the program in theory*. The diversion in commercial trade of agricultural export countries is less favorable to these nations, but even here a larger GNP in Israel as a result of increased development may provide long-term gains for export countries to offset short-term losses. Israeli programs for domestic agriculture insulated the farmers from import competition and, through feed grain imports, provided new opportunities.

Colombia

Let us turn more briefly to Colombia, recipient of much smaller quantities both in the aggregate and on a per capita basis. Between 1955 and 1961, some $53 million of Title I and $26 million of Title III commodities were received.[17] Most of the Public Law 480 imports were received after 1957, when export earnings were falling following the decline in world coffee prices. Despite this, and with a relatively small amount of overall planning, Colombia was able to maintain economic growth, though very small in several years.[18] The major products imported under Title I of Public Law 480 were wheat, cotton, and edible oils; under Title III, wheat and nonfat dry skim milk were the major items.

Internal production of cotton was stimulated, despite the import programs, through a special semi-official agency, partly by price guarantees, mostly through technical assistance, to such an extent that Colombia became a cotton exporter.[19] On the other hand, wheat prices lagged behind other prices, production was more or less constant despite

[16] Kahn, *op. cit.*, p. 591.

[17] Lawrence Witt and Richard Wheeler, "Effects of Public Law 480 Programs in Colombia: 1952–62," Medellin, Colombia, October, 1962, mimeographed, pp. 6 and 11.

[18] *Ibid.*, pp. 22–24.

[19] *Ibid.*, pp. 61–64.

varietal improvements, and some wheat farmers apparently shifted to barley and dairy production in efforts to maintain or increase their income.[20] Both concessional and commercial imports of edible oils expanded, but prices advanced more rapidly than the general price level. Internal production expanded slowly, and without much technical and marketing assistance.

Consumption levels increased slightly for wheat, cotton, and edible oils. There is some evidence that consumption would have dropped without the program, since lower foreign exchange earnings would have forced a curtailment of imports, and internal shortages might have appeared, particularly for wheat. The accumulation of local currency increased the number and volume of development projects related to agriculture, perhaps at the expense of greater internal inflationary pressures.[21]

There also are indications of trade diversions in Colombia's farm imports. Colombia purchased commercially the agreed-upon volume of cotton, wheat, and edible oils. A comparison of 1950–1954 purchases with 1955–1960 purchases, however, shows a mixed pattern.[22] There were smaller purchases of wheat from Canada as United States-supplied Title I shipments came into Colombia. Cotton imports disappeared as local production expanded. Edible oil imports increased in both commercial and concessional categories. An appraisal of how Public Law 480 imports affected the external assistance for development must be conjectural, but it appears that concessional wheat imports forestalled a greater pressure on foreign exchange earnings, kept bread price increases within modest limits, and aided the Colombian Government in refraining from expansion of its comparatively high-cost wheat industry.

Thus, the Public Law 480 program has had mixed effects upon individual farmers. National policy insulated some producers from adverse income effects, and left others exposed to lagging prices so that potential income gains through improved crop varieties were neutralized. Development both in agriculture and in industry probably was enhanced as Title I imports softened the effect of declining incomes from coffee exports. The eventual value to the United States of local currency sales in Colombia probably is higher than in Israel and in many other recipient nations. More of the pesos are utilized for normal United States government expenditures; the remainder are scheduled for eventual repayment to the United States. However, the dollar value of Colombian pesos is depreciating more rapidly than the value of the Israeli pound.

[20] *Ibid.*, pp. 73–75.
[21] T. J. Goering and L. W. Witt, *United States Agricultural Surpluses in Colombia: A Review of Public Law 480*, Michigan State Experiment Station Technical Bulletin 289, 1963, pp. 130–145.
[22] *Ibid.*, pp. 35–38.

Pakistan

During the 1950s, Pakistan changed from an exporter of grain products into a substantial importer, much of it on a concessional basis. Between 1955 and 1962, about $475 million of commodities were exported to Pakistan under Title I, in one of the three largest national programs. The Pakistan government, through deficit financing, had pushed the economy beyond its resource base. Food grain aid between 1955 and 1958 amounted to nearly 50 per cent of economic and technical aid to Pakistan from all sources.[23] Impending inflation and food shortages were alleviated by concessional grain imports, primarily from the United States and Canada, and by commercial imports from Thailand (rice), Mainland China (rice through barter), Australia (wheat), and other countries. The amount of land devoted to wheat and rice has increased slightly while yields have been static. Prices for grains have been less than import costs in rupees, but have averaged about the same as the general price level. Food grains, of course, are a principal item of consumer expenditure, and the Government is interested in keeping such prices from advancing.

It is difficult to judge what Pakistani agricultural policies would have been in the absence of concessional sales programs. Moreover, Pakistan has received concessional grain for several years from Canada, the U.S.S.R. and the United States, prior to Public Law 480, and might have obtained more in the absence of Public Law 480. Without food aid it is likely that major changes in Pakistani policies, perhaps including an earlier or more drastic change in government, would have been necessary to cope with the food problem. In short, Pakistan has imported and consumed substantial quantities of food grains, but with little evidence either of an accelerated development program or of an improvement in domestic agriculture as a direct consequence of Public Law 480 shipments. There are indications that levels of consumption were larger because of the program.

India

While Israel has the largest Public Law 480 program on a per capita basis, India has received the largest total volume, $1,363 million of farm commodities from 1954 through 1962, or nearly 25 per cent of total Title I shipments. The effect of these shipments upon the Indian economy and economic development can be examined within the framework of the three Five-Year Development Plans.

[23] United Nations Food and Agriculture Organization, *A Note on the Utilization of Agricultural Surpluses for Economic Development in Pakistan,* Economic Commission for Asia and the Far East, Bangkok, 1961.

The First Plan in 1951 devoted major attention to investments and services to stimulate an increase in agricultural output, recognizing that three-fourths of the people were dependent upon agriculture. Technical assistance and favorable weather enabled the major goals to be met, or nearly met. Food grain output increased 22 per cent instead of the anticipated 14 per cent.

The Second Plan in 1956 gave less emphasis to agriculture and much more to heavy industry. In part, the authors of the plan believed that agricultural expansion was well under way; in part, they wished to put more emphasis on import-replacing industries, since exports had been static during the First Plan. In any case, three events brought India a foreign exchange gap. Small crop years led to food imports, underestimated capital equipment requirements expanded industrial imports, and an unexpectedly large population growth increased the demand for imports. All three placed added burdens upon foreign exchange balances. Two Title I agreements, in 1956 and 1958, and a sharp curtailment in capital goods imports enabled India to pursue the Second Plan without a major disaster.

The Third Plan, in 1961, attempted to take account of the increased rate of population growth. In formulating the Plan, India asked for and received a four-year Title I Agreement. This enabled the Third Plan to schedule continued investments in industrialization with a fair assurance of adequate food supplies. Even with this $1.2 billion agreement, the Third Plan placed more emphasis on agriculture than did the Second.

With this brief résumé, let us turn to some appraisals of the Indian program. We mentioned that an early FAO report[24] was optimistic about the uses of agricultural surpluses for development. S. R. Sen[25] indicates that Public Law 480 shipments were meshed operationally into India's development program. Crawford[26] introduces a critical note. While making a strong case for Public Law 480 shipments as a contribution to Indian development, he also points out that India's commercial purchases of food grains were substantially reduced. He suggests that India would have developed somewhat more rapidly had she been able to receive more dollars and less commodity aid. In fact, he suggests that the size of the 1960 four-year Public Law 480 Agreement required some transfer of Indian resources from industrial and agricultural development to marketing and storage facilities to handle the increased commodity

[24] FAO, "Uses of Agricultural Surpluses to Finance Economic Development in Underdeveloped Countries: A Pilot Study in India," Rome, 1955.

[25] For a discussion of Indian Planning see S. R. Sen, *The Strategy for Agricultural Development,* Asian Publishing House, Bombay, India, 1962, Part II.

[26] J. G. Crawford, "Using Surpluses for Economic Development," in *Proceedings of the International Conference of Agricultural Economists,* London, 1963.

aid. Finally, Khatkhate[27] indicates that the deflationary monetary effect of Public Law 480 shipments was neutralized by increased government debt (and a larger development program) and suggested that the monetary impact of the subsequent spending of accumulated rupees could also be offset by debt management.

These reports indicate that the 1956 and 1958 agreements provided needed consumption goods and partially aided in fulfilling the major goals of the Second Plan. The 1960 Public Law 480 agreement was carefully integrated into the Third Plan and into monetary and fiscal policies. Per capita food consumption increased slightly as a result of commodity aid. A reduction in commercial imports enabled India to stretch its foreign exchange earnings. The fears of some analysts about the detrimental effects on Indian agriculture[28] notwithstanding, these reports do not indicate a serious problem. Nonetheless, it is still appropriate to ask whether the agricultural investment priorities of the Third Plan would have been even higher without Public Law 480.

Food for Wages: The Tunisian Experience

An unusual Title II program in Tunisia has become a pilot or model for using surplus food in a food-for-wages program. (Most Title II programs are natural disaster or famine relief operations.) In Tunisia certain labor-intensive, locally administered capital creating projects are carried on with previously unemployed or underemployed workers through wage payments in food and cash. Similar projects are in operation in about ten other countries. Moreover, some recent United Nations-sponsored programs are drawing on this experience. Let us examine the program more closely.

A grant of United States wheat to Tunisia in 1958 was used "to carry out worthwhile work relief projects having economic value, mainly in the agricultural field."[29] By April 30, 1958, a total of 184 projects averaging two months duration had been selected by the governors of the provinces and approved by the central government. The governors provided straw bosses for each twenty to twenty-five men and a foreman or project director for each 100 men. Since Tunisia is basically an agricultural country, with water shortages in the center and south, most of the projects were related to water conservation, removal of undesirable shrubs, tree planting, road repair, and firebreaks.

[27] D. R. Khatkhate, "Money Supply Impact of National Currency Counterpart of Foreign Aid: An Indian Case," *The Review of Economics and Statistics*, vol. 45, pp. 78–83, February, 1963.

[28] See T. W. Schultz, *op. cit.* For an Indian view see S. R. Sen, "Impact and Implications of Foreign Surplus Disposal on Underdeveloped Economies—The Indian Perspective," *Journal of Farm Economics*, vol. 42, no. 5, pp. 1031–1042, December, 1960.

[29] ICA, Airgram, April 30, 1958.

The early program consisted of a daily wage of four kilos of American hard red winter wheat supplied under Title II of Public Law 480 and 100 milliemes in cash supplied by the Tunisian government. This wage amounted to about 71 cents per day, with about one-third paid in cash and the remainder in wheat. This payment was equal to the basic wage in rural areas. Since the Tunisian national dish, "couscous," was made best from durum wheat, which was ground into a coarse meal called semolina, the American hard winter wheat was unsuitable for direct use by the Tunisian peasant. Therefore, approval was secured to permit the exchange of American hard wheat on a local value basis for semolina which was made from local durum wheat. The ratio of semolina to cash was changed several times, and in January, 1960, the workers were paid a daily wage of 68 cents of which two-thirds was in cash.

The program employed some 50,000–70,000 unemployed rural workers on a ten-to fifteen-day rotation basis, equivalent to about 25,000 workers full-time, until November 1959. Since then, workers have been employed on a full-time, forty-eight-hour week and their numbers had been increased to 120,000 by July 1, 1960, and to nearly 200,000 by November, 1961.

The program was evaluated as extremely successful by the Tunisians. Some of the features accounting for the success of the experience according to ICA[30] administrators were local planning of projects, governors of good administrative ability, and the fact that local projects were tied into the Office of the Presidency through a work relief administrator. This suggests that the quality of local planning and administration are extremely important variables in a food-for-wages program.

Other Provisions of Public Law 480

Since 75 to 80 per cent of United States commodity aid has been sent abroad through Title I agreements, the above discussion has concentrated on Title I programs, with a single example of one type of Title II program in Tunisia. Other Title II, Title III, and Title IV programs are integral parts of Public Law 480.

Most Title II and Title III donations are distributed outside usual international and domestic market channels to provide more nutritious meals than would otherwise be available. If the program has an economic development impact, it is in the greater human energy and output of participants. Both Leibenstein and a United Nations report recognize this possibility.[31]

[30] Now called AID or Agency for International Development.

[31] Harvey Leibenstein, "The Theory of Underemployment in Backward Economies," *Journal of Political Economy*, vol. 55, pp. 91–104, April, 1957. United Nations Food and Agricultural Organization, "Nutrition and Working Efficiency," Basic Study no. 5, Rome, 1962.

The only way in which Title III barter programs would stimulate development is through the additional purchase of minerals or other commodities which the United States would stockpile. The stimulus, if any, comes from the United States decision to purchase, and not from the sale or use of farm products.

Title IV perhaps could be examined in a developmental framework. However, since the farm aid subsequently is repaid to the United States in dollars, the transaction comes closer to being a sales program with a price discount, to the extent that interest charges are less than usual international rates.

Thus, the major effect on economic development comes from Title I and one provision of the Title II programs. There are a number of complex and subtle issues which come out of these experiences. Let us review these in light of the country experiences.

DEVELOPMENT AND INTERNATIONAL POLICY ISSUES

The effects of Public Law 480 programs in five countries have been reviewed to show the importance of internal policies and individual country differences. Many factors can affect the results of the program in the recipient country. Public Law 480 supplies can advance the development program, can help maintain such a program in adverse circumstances, or can flow primarily into channels which enhance human welfare, such as increased per capita consumption. In short, Public Law 480, like other foreign aid programs, must be reviewed against the broad pattern of economic, political and social variables of the individual country. Either a sweeping attack on the program or a comprehensive defense will miss the mark. There are too many individual exceptions.

In economic terms, commodity aid allows for the expansion of spending on either consumer or investment goods. Commodity aid may expand investments and development efforts through the employment of unused resources—mainly underemployed labor. Moreover, the sale of Public Law 480 commodities in local channels will absorb the purchasing power created through the expanded investment and development program. For example, consumers exchange local currency for the commodities, and as the local currency is withdrawn from the economy, excessive inflationary pressures can be avoided. If the local currency is subsequently spent by the government, it may have an inflationary effect; it does not, as some would argue, make a second contribution to development. Such double counting implies that the bank accounts of local currency are an additional developmental resource; actually they only represent a possible future claim against the developing nation's resources.

The issue of most concern to policy makers is the effect which commodity imports may have on domestic production in the recipient country. On this issue the evidence is mixed. Fisher[32] has recently pointed out that domestic programs can be developed at small cost to offset the unfavorable price effects of additional imports. Economic circumstances in Israel provided more favorable farm prices after Public Law 480 began to operate. In Colombia an aggressive cotton expansion program more than offset the price effects of Public Law 480 cotton imports, whereas the Colombian wheat producer was not protected. In Pakistan, food grain production did not expand. Prices paid to local producers usually were less than the cost of imported supplies, with the government paying a subsidy on imports to keep consumer prices from rising "too fast." In India, the major point evident in studies to date is that Public Law 480 *may* have helped prevent an even stronger effort to expand Indian agriculture in the Third Five-Year Plan. Finally, it should be emphasized that price alone is an inadequate stimulus to agricultural production in an underdeveloped country. Other types of effort also are needed, such as credit, technical information, and market facilities.

Turning from domestic agriculture to international trade, another issue comes into view. Does Public Law 480 depress world prices and therefore the foreign exchange earnings of agricultural exporting nations? The recipient country often is an exporter of products other than those received under Public Law 480. They, along with other export countries, compete with the United States for commercial markets. One must be careful here to differentiate among the Title III barter provision of Public Law 480, the other sections of Public Law 480, and the export subsidy program.[33] All are part of an aggressive United States farm export program, but the price effects of export subsidies are more important than the other two programs. With the use of export subsidies, the United States ceased to hold a price umbrella over the world market, but instead began to play the role of price leadership. Markets are to a large extent interrelated. If a recipient nation finds ways to cut its normal commercial imports, other exporters are affected.[34] A reduction in their export earnings, whether caused by United States export subsidies, by aggressive barter programs, or by trade diversion under

[32] Franklin M. Fisher, "Food Surplus Disposal, Price Effects and the Costs of Agricultural Policies in Underdeveloped Countries: A Theoretical Analysis," Report 6307, Econometric Institute, Netherlands School of Economics, 1963.

[33] See Karl Fox et. al., *op. cit.*, pp. 166–168.

[34] Jerome Stam in an unpublished Michigan State University M.S. thesis points out that Title I sales reduced both Canadian and U.S. commercial sales to sixteen less developed countries, with the latter declining more rapidly. He also indicates that Canadian sales in 1954–1957 were smaller than in 1958–1960, when the barter rules were much tighter and the volume smaller.

Title I programs, does affect the development potential of less developed farm product exporting nations.

A related issue is the question of what prices underdeveloped countries would pay for surplus products were there free international markets and no concessional sales programs. It is argued that much lower international commodity prices would greatly reduce the foreign exchange costs of food imports,[35] but there is little reason to expect that internal political forces would permit such a deterioration in farm income and welfare of export nations. Concessional sales permit a large degree of price discrimination, which probably provides more food to developing nations and requires that importing developed nations pay higher prices than they would with less intervention in international trade.

Another unresolved question relates to an increase in food production in a world of rapid population growth. Is it less costly for developed nations to produce food surpluses and sell it on concessional terms, than for the less developed countries to reorganize their resources to expand farm production? If the food is to be produced in the less developed world, then costly programs to idle and transfer agricultural resources to other uses are required in the developed countries. Past experience indicates that developed countries do *not* easily curtail farm production, and that less developed nations do *not* easily expand agricultural production.

Next let us return to the local currency issue. This currency is sometimes viewed as nearly equivalent to additional dollar aid and sometimes viewed as a potential threat of inflation—a United States-held mortgage on the money supply. It may be "Foreign Money We Can't Spend" in the words of Mason,[36] but it may also be a useful source of financing, when there are internal institutional rigidities. Some of the local currency is used for regular United States government expenses, but this has little or no development impact. In some countries the local currency can serve no useful purpose, because the host country follows sound and sophisticated monetary and fiscal policies, creating money and credit as needed for expanded development programs. In such cases, local currency *is* an embarrassment to the United States government and serves no purpose. In between are cases where the local currency can expand the use of underemployed resources, shift the developmental priorities in a favorable (or unfavorable) direction, or provide increased financing for social reform or overhead capital formation, when the local government may be unable to act. In other words,

[35] T. W. Schultz, *op. cit.*, and my comments on his article in the same journal, pp. 1046–1051.

[36] See E. S. Mason, "Foreign Money We Can't Spend," *The Atlantic Monthly*, vol. 205, May, 1960.

there may be a way in which local currency can encourage development, usually through supporting programs for which the local government is unwilling or unable to act. A clarification of the circumstances under which this may be true is warranted. If these funds are to be useful they must be viewed realistically as claims on the recipient country's resources. They are expendable funds and should not be budgeted and controlled as if they were dollars.

Finally, the use of food-for-wages programs can be a useful way to cut through institutional rigidities which prevent more normal programs from utilizing unemployed labor resources. The same effects as attained in the Tunisia experience could be obtained by employing these laborers, paying a cash wage, and expanding the volume of food available through private market channels. But this may not always be possible. Government fiscal authorities may resist additional spending for such projects, or the private trade channels may be incapable of substantial, rapid expansion. In such cases it may be far easier to establish a food-for-wages program, despite its cumbersomeness. In actual fact, this criterion is not dominant. Some of these programs are found in the more traditional, less monetized economies, but there are also programs in Brazil, Hong Kong, and Taiwan, economies which certainly are in a position to proceed by revisions of their overall economic plans.

In conclusion, let us briefly review the implications of Public Law 480 for United States farm policy.

UNITED STATES AGRICULTURAL POLICY AND PUBLIC LAW 480

The Public Law 480 program has persisted and grown, despite its origin as a temporary surplus disposal program in 1954. The economic events which supported this growth through increasing agricultural productivity are likely to be repeated in the 1960s in other developed nations, such as the European Common Market nations and possibly Japan. Advances in agricultural technology, increases in efficiency at stable prices, farm consolidations, specialization, better management, and more capital all lead to increases in agricultural production; yet in these developed countries, income and price elasticities are low. Low demand elasticities combined with low downward supply elasticities result in lower farm prices and incomes. Political responses to agricultural pressures tend to provide prices high enough to continue the process. Government intervention to support agricultural prices piles up "surpluses," which gradually become sufficiently large to threaten internal policy.

In these circumstances, Public Law 480 became a "second best" solution. The concept is likely to be applied by other developed nations. Since Public Law 480 exports involve little additional expenditure of government funds, promise to reduce storage costs and losses, and contribute to humanitarian values, it is not surprising that they are politically appealing. Over time they tend to reduce the pressures for a change in farm policy, despite a widespread recognition that the agricultural sector is producing more goods than are needed. Fundamental restructuring of policies is difficult, and the proper solutions for United States agriculture are all the more complex because of the time required, the geographical variables, the large number of underemployed farmers, the political and social implications of large-scale rural to urban migration, and the slow rate of United States economic development.[37]

The growth of Public Law 480 shipments also has meant that little progress is made in pushing towards the policies which will better use the skills and capacities of those whose lives will continue to be dedicated to agriculture, but who could contribute more fully if used in other, nonfarm occupations. Public Law 480 thus represents a weakness of the American economy, not just a weakness of American agriculture.

In evaluating Public Law 480 one also must ask whether Public Law 480 authorizations compete with or are supplementary to foreign aid authorization. This issue cannot be resolved precisely, since it involves political judgments and political decisions. In the short run, Public Law 480 is supplementary. The dollars represented already have been spent on commodity purchases and stockpiling. Their shipment overseas is not a further drain on public funds; in fact, they may reduce storage expenditures. For the longer run, the problem is more difficult. If there were a gradual reduction in United States federal expenditures on agricultural programs from the present annual $6 to $7 billion to $2 or $3 billion, would some of these "not spent" federal dollars be available for foreign aid, for tax reduction, for domestic slum clearance, for internal development programs, or for a host of other items? The question is easy to pose, but difficult to answer.

Meanwhile, part of the excess capacity of American agriculture contributes to greater supplies of farm products abroad. They can and do contribute to development, but there are many limitations in their use. Better use of these food resources abroad demands clearer understanding of the development process, necessitates improved administration of programs by both the United States and recipient countries, and requires that commodity aid be skillfully integrated into a carefully constructed and effectively managed development program. Programs such as Public Law 480 still are convenient for the presently advanced nations. Continued technological advance in the developed countries indicates that these countries may be able to expand food output and ship food at less resource cost than the less developed countries would require in providing their own sustenance. Unless there are significant agricultural

[37] For further insight into these problems see Selection 12 by Dale Hathaway.

advances in less developed nations in the near future, the rapidly expanding populations and lagging agriculture will require the extension of Public Law 480 and the introduction of similar programs by other nations and international agencies.

22. Programming Changes in Marketing in Planned Economic Development*

N. R. COLLINS AND R. H. HOLTON[1]

Plans for economic development now generally recognize the interdependence of industrial sectors in the economy. If the rate of economic growth is to be as great as possible for any given level of effort, a planned increase in the output of a given industry must be coordinated with changes on the part of that industry's suppliers and customers. Otherwise frustrating bottlenecks can develop.

Rarely, however, is it recognized that industrial and agricultural sectors in turn are dependent on the development of a distributive sector to bridge the gap between producer and ultimate consumer. In a sense the goods are not fully "produced" until they reach the hands of this final buyer; new production goals cannot be considered successfully achieved in any viable long-run sense unless firm and continuous contact is made with markets.

Plans for economic development normally assume that this link between producers and ultimate buyer will be provided more or less automatically as marketing firms spring up in response to price incentive.[2]

* From *KYKLOS*, vol. 16, pp. 123–136, January, 1963. Reprinted by permission of *KYKLOS* and the authors. The authors are professor of agricultural economics and professor of business administration, at the University of California, Berkeley. Professor Holton is now serving as special assistant for economic affairs, U.S. Department of Commerce.

[1] This paper was written when the authors held Fulbright grants to the University of Naples. The work was supported by Professor Manlio Rossi-Doria's Istituto di Economia Agraria and by Professor Carlo Fabrizi's Istituto di Tecnica Aziendale. Professor Holton is indebted also to Professor A. G. Papandreou's Center of Economic Research in Athens, Greece.

[2] The extensive UN-studies of Brazil and Colombia, for example, give virtually no attention to needed changes in marketing, partly for this reason, presumably. United Nations, *Analyses and Projections of Economic Development,* Vol. II, *The Economic Development of Brazil,* and Vol. III, *The Economic Development of Colombia.*

The purpose of this note is to question the proposition that such firms will necessarily appear or, if they do, that they will always provide the kind of marketing services most appropriate for the new production situation. This is especially true in the case of agriculture, to which we will devote most of our attention.

The welfare of the agricultural producer depends on the distributive sector not only because *ceteris paribus* the greater the cost of distribution, the lower the price received by the producer.[3] Especially in agricultural marketing the historical interest in reducing the cost of distribution has obscured the point that perhaps the costs of distribution are actually too low in many respects, rather than too high. The ideal set of marketing services for a given agricultural product may be one which is more costly, rather than less costly, per unit of physical product marketed. Development plans which do give attention to agricultural marketing problems usually emphasize the simple cost-reduction problems and call for improved physical distribution facilities, especially new buildings for central wholesale markets. But more often the really critical need is a change in the organization and operation of the distributive sector rather than a few new physical facilities. Planners no doubt prefer the latter to the former kind of change because of their fondness for activity with obvious physical manifestations. Moreover, materials are notably more malleable than men, and this simple principle dictates that the planner first alter the physical facilities in the hope that the more intangible aspects of distribution will follow suit with a new configuration of their own accord.

Effective planning for economic development, then, must recognize that expansion of agriculture and agriculture-based industries may call for correlative changes in the organization and practices, not just in the physical facilities, in the distributive sector. But one can go beyond this and argue that the distributive sector can in fact be a leading sector in economic development. The discussions of distribution in development plans generally focus on removing the obstacles in the marketing process. This implies, however, that the distributive sector plays only a passive role in development, whereas it can under certain circumstances play a very active role by changing demand and cost functions in agriculture and manufacturing in such a way as to encourage their expansion.[4]

[3] For a discussion of marketing costs in less developed areas, see P. T. BAUER and B. S. Yamey, "Economics of Marketing Reform," *Journal of Political Economy*, LXII (June, 1954), pp. 210–235; R. H. Holton, "Marketing Structure and Economic Development," *Quarterly Journal of Economics*, LXVII (August, 1953), pp. 344–361; and J. K. Galbraith and R. H. Holton and others, *Marketing Efficiency in Puerto Rico*, Cambridge, Harvard University Press, 1955.

[4] A. O. Hirschman has briefly noted the backward linkage effect from tertiary back to primary and secondary production. See his *Strategy of Economic Develop-*

We now turn to the problems of programming actions to facilitate changes in the distributive sector, changes that must be instituted to complement the plans for expanding physical production of goods.

GOALS FOR THE DISTRIBUTIVE SECTOR

Usually a country's development program reflects not a single goal but rather a set of goals, which may not be wholly consistent with each other. The well-designed strategy for the distributive sector will take into account these conflicts, and the planners will have to recognize the consequences of sacrificing some objectives for the sake of others.

One goal for the distributive sector might be a set of institutions and operating practices that would permit distribution of the output of primary and secondary industries at the lowest possible cost per unit of product, given the present organization of production on the one hand and of the industrial groups or consuming groups on the other. If the high distribution costs which so often are found in underdeveloped areas were to be lowered, the derived demand curve facing the producer would tend to be shifted to the right with a consequent encouragement to greater output, employment, and income. When the plans for economic development do not anticipate any substantial changes in the production and consumption patterns, and when the marketing system is performing the proper mix of services (although at too high a cost), this may be the most appropriate goal for development of that portion of the distributive sector handling the commodity in question.

But if we adopt a more realistic assumption, namely that the economic development plan for the country calls for changes in the methods, organization and level of production, or in the mix of goods produced, it is probable that the distributive apparatus ideally suited to the present production pattern would not be well designed for the characteristics of the output planned in the target year. Hence a second alternative goal for the distributive sector might be to develop a set of institutions and practices that will give minimum costs per unit of product given the planned organization of production and given the anticipated nature of final consumer markets.

These two goals, however, may overemphasize costs and give too little attention to the distributive services performed. A third goal for the distributive sector might be to establish a set of organizations and practices which would maximize the rate of growth of the primary and secondary sectors. This goal views marketing as playing an active,

---

ment, New Haven, Yale University Press, 1958, p. 112. P. T. Bauer has also noted changes in the marketing environment which have made consuming centers accessible to agricultural producers. See his *Economic Analysis and Policy in Underdeveloped Countries,* Durham, Duke University Commonwealth Study Center, 1957, pp. 58/59 and 75/76.

rather than merely a passive, cost-reducing role in economic development, and admits the possibility that more, instead of fewer, resources might well be devoted to the distributive sector. The marketing system can often make or break the development plans for agriculture, and it may be especially crucial during the early years of the development program. It is possible that during the initial years, special temporary practices or organizational features of marketing might be adopted to give agricultural development extra thrust, designed to accelerate the first stages of the transformation of that sector.

We turn now to the design of strategy for achieving the goal of a distributive sector that facilitates the development of primary and secondary production. But under several combinations of circumstances the most appropriate strategy may consist of no intervention into the distributive sector. Before discussing the components of an active strategy for effecting change in the marketing system, let us consider possible reasons for inaction.

A STRATEGY OF INACTION

No action may be called for if the mix of distributive services and scale of operations are generally adequate. This might be the case, for example, if the development plan calls for an increased output of deciduous fruits or vegetables and if it is possible to export these effectively through an existing channel handling large quantities of citrus. Certain other changes at the producer level, such as shifts toward more desirable varieties, also might make no new demands on the marketing system for agricultural commodities. Similar cases can be found in the case of manufactured goods.

Inaction may also be advisable simply because the weak points in the distributive network are beyond the reach of the planning agency. If a region's output is sold into foreign markets, for example, it might not be possible for the development agency to effect requisite alterations in the wholesaling or retailing practices in these outside areas. Furthermore, the development activity may be limited functionally as well as geographically. For example, the Cassa per il Mezzogiorno, the principal development agency for southern Italy, limits its activities not only to this geographic area but also to extending financial and other inducements almost exclusively to agricultural and manufacturing enterprises. Thus marketing facilities, both wholesale and retail, outside southern Italy are beyond both the geographic and functional jurisdiction of the Cassa.[5] It may be technically feasible to produce in a newly developing

[5] A well-designed development plan, however, could give this functional jurisdiction to one development agency or another; but the geographical problem is more difficult to avoid if international boundaries are involved.

area varieties of fruits and vegetables suitable for freezing. But in order to place frozen products in the hands of the consumer in distant markets, an uninterrupted cold chain must be developed. This latter requires drastic changes in wholesaling and retailing. Such changes may simply be beyond the reach, geographically and functionally, of the development agency, in which case it may be unwise to allocate the limited funds for adjustments at the producer or first handler level.

A strategy of inaction may also be appropriate if the ambient circumstances are such that, although a distributive network suitable for the changing production may not now exist, a reasonably satisfactory marketing system is expected to spring up in response to the new economic opportunities. It is clear that many underdeveloped areas hold this view.

Often, too, the development plan can ignore the problem of the marketing network because the firms called for in the given primary or secondary industry are large enough to support their own integrated marketing operations. The cement mill and the large-scale exploitation of mineral resources offer cases in point.

Intervention into distribution may also be shunned because the returns to development capital in this direction are lower than for other development projects. If development capital is limited, as it invariably is, some proposed projects may be dropped because the ratio of social benefits to social costs falls below some cut-off point. Inaction is appropriate if investments in improved marketing organization and practices would bring returns below this point. But it might be argued that so little is known about the probable returns from improved marketing that planners may consistently underestimate the real potentialities of such a program.

A strategy of inaction may also be dictated because the required changes in the distributive apparatus in the society call for talents which do not exist or else are very expensive to hire. One may hire specialized firms to build dams, but building a new marketing system means changing business behavior, and this is slippery stuff. The oft-repeated expression that it is easier to build dams and roads because only money is required simply reflects the difficulty of modifying human behavior.

OBSTACLES TO NECESSARY CHANGE

The distributive sector may not develop along the appropriate path in response to market opportunities for a number of reasons which must be appreciated if positive policies for change are to be designed and implemented. First, the absence of such institutions as grading systems, standard weights and measures, and an adequate legal code covering rights and obligations under contracts may retard development.

It has been noted that the lack of these institutions may serve to perpetuate an industrial structure whose performance is antithetical to rapid economic development and that the already difficult task faced by market prices in effectively directing investment decisions is compounded by market imperfections of this kind.[6] These institutions provide rules serving to reduce the number of dimensions which must be negotiated in a market transaction, and generally permit business to be transacted without each aspect of each transaction being carefully monitored. With negotiation simplified, a firm with a given amount of managerial talent can achieve a much larger scale because each transaction takes less time and because certain physical handling processes are also simplified.

Second, the operation of the price mechanism may not induce the individual firm to establish certain ancillary distributive services or procedures, the benefits from which are diffused among the industries as a whole, since the gains from such changes are not reflected accurately in the profit account of the initiating agency. Examples of such may include improvements in the industry's information system or the development of contracting and buying procedures to be used, say, by processors in dealing with farm producers. Since such "public" services will not be forthcoming from a decentralized decision-making organization to an extent warranted by general efficiency considerations, a centralized program must be considered.[7]

For some ancillary services, furthermore, economies of scale may dictate that the service be performed for a whole industry or not at all. But in some cases, as Bauer has pointed out, the economies of scale in the organization and establishment of a service, as distinct from the later operation of the service, may urge that it be set up on an industry-wide basis at the outset.[8]

Third, significant innovations by private entrepreneurs in distribution may be blocked because the initial investment required is very large indeed relative to the funds to which the entrepreneur has ready access. The typically easy entry into trade in underdeveloped areas causes most traders to be financially weak; and the strong traders are likely to prefer the *status quo* to the uncertainties of innovation.

Fourth, the shortage of managerial talent may cause the successful merchant to invest not in changes in distribution but in real estate, foreign securities or other investments which not only diversify his risks but also make limited demands on his managerial time. The widespread inability to expand the firm's managerial capacity beyond the limits

[6] W. F. Mueller, "Some Market Structure Considerations in Economic Development," *Journal of Farm Economics*, XLI (May, 1959), p. 417; and P. N. Rodenstein-Rodan, "Notes on the Theory of the Big Push" in: H. S. Ellis (ed.), *Economic Development for Latin America*, London, Macmillan, 1961, p. 58.

[7] F. M. Bator, "The Anatomy of Market Failure," *Quarterly Journal of Economics*, LXXII (August, 1958), pp. 351–379.

[8] Bauer, *op. cit.*, p. 110.

imposed by the size of the family may be just as great a barrier to the unaided development of distribution as of manufacturing.

Fifth, the potential innovator in distribution may be discouraged because imitators may enter easily and quickly to beat down operating margins before the innovator can recoup his investment. For example, the first firm to begin processing fruits and vegetables in an area may have to spend substantial amounts to persuade farmers to produce proper varieties and to use appropriate cultivation and harvesting techniques. The firm in effect would be establishing the requisite coordination among the farm firms and between the producers and the processing activity.[9] Later entrants can take advantage of the innovator's organizational work and they may push down operating margins before the innovator has recovered his initial outlays.

The desired changes in the distributive system may also be blocked because the potential innovator has control only over a limited portion of the distribution channel, while his innovation to be effective must be coordinated with changes in other stages of the marketing process. The dependence of the frozen food processor on adequate storage and selling facilities, discussed earlier, is a case in point.

Yet another barrier to development of the appropriate kind of distribution system is often found in complicated licensing procedures and closed socio-economic groups which collectively resist competitive intrusion, especially of firms such as supermarkets, which represent significant and threatening innovations.

Finally, automatic transformation of the marketing system may be impeded if the economies of scale in distribution are much greater than in production; under these circumstances the proper kind of distributive sector may not develop until the new pattern of production has already been established, but the establishment of this new pattern of production may in turn be dependent on the existence of the right kind of distributive sector. In southern Italy, for example, a program of land reform, land reclamation and irrigation is designed to shift the region from extensive agriculture to intensive production of such commodities as commercial fruits and vegetables. The new small-holders find, however, that there is no developed marketing organization to link them with the major consumer centers. Without tangible outlets at hand, these farmers are reluctant to risk their limited capital in the production of fruits and vegetables in the expectation that markets will materialize in the future. But on the other hand, marketing firms do not want to enter the area merely in the hope that fruit and vegetable production in adequate volume will be forthcoming after they are established.

[9] The need for a high degree of coordination between food processor and suppliers is widely recognized in the U.S. See N. R. Collins and J. A. Jamison, "Mass Merchandising and the Agricultural Producer," *Journal of Marketing*, XXII (April, 1958), pp. 357–366.

It can be seen, then, that a special effort may be required to transform the distributive sector simultaneously with the transformation of primary and secondary production. Although presumably the network of production and marketing, once established, can function satisfactorily with only the normal level of government surveillance and regulation, the *shift* from the present to the desired system of organization may well require management and financial capabilities beyond those found in tertiary industry. When this is the case, public policy should provide devices that facilitate the transition from the present to the desired organizational pattern. Then after the mutation of the interrelated production-distribution organization is completed, the facilitating devices can be dismantled, leaving the new organism free to operate.[10]

THE DESIGN OF THE FACILITATING MECHANISMS

The precise nature of the best facilitating mechanisms will of course depend on the individual case. But possible components of a program can be suggested. The most straight-forward inducement may be subsidies to private firms which make the desired modifications so that these firms could avoid operating losses during the transition. For example, direct payments or some tax advantage might be used to encourage establishment of large-scale assembly, wholesaling, or even retailing firms; and such might be done before the production of the commodities requisite for the effective and profitable operation of such firms has been obtained.

The reasoning behind this time sequence is that building the distributive capacity stimulates the productive sector to supply the desired product mix. In the United States, for example, the large-scale food retailers have been both persistent and effective in encouraging the supply of the kinds of food products best suited to a mass-merchandising, mass-consumption industry.[11]

Subsidies to farmers might be used to obtain uniform planting of, say citrus groves in a newly irrigated and levelled area in advance of the establishment of a marketing network. (Although one has no small amount of trepidation recommending features of the US farm program

[10] The argument for facilitating mechanisms to assist during the period of rapid economic growth parallels Stigler's suggestion that integration under such conditions can obtain the requisite level of coordination among the interdependent sectors. After the growth rate declines, Stigler concludes, there would be less need for such administrative arrangements and disintegration would be induced. See G. Stigler, "The Division of Labor is Limited by the Extent of the Market," *Journal of Political Economy*, LIX (June, 1951), pp. 185–193.

[11] G. L. Mehren, "The Changing Structure of the Food Market," *Journal of Farm Economics*, XXXIX (May, 1957), pp. 339–353; W. W. Cochrane, "Changing Structure of the American Economy: Its Implications for the Performance of Agriculture Markets," *Journal of Farm Economics*, XLI (May, 1959), pp. 401–413.

for adoption elsewhere, subsidies there in recent years have been effective in inducing farmers to shift marginal crop lands to their best alternative use, pasture.) Temporary subsidies might also be paid to new marketing firms to encourage their entry even before the volume of production reaches the level which, without the subsidy, would be required to justify entry into the market.

In the modern world, however, the recipients of subsidies have been notably successful in persuading their countrymen that the welfare of the entire economy depends on the continuation, if not the expansion, of the subsidy. It may be argued, therefore, that subsidies would perhaps be avoided not because they are ineffective, but because they are immortal. Besides, other devices may accomplish the same ends. For example, extending credit on preferential terms to the distributive and farm firms described above, while denying credit to those not making the adjustments desired or to those not of adequate size, may aid significantly in moving the system through the transitional phase.

Subsidies and credit and tax devices may suffice to attract new distributive firms quickly, especially if the optimum scale for the new firms is relatively small. But if the optimum size is large or if the organization cost is high, and particularly if a substantial amount of managerial talent is needed to operate the kind of firm required, these devices may not do the job. Perhaps only a very small number of large firms would be required, or the conditions of natural monopoly may even be present. The cooperative comes to mind immediately as a possible instrument under such circumstances, since the producers own and operate these enterprises and so are not damaged by the cooperative's monopsonistic position.

But for maximum success, the marketing cooperative in many cases must have the power to require its producer-members to follow certain practices so that the cooperative's produce can be marketed with effective advertising and merchandising. Producers are often reluctant to relinquish to the cooperative this degree of sovereignty over their farm operations. The fact that Sicily's huge citrus production is sold through a highly fractionized packing and shipping industry, in contrast with the highly centralized selling activity of the large California cooperative, Sunkist, may reflect among other things the greater willingness of the producers in California to let some of their operating decisions be made by their cooperative. Perhaps it would be necessary to require by law a certain minimum of grower participation in his cooperative in a developing area, but it would obviously be preferable for a cooperative to gain the necessary compliance with its wishes by using price incentives.

The problem of inadequate managerial talent may call for special tactics. When it seems clear that private firms are unlikely to enter a given industry, it is tempting to recommend that a cooperative or a state-owned firm should be organized to fill the gap. But if private firms have been reluctant to enter because of inadequate managerial talent, there is little reason to think that the state will have such talent at its disposal. Here the appropriate solution might be a cooperative or possibly a state-owned firm operated by a private firm, perhaps a foreign one, under a management contract. There may be in the country private firms in the same or related kinds of business who would not be interested in setting up the necessary firm with their own or with borrowed capital simply because of their estimation of the risk involved. But if the state were to take the burden of the risk, the firm might be able to provide the management services. We need not go into the details of possible arrangements, but they might permit the firm providing the management services to receive its costs and fixed fee plus a percentage of profit plus options to buy a part of the stock of the company. Some such set of devices could permit the risk of the venture to lie with the producers (in the case of a cooperative) or with the development agency, while the private firm providing the managerial services would be motivated to make the new venture succeed.

If the scale economies of the operation in question are such that only one firm is called for, and if producers have little opportunity to sell to any other buyer, the firm could well be treated as a public utility. If it is a private firm, perhaps some maximum rate of profit should be stipulated, although since these ventures are likely to involve considerable risk, supposedly the development agency should be prepared to cover operating losses in excess of some amount. The application of the public utility idea would also include the joint private-public firm, as illustrated by Migros-Turk, the food chain in Turkey. This retailing and wholesaling organization is owned by Migros, the famous Swiss retail food chain, and the Turkish government, with Migros having a controlling interest in the company.

Besides these specific devices for facilitating the development of the required distributive organization, measures to correct the commonly noted imperfections in the market should of course be pushed. Improved market information, more enlightened taxing and licensing policies, removal of legislative or administrative barriers to lower-cost distribution are all generally-recognized needs and it is not necessary to discuss them in detail here.

Finally, the rationalization of distribution is often slowed because the limited employment opportunities in the rest of the economy, coupled with the ease of entry into trade, leads to a fragmented, "sick" industry. In an environment marked by chronic unemployment, "from the point of view of the government the phenomenon of the unemployed taking refuge in trade may be a satisfactory substitute for a comprehensive unemployment insurance program."[12] These small firms may have sales

[12] Holton, op. cit., p. 345.

volumes so small that although the owners' weekly earnings are extremely low, the percentage mark-up may nonetheless be very high. Such high margins would seem to invite large scale, efficient competition to enter the market. But if all firms in the industry are so very small, their capital and their experience are too limited to give rise to innovations requiring large scale investment and management. A successful economic development program would encourage shifts to alternative employment in order to dull the lobbying effectiveness of this group.

No doubt the rationalization of the distributive apparatus could, under many circumstances, be accelerated sufficiently just by clearing away the imperfections in the market and by providing an environment of better employment opportunities. But often the interdependence of the distributive apparatus and the industry producing the physical good can prevent the establishment of either one without the other, unless there is some sort of intervention in the normal operation of the market. It is in this situation that a great deal of imagination must be brought to bear on the design of facilitating devices which accelerate the development of the distributive apparatus but which can be dismantled after the volume of product moving through the system has reached the planned level.

23. Research Costs and Social Returns: Hybrid Corn and Related Innovations*

ZVI GRILICHES[1]

INTRODUCTION AND SUMMARY

Both private and public expenditures on "research and development" have grown very rapidly in the last decade. Quantitatively, however, we

* From *The Journal of Political Economy*, vol. 66, pp. 419–431, October, 1958, with an added correction note. Copyright 1958 by the University of Chicago. Reprinted by permission of the University of Chicago Press and the author. The author is associate professor of economics at the University of Chicago.

[1] This article is an outgrowth of a larger study of the economics of hybrid corn. See my article, "Hybrid Corn: An Exploration in the Economics of Technological Change," *Econometrica*, October, 1957. I am indebted to A. C. Harberger, Martin J. Bailey, Lester G. Telser, and T. W. Schultz for valuable comments and to the National Science Foundation and the Social Science Research Council for financial support.

know very little about the results of these investments. We have some idea of how much we have spent but very little of what we got in return. We know almost nothing about the realized rate of return on these investments, though we feel intuitively that it must have been quite high. This article presents a first step toward answering some of these questions. However, all that is attempted here is to estimate the realized social rate of return, as of 1955, on public and private funds invested in hybrid-corn research, one of the outstanding technological successes of the century. The calculated rate of return is an *estimate*, subject to a wide margin of error but it should provide us with an order of magnitude for the "true" social rate of return on expenditures on hybrid-corn research. Actually, I believe that my estimate is biased downward, for, whenever I had to choose among alternative assumptions, I chose the assumption that led to the lowest estimate. This estimate will not tell us the global rate of return on research expenditures, but even a modest step in that direction may be of some use.

The following procedure is used to arrive at the estimate: First, private and public research expenditures on hybrid corn, 1910–55, are estimated on the basis of a mail survey and other data. Then the annual gross social returns are estimated on the assumption that they are approximately equal to the value of the resulting increase in corn production plus a price-change adjustment. The additional cost of producing hybrid seed is subtracted from these gross returns to arrive at an annual flow of net social returns. Using first a 5 and then a 10 per cent rate of interest, I bring all costs and returns forward to 1955, when the books are closed on this development and a rate of return is computed. Research costs are expressed as a capital sum, and returns are converted into a perpetual flow. The estimated perpetual flow of returns is divided by the cumulated research expenditures to arrive at a rate of return that will equalize the present value of the flow of returns with the cumulated value of research expenditures. This procedure leads to the estimate that *at least* 700 per cent per year was being earned, as of 1955, on the average dollar invested in hybrid-corn research.

Since this is not the only way in which a rate of return could be computed from these data, some alternative ways of defining and estimating the social rate of return are explored briefly. Comparisons are also made with estimates of returns in some other areas of technological change. Finally, I discuss the limitations of the procedure used and the implications of the results. In particular, I shall emphasize that almost no normative conclusions can be drawn from these few estimates.

RESEARCH EXPENDITURES

Inbred lines and hybrids have been developed by state agricultural experiment stations, the United States Department of Agriculture

(USDA), and private seed companies. The distinction between the first two developing agencies is mainly in the source of funds. Except for funds spent on research and coordinating activities at Beltsville, Maryland, most of the USDA funds were spent on co-operative corn-breeding research at various experiment stations.

A mail inquiry to ascertain expenditures on hybrid-corn research was sent to all the agricultural experiment stations, and usable data were obtained from twenty of them. The twenty states represented by these replies include most of the important corn states in the country. Expenditures of non-responding stations were estimated by setting the expenditures of each of them equal to the expenditures of a "similar" station.[2]

Data on USDA expenditures on "corn-production research: agronomic phases" beginning with 1931 were obtained from the Agricultural Research Service and extrapolated back to 1910. They overestimate the USDA contribution substantially, because they include various other aspects of corn research besides hybrid corn. Moreover, some of the USDA funds have already been counted in the expenditures of agricultural experiment stations.

The research expenditures of one of the major private seed companies for the years 1925–55 were extrapolated back to 1911 and divided by that firm's estimated share of the total market for hybrid seed corn to arrive at an estimate of the research expenditures of the "private" segment of the industry.[3]

The figures for 1955 may be used as an example of the numbers involved. I estimate that in 1955 the USDA spent about $300,000 on hybrid-corn research, the experiment stations about $650,000, and the private companies about $1,900,000.[4]

The historical research expenditure data, deflated by the Consumers Price Index (1955 = 100), are reproduced in column 1 of Table 1. In view of all the assumptions made, these figures should be taken with several grains of salt, the dosage increasing as one goes back into the

---

[2] The pairing was made on the basis of geographic proximity and general information about the industry. For example, Indiana expenditures were assumed to equal the reported Illinois expenditures; Oklahoma's to equal Kentucky's, and so forth. These pairings probably overestimate the total expenditures on hybrid-corn research.

[3] This will again overestimate expenditures, because "public" hybrids make up 25–30 per cent of the total market, and research expenditures on these have already been counted once.

[4] In 1951 M. T. Jenkins, of the USDA, estimated the total annual expenditures on hybrid-corn research as follows: USDA, $220,000; states, $600,000; and private industry, $1,100,000. My own independent estimate for 1951 is: USDA, $190,000; states, $550,000; private industry, $1,300,000. The two totals are $1,920,000 and $2,040,000, respectively. The agreement is very close, considering how arbitrary some of my assumptions are (see M. T. Jenkins, "Corn Breeding Research—Whither Bound," *Proceedings of the Sixth Annual Hybrid Corn Industry–Research Conference* [Chicago: American Seed Trade Association, November, 1951], pp. 42–45).

past. In particular, for the years 1910–25, the figures are little more than guesses.

For the purpose of estimating the rate of return on these expenditures, I assume that the public sector will continue to invest in hybrid-corn research at an annual rate of $1 million, and the private sector at an annual rate of $2 million. No incremental returns, however, will be ascribed to these expenditures. I assume them to be "maintenance" expenditures in face of a malevolent nature.

Cost of Additional Resources Devoted to Production of Hybrid Seed

I assume that the price of hybrid seed, approximately $11 per bushel in 1955, measures adequately the value of resources devoted to its production. If there were no hybrid corn, farmers would use mainly home-produced open-pollinated seed, which I value at $1.50 per bushel.[5] The quantity of hybrid seed used annually was estimated by multiplying the reported corn acreage planted with hybrid seed by the average seeding rate of corn. Multiplying the result by $9.50, the difference between the price of hybrid and non-hybrid seed, and subtracting $2 million research expenditures, I get $90 million as my estimate of the additional resources currently devoted each year to hybrid-seed production.[6] Using the average 1939–48 corn acreage (90 million), the 1951 seeding rate (7.5 pounds per acre), and the percentage planted with hybrid seed, I computed the additional cost of hybrid seed for the years 1933–55 and subtracted this from the subsequent estimate of gross returns to arrive at a net return figure.[7]

The Value of Hybrid Corn to Society

As everyone knows, hybrid corn increased corn yields. The figure most often quoted for this increase is 20 per cent. For my purpose, I assume that the superiority of hybrid over open-pollinated varieties is 15 per cent, the lower figure in most estimated ranges.[8] The value of this in-

---

[5] This is somewhat higher than the market price of corn because of the better quality of seed corn and the labor that would go into its selection. Since open-pollinated seed is now quoted at about $3.00 to $4.00 a bushel, this assumption also contributes to an over-all overestimate of cost.

[6] This result is reached as follows: 80 million acres × 90 per cent in hybrids × (8.6/64) average seeding rate × $9.50 = $92 million. Subtracting $2 million research expenditures, we get $90 million (source: *Agricultural Statistics, 1955*).

[7] Throughout the period these computations use the average corn acreage planted in 1939–48; they disregard annual fluctuations in total corn acreage and seeding rates. For any year before 1956, the extra cost of seed equals the percentage planted with hybrid seed times $98 million (90 million × [7.5/64] × $9.50 − $2 million [research expenditures] = $98 million).

[8] For example: "Plant breeders conservatively estimate increase in yields of 15 to 20 per cent from using hybrid seed under field conditions. They expect about the same relative increases in both low—and high—yielding areas" (USDA, *Technology on the Farm* [Washington, 1940], p. 7).

crease to "society" will be measured by the loss in total corn production that would have resulted if there were no hybrid corn. This hypothetical loss will be valued at the estimated equilibrium price of corn plus a price-change adjustment, a procedure equivalent to computing the loss in "consumer surplus" that would occur if hybrid corn were to "disappear."

The amount of this loss will depend on our assumptions about the relevant demand-and-supply elasticities. As will be seen from the formulas presented below, these elasticities have only a second-order effect, and hence different reasonable assumptions about them will affect the results very little. I assumed that the price elasticity of the demand for corn is approximately —0.5.[9] Since we know much less about the supply elasticity of corn, I shall first explore the consequences of two different extreme assumptions about it.

Let us assume, first, that in the long run the supply of corn is infinitely elastic; that is, we face long-run constant costs. The "disappearance" of

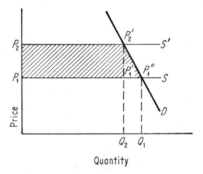

Fig. 1

hybrid corn would shift the supply curve upward by the percentage reduction in the yield of corn. The "loss" to society, in this case, is the total area under the demand curve between the new and the old supply curves. In Figure 1 this area is $P_1 P_2 P_2' P_1''$. This area can be interpreted as the increase in the total cost of producing the quantity Q_2 in the new situation, the rectangle $P_1 P_2 P_2' P_1'$, plus the loss in consumer surplus caused by the rise in price, the triangle $P_1' P_2' P_1''$. A linear approximation of this area is given by the formula

$$\text{Loss } 1 = k P_1 Q_1 (1 - \tfrac{1}{2} k n),$$

where k is the percentage change in yield (marginal cost and average cost), P_1 and Q_1 are, respectively, the previous equilibrium price of corn and quantity of corn produced, and n is the absolute value of the price elasticity of the demand for corn.

[9] This figure is based on a USDA demand analysis (see R. J. Foote, J. W. Klein, and M. Clough, *The Demand and Price Structure for Corn and Total Feed Concentrates* [Technical Bull. 1061 (Washington: USDA, October, 1952)]).

Alternatively, it could be assumed that the elasticity of the supply curve is zero. In this case, the loss is measured by the area $Q_2P_2'P_1''Q_1$ in Figure 2. Instead of assuming that the supply curve shifts upward, we now assume that it shifts k per cent to the left. The rectangle $Q_2P_1P_1''Q_1$ measures the loss in corn production at the old price P_1. The triangle $P_1'P_2'P_1''$ can be viewed as the additional loss in consumer

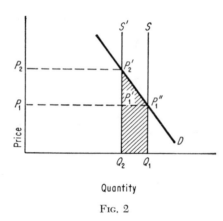

Quantity

FIG. 2

surplus or as an adjustment for the increase in price from P_1 to P_2. The total loss is now given by the formula

$$\text{Loss } 2 = kP_1Q_1(1 + \tfrac{1}{2}kn).*$$

It is easily seen that the second assumption leads to a higher estimate of the loss. It can be also shown that the two estimates bracket estimates implied by assuming other intermediate supply elasticities. The ratio of the loss under assumption 2 to the loss under assumption 1 is $(1 + \tfrac{1}{2}kn)/(1 - \tfrac{1}{2}kn)$. In our case, this ratio is approximately 1.07.[10] The difference between these two extreme assumptions implies only a 7 per cent difference in the final estimate of the total loss. Because this difference is so small and because I am striving for a lower-limit estimate, I have chosen the first assumption—that of an infinitely elastic long-run supply of corn.

To calculate the loss, we must assume an equilibrium price of corn. I shall use $1.00 per bushel in 1955 dollars as a minimal estimate of the value of corn to society. The current price of corn, about $1.25, is affected by the existence of price-support programs and probably overestimates the social value of corn.[11]

* EDITOR'S NOTE: See correction in the formula for "Loss 2" on page 385.
[10] Assuming k = 13, i.e., 15/115, and n = 0.5, the ratio is $(1 + 0.5 \times 0.13 \times 0.5)/(1 - 0.5 \times 0.13 \times 0.5) = 1.07$.
[11] An approximate formula for determining the price of corn in the absence of price supports is given by Marc Nerlove in "Estimates of the Elasticities of Supply of Selected Agricultural Commodities," *Journal of Farm Economics*, XXXVIII (May,

Because not all corn acreage was or is planted with hybrids, I multiply the percentage shift k by h, the percentage of all corn acres planted with hybrids (loss = $hkPQ[1 - \frac{1}{2}hkn]$).This procedure disregards the fact that the acres first planted to hybrids were higher-yielding acres than those planted later, and hence the procedure underestimates total returns.

In estimating past returns from hybrid corn, I ignore annual fluctuations in prices and production, basing my computations on the average 1937–48 level of production of 2,900 million bushels[12] and a real price of corn of $1.00 per bushel in 1955 dollars. On the returns side, only the percentage planted with hybrid seed varies over time. To calculate the annual flow of future returns, I assume that the average 1943–52 level of production—approximately 3,000 million bushels annually—will continue and that the percentage planted with hybrid seed will stabilize at 90. Both these assumptions are conservative and will result in an underestimate of returns.

Assuming that k, the relative shift in the supply curve, is 0.13 (15/115); that PQ is $3,000 million; that n, the demand elasticity, is 0.5; and that h, the current and future fraction of all corn acres planted with hybrid seed, is 0.9, we can calculate the current and expected annual flow of gross social returns from hybrid corn as follows:

$$0.9 \times 0.13 \times \$3,000 \text{ million } (1 - \frac{1}{2} \times 0.9 \times 0.13 \times 0.5) = 0.117 \times \$3,000 \text{ million } (1 - 0.029) = 0.117 \times 0.971 \times \$3,000 \text{ million } = \$341 \text{ million}$$

Subtracting the projected annual cost of hybrid-seed production and research—$93 million—we get $248 million as the current and expected annual flow of net social returns.

Similarly, returns for the past years, beginning with 1933, are calculated by multiplying 2,900 million 1955 dollars, the average total value of corn production, by the percentage of total corn acreage planted with

---

1956), 497: $dp/p_0 = (dq/q)/(n + e)$, where p_0 is the equilibrium price, n and e are the demand-and-supply elasticities, and dq is the quantity placed under loan. In recent years about 7 per cent of the annual corn crop, on the average, has been placed under loan with the Commodity Credit Corporation. The assumptions $n = 0.5$, $e = 0.2$, imply that the current price is about 10 per cent above the equilibrium price. The current price is about $1.25 per bushel, which implies an "equilibrium" price of corn of about $1.13. But this estimate does not take into account the impact on corn prices of the elimination of price supports on all other agricultural commodities. Taking this into account, the equilibrium price would be closer to $1.00 per bushel. In any case, it is unlikely to be lower than $1.00.

[12] This assumption was made to simplify the calculations. In the first part of the period, production was below this figure, and, since I use a relatively high rate of interest, this will result in an overestimate of returns. But the percentage planted with hybrids was also low then, while it was much higher during the period when production exceeded its average, and this will result in an underestimate of returns. On balance, the second effect should outweigh the first by a fair margin.

TABLE 1. HYBRID CORN: ESTIMATED RESEARCH EXPENDITURES
AND NET SOCIAL RETURNS, 1910–55
(*Millions of 1955 Dollars*)

Year	Total research expenditures (private and public)	Net social returns*	Year	Total research expenditures (private and public)	Net social returns*
1910	0.008		1935	0.593	2.9
1911	0.011		1936	0.661	8.3
1912	0.010		1937	0.664	21.2
1913	0.016		1938	0.721	39.9
1914	0.022		1939	0.846	60.3
1915	0.032		1940	1.090	81.7
1916	0.039		1941	1.100	105.3
1917	0.039		1942	1.070	124.3
1918	0.039		1943	1.390	140.4
1919	0.044		1944	1.590	158.7
1920	0.052		1945	1.600	172.6
1921	0.068		1946	1.820	184.7
1922	0.092		1947	1.660	194.3
1923	0.105		1948	1.660	203.7
1924	0.124		1949	1.840	209.8
1925	0.139		1950	2.060	209.0
1926	0.149		1951	2.110	218.7
1927	0.185		1952	2.180	226.7
1928	0.210		1953	2.030	232.1
1929	0.285		1954	2.270	234.2
			1955	2.790	239.1
1930	0.325				
1931	0.395		Annually		
1932	0.495		after 1955	3.000	248.0
1933	0.584	0.3			
1934	0.564	1.1			

* Net of seed production cost but not net of research expenditures. Net social returns are zero before 1933.

hybrid seed in each year. Subtracting the estimated past costs of hybrid-seed production, we get the net social returns for the years 1933–55 shown in column 2 of Table 1.[13]

[13] These are calculated from the following formula: $h \times [0.13 \times \$2,900$ million $(1 - \frac{1}{2} \times 0.9 \times 0.13 \times 0.5) - 90$ million $\times (7.5/64) \times \$9.50 - \$2$ million] $= h \times \$268$ million. This procedure is an approximation, since h should also have entered into the second part of the first term of the formula, the "triangle." I neglect this. Because h is less than 1 and because that part is always subtracted, this procedure again underestimates total returns.

CALCULATION OF A RATE OF RETURN

Table 1 presents estimates of costs and returns. There are several ways in which these figures could be summarized and a rate of return calculated. My procedure is as follows: Consider the development closed as of 1955. Future expenditures will not increase returns, nor will there be an expansion of hybrid-corn acreage. Standing in 1955, I cumulate and bring forward to 1955 all past costs and returns at a reasonable *external* rate of interest. To explore the impact of two quite different rates of interest, I perform the calculations twice, using first a 5 per cent and then a 10 per cent rate of interest. Past research costs are cumulated and expressed as a capital sum. Past returns are cumulated to 1955, and a 5 or 10 per cent rate of return on these cumulated returns is projected into the future. The estimated flow of future net returns is added to the flow from past returns to arrive at a perpetual flow of net social returns from hybrid corn. This flow, divided by the cumulated research expenditures, gives us our estimate of the realized perpetual rate of return.

Table 2 presents the calculations that lead to my estimate of approximately $7.00 as the annual return in perpetuity, as of 1955, for every dollar that has been invested in hybrid-corn research. Actually, even if we ignore all past returns completely, the figure is still very high—approximately $4.00 annually (using the 5 per cent interest rate) for every research dollar.

This way of calculating a "rate of return" is not really different from a benefit-cost ratio calculation. It may be useful to bring out explicitly the relationship between these two concepts. The preceding rate of return is defined as follows: $r = 100 \ (PR \times k + AFR)/RC$, where PR = cumulated past returns, k = the external rate of interest used to cumulate or discount returns, AFR = annual future returns, and RC = cumulated research costs.

A benefit-cost ratio from these same data would be

$$\frac{B}{C} = \left(PR + \frac{AFR/k}{RC} \right)$$

Hence $r = 100 \ k \ (B/C)$, and we can translate our calculation into a benefit-cost ratio, and vice versa. Using 5 and 10 per cent as the external rates of interest, the benefit-cost ratios for hybrid-corn research expenditures are 150 and 70, respectively.[14] When we recall that most Bureau

---

[14] If before cumulating we were to subtract the research costs from net returns annually (that is, have in our denominator only research expenditures before 1934, the year when net returns began to exceed research costs), the benefit-cost ratios would be substantially higher (about 700 and 200, respectively), and so would also the rate of return as defined in the text.

of Reclamation watershed projects have ex-post benefit-cost ratios of 1 or less, this does imply a certain misallocation of public resources.[15]

These calculations use an external rate of interest to bring all sums forward to 1955. It is reasonable to assume that the marginal productivity of capital in alternative investments is between 5 and 10 per cent and to use these rates as conversion factors for funds expended or earned at different dates. Alternatively, however, one could calculate an *internal rate of return*—that rate of interest which will equate the flow of costs and the flow of returns over time.[16] Such a rate has to be calculated using an iterative procedure, changing the rate used until the cumulated costs are equal to the discounted returns. The two procedures will give different answers when the time shape of costs differs markedly from the time shape of returns, as in our case. The internal rate of return on hybrid-corn research expenditures is between 35 and 40 per cent.[17] My objection to this particular procedure is that it values a dollar spent in 1910 at $2,300 in 1933. This does not seem very sensible to me. I prefer

TABLE 2. RATE OF RETURN ON HYBRID-CORN, RESEARCH
EXPENDITURES AS OF 1955
(*Millions of Dollars*)

	$r = 0.05$	$r = 0.10$
(1) Net cumulated past returns.........................	4,405	6,542
(2) Past returns expressed as an annual flow..............	220	654
(3) Annual future gross returns.........................	341	341
(4) Annual additional cost of production and research.......	93	93
(5) Total net annual returns, (2) + (3) − (4).............	468	902
(6) Cumulated past research expenditures.................	63	131
(7) Rate of return 100 × (5)/(6)........................	743	689

to value the 1910 dollar at a reasonable rate of return on some alternative social investment. Also, this procedure gives tremendous weight to the early expenditures, which are subject to the largest error of measurement. Actually, however, the two estimates are not very far apart. The estimate using an *external* rate of interest says that a dollar invested in hybrid-corn research earned 10 cents annually until 1955 and $7.00 annually thereafter. The *internal* rate estimate says that the dollar earned 40 cents annually throughout the whole period. If the average delay between

[15] For an evaluation of public investments in watershed projects see E. F. Renshaw, *Toward Responsible Government* (Chicago: Idyia Press, 1957).

[16] I am indebted to Martin J. Bailey for suggesting this alternative way of calculating the rate of return.

[17] That is, 40 per cent is too high and 35 is too low. The iterative procedure was not carried further.

investment and fruition is about ten years, then the two figures represent different ways of saying the same thing.[18]

LIMITATIONS

The estimate of 700 per cent is probably too low. At almost every point at which there was a choice of assumptions to be made, I have purposely chosen those that would result in a lower estimate. This is an attempt to arrive at an estimated lower limit of the social rate of return from hybrid corn.

Both the public and the private research expenditures are probably overstated substantially. In fact, the expenditure estimates supplied by some experiment stations are obviously too high. Of the USDA expenditures, perhaps less than half were devoted to hybrids. I did leave out all expenses incurred before 1910, but these in total could not have been more than a few thousand dollars. This should remind us, however, that the estimated rate of return is mainly a rate of return on applied rather than basic research. The basic idea of hybrid corn was developed between 1905 and 1920, with the help of very little money. The rate of return on this basic research, if it could be calculated, would be much higher. However, the idea had to be translated to commercial reality, and separate adaptable hybrids had to be developed for different areas. These are the activities reflected in my estimate of research cost.

The returns, on the other hand, are understated. The assumed price of corn of $1.00 per bushel in 1955 dollars and the assumption of a 15 per cent superiority of hybrids are both conservative and probably result in an under-estimate of the real returns to society. I have also assumed that all past research has already borne all its fruit and that all future research on hybrids will result in no benefit whatsoever. Nor has credit been given for the impact of hybrid corn on other fields: the research on hybrid poultry and hybrid sorghum which it stimulated or the reduction of farmer resistance to new technology as a result of the spectacular success of hybrid corn.

Hence, as far as costs and returns from hybrid corn per se are concerned, the estimate is too low. One troublesome problem, however, remains to haunt us. Does it really make sense to calculate the rate of return on a successful "oil well"? What is the point of calculating the rate of return on one of the outstanding technological successes of the century? Obviously, it will be high. What we would like to have is an

---

[18] An annual flow of 40 cents discounted at 40 per cent has a present value of $1.00. An annual flow of $7.00, discounted at 40 per cent, will also have a present value of $1.00 if there is a lag of approximately ten years between the date of investment and the date at which the perpetual flow of returns begins.

estimate that would also include the cost of all the "dry holes" that were drilled before hybrid corn was struck.

The estimate does include the cost of all the "dry holes" in hybrid-corn research itself. Hybrid corn was not a unique invention—it was an invention of a method of inventing. Many different combinations were tried before the right ones were found. One major seed company annually tests approximately fifteen hundred different combinations of inbred lines. Of these, at most three or four prove to be successful. The cost of the unsuccessful experiments is included in my estimate. What is excluded is investment in various other areas of agricultural research which has not borne fruit.

The problem of dry holes, however, can be reduced *ad absurdum*. What is the relevant segment for which an aggregate rate of return is to be computed? Is it really reasonable to ascribe the cost of unsuccessful gold exploration to the oil industry? If one takes this kind of reasoning too seriously, there is only one rate that has any meaning—the rate of return on research for the economy as a whole.

Nevertheless, the rate of return on a successful innovation may be of some interest. In particular, it may be useful, ex ante, to break down the probable rate of return into two components: the rate of return if the development turns out to be a success and the probability that it will be a success. The approach outlined here is a way of estimating the first component. An estimate of the probability of success, however, must be made on the basis of data other than those presented in this article.

Returns in Some Other Areas

T. W. Schultz has provided us with estimates of costs and returns of research for United States agriculture as a whole.[19] His data can be used to estimate the rate of return on agricultural research as a whole. Schultz gives an upper- and a lower-limit estimate of how much more input it would have taken to produce the 1950 output with 1940 techniques and inputs. His upper estimate is that it would have taken 18.5 per cent more input; his lower estimate is 3.7 per cent. Let us use Schultz's figures to estimate the perpetual gross annual returns, beginning with 1951, from the agricultural research that bore fruit between 1940 and 1950. Using the lower estimate, there would be a loss of 3.7 per cent in output if the new technology were to disappear. Taking the total annual value of farm output as $30 billion ($32 billion cash receipts from farm marketings in 1951, minus approximately 10 per cent to allow for the impact of the

[19] *The Economic Organization of Agriculture* (New York: McGraw-Hill Book Co., 1953), pp. 114–22.

support programs), and assuming a price elasticity of demand for agricultural products of —.25 and an infinite supply elasticity, we get

$$k(1 - \tfrac{1}{2}kn) \times \$30 \text{ billion} = 0.037 \times (1 - 0.5 \times 0.037 \times 0.25)$$
$$\times \$30 \text{ billion} = 0.037 \times 0.995 \times \$30 \text{ billion} = \$1,110 \text{ million}$$

Using the upper limit estimate of 18.5 per cent saving in inputs, we get

$$0.185(1 - 0.5 \times 0.185 \times 0.25) \times \$30 \text{ billion} = \$5,430 \text{ million}$$

as an upper-limit estimate of the gross annual social return from the technical change that occurred between 1940 and 1950.

Schultz also provides an estimate of total public expenditures on agricultural research for the years 1937–51. I assume that all these expenditures were used to produce the increase in output in 1951. This leaves out the contributions developed from funds spent before 1937, but, on the other hand, it disregards the possible returns after 1951 from the 1937–51 expenditures. On balance, we will probably overestimate the funds spent on the 1940–50 improvement in technology.

I will assume that total private agricultural research expenditures were of about the same magnitude as the public expenditures. This is approximately half the corresponding ratio for hybrid corn but is probably an overestimate for agriculture as a whole.[20]

Multiplying the 1937–51 public expenditures by 2, deflating them by the Consumers Price Index, and cumulating them at the rate of 5 per cent, I get the figure of 3,180 million 1951 dollars as my estimate of total cumulated research expenditures in agriculture. Comparing this with the two estimated limits of the annual social returns of $1,110 and $5,430 million, I get a lower limit of 35 and an upper limit of 171 per cent as estimates of the annual rate of return per dollar spent on agricultural research. These are substantially lower than the estimated returns from hybrid corn but are comparable to estimates made by Ewell for the economy as a whole (100–200 per cent per year per dollar spent on "research and development") and to figures quoted by major industrial companies on their returns on research.[21]

Of course, these estimates are quite consistent with the estimated returns on hybrid corn, if the probability of success in research on inno-

---

[20] Mighell has estimated that recent annual expenditures by industry for research on agricultural products and on machinery and materials used in agriculture were in excess of $140 million. At the same time the USDA and state agricultural experiment stations spent about $118 million annually on research. However, only one-third of the industry research was in aid of farm production, mainly in machinery and chemicals: the rest was used in product research, while four-fifths of public expenditures were for research in aid of farm production (see R. Mighell, *American Agriculture* [New York: John Wiley & Sons, 1955], p. 130).

[21] R. H. Ewell, "Role of Research in Economic Growth," *Chemical and Engineering News*, XXXIII (1955), 298–304.

vations like hybrid corn is on the order of one-tenth or one-twentieth. Nevertheless, all these figures indicate that, in spite of the large growth in research expenditures during this century, the social returns to this activity are still very high.

HYBRID SORGHUM

The approach previously outlined can be used to estimate the probable rate of return on a new development: for example, hybrid sorghum. The development of hybrid sorghum began seriously only after World War II but has gained momentum rapidly since. Hybrid sorghum is now being introduced commercially. Very little was planted in 1956, but substantial amounts were planted in 1957. The experimental data to date suggest that the superiority of hybrid sorghum over previous seed may be even greater than that of hybrid corn.[22]

The 1956 value of the grain sorghum crop was approximately $232 million. Assuming a 15 per cent superiority of hybrids, a demand elasticity of −1.0, and an infinitely elastic supply curve, the estimated gross social returns from sorghum hybrids would be about $37 million annually.[23] Assuming that the extra cost of hybrid seed will be about $7 million annually, the net annual returns would be about $30 million.[24] I have no official data on research expenditures on hybrid sorghum. The head of one of the major seed companies has estimated that to date all public and private expenditures on hybrid sorghum total approximately $1 million and that current expenditures are at an annual rate of $300,-000. Doubling his estimate of past expenditures and projecting into the future an annual research expenditure rate of $500,000, I get $10 or $13 million, depending on the rate of interest used, as my "estimate" of cumulated hybrid-sorghum research expenditures in 1967. I choose 1967 as the reckoning date on the assumption that it will take ten years for hybrid sorghum to capture most of the sorghum seed market. While the projected rate of development is faster than that of hybrid corn in the United States as a whole, it is equivalent to the rate of acceptance of hybrid corn in Iowa. It is reasonable to assume that hybrid sorghum will spread much faster than hybrid corn did. Sorghum production is more

[22] *Sorghum Hybrids* (USDA, ARS, Special Report 22–26 [Washington, May, 1956]).

[23] This figure is derived as follows: 0.15 $(1 + \frac{1}{2} \times 0.15 \times 1.0) \times \$232$ million = $0.16 \times \$232 = \$37$ million. The figure would have been approximately twice as large if I had used the value of the 1957 crop—$493 million—as my base.

[24] The additional cost of hybrid seed, seven million dollars, is estimated from the following data: 10 million acres sown to sorghum; ten dollars difference between the average prices per hundredweight of hybrid and open-pollinated grain sorghum seed (*Agricultural Prices*, April, 1958, p. 42); and an average seeding rate of seven pounds per acre.

localized than corn production, almost all sorghum is grown for commercial purposes, and hybrid sorghum will probably encounter much less
resistance than hybrid corn encountered. I also assume that the use of
hybrid sorghum in the United States will follow the same time path that
the use of hybrid corn followed in Iowa.[25] This assumption allows me to
estimate the social returns during the "transition period," 1957–67.

TABLE 3. ESTIMATED COSTS AND RETURNS OF HYBRID-SORGHUM
RESEARCH AS OF 1967
(*Millions of Dollars*)

	$r = 0.05$	$r = 0.10$
Cumulated social net returns, 1957–66..........	155	171
Value in 1967 of returns beyond 1967...........	590	295
Total value of net returns in 1967..............	745	466
Cumulated research expenditures..............	9.4	13
Benefit-cost ratio............................	79	36
"Rate of return" in per cent per annum........	395	360

Table 3 outlines the calculation of the estimated rate of return on
research expenditures on hybrid sorghum, which is approximately 400
per cent per annum. While this is somewhat lower than the estimated
rate of return on expenditures on hybrid-corn research, it is still very
high indeed.

SOME IMPLICATIONS

One might have expected, on a priori grounds, that the rate of return
on expenditures on hybrid-sorghum research would be higher than the
return on hybrid-corn research. The cost of hybrid sorghum has been and
will be lower than the cost of hybrid corn both because of the cumulated
experience in hybrid-corn breeding and because sorghum-growing is
much more localized than corn-growing. Therefore, adaptable hybrids
will have to be developed for a much smaller portion of the United
States. Nevertheless, the estimated returns from hybrid sorghum are lower
than those from hybrid corn. Why? To some extent this lower rate may
be a result of overestimating research costs for hybrid sorghum, but the
principal explanation is that the total value of the sorghum crop is substantially smaller than that of corn; sorghum is a relatively unimportant
crop. It has recently been suggested that we should redirect our research
efforts away from the major commodities that are in "surplus" and away
from commodities with low elasticities of demand, where technical improvements result in reduced total returns to farmers in the long run.

[25] The percentage of all corn planted with hybrid seed in Iowa followed the following time path by years: 0.02, 0.06, 0.14, 0.31, 0.52, 0.73, 0.90, 0.99, and 1.00.

However, if we assume, in the absence of any other information, that technological change operates somewhat like a percentage increase in yield, and that the cost of achieving a given percentage boost in yield is the same for different crops or at least independent of their price elasticities and relative "importance," then the highest *social* returns per research dollar are to be found in the important, low-elasticity commodities. For it can be easily shown that the absolute social gain from a given percentage increase in yield will vary proportionately with the total value of the crop and that the impact of different demand-and-supply elasticities is of a second order of magnitude. The latter affect only the "triangle," or the magnitude of the price-change adjustment. Among all the different factors, the total value of the crop is by far the most important determinant of the absolute social gain from a given percentage increase in yield.

No matter how we calculate them, there is little doubt that the over-all social returns on publicly supported technological research have been very high. It is not clear, however, whether or not this fact has any normative implications. I am afraid it has very few. More knowledge than is now at hand is required for presciption.

It is clear that we have not succeeded in equalizing the returns on different kinds of public investments. The returns from technological research have been much higher than the returns from reclamation and watershed projects. But should we have had more technological research? Surely, we have yet to reach the optimal level of expenditures on research, but this can only be a hunch. Should the public support agricultural research? My analysis illustrates and quantifies one of the major arguments for *public* investments in this area—the divergence between the social and private rates of return. Almost none of the calculated social returns from hybrid corn were appropriated by the hybrid-seed industry or by corn producers. They were passed on to consumers in the form of lower prices and higher output. Entry into the hybrid-seed industry was easy, and in the long run no "abnormal" profits were made there. By valuing the extra cost of seed production at the market price, I have counted as a cost whatever profit was made in this area by private producers, and the resulting estimate of returns consists almost entirely of social rather than private returns. These social returns were diffused widely among consumers of corn and corn products. Given the difficulty of patenting most of the valuable ideas in this area, the short life of a patent, and the general precariousness of a monopoly position in the long run, the incentive for private investment was very much smaller than that implied by the social rate of return.

While a divergence between social and private rates of return is a necessary reason for public intervention, it is not, by itself, a sufficient reason. We must ask not only whether social returns are higher than private—this is also true of many private investments—but also whether the private rate of return is too low, relative to returns on alternative private investments, to induce the *right* amount of investment at the *right* time. The social returns from nylon were probably many times higher than DuPont profits, but the latter were high enough to induce the development of nylon without a public subsidy, although, perhaps, not soon enough. To establish a case for public investment one must show that, in an area where social returns are high, private returns, because of the nature of the invention or of the relevant institutions, are not high enough relative to other private alternatives. This was undoubtedly true of hybrid corn, and it is probably true of many other areas of agricultural research and basic research in general. But it is not universally true. Hence a high social rate of return is not an unequivocal signal for public investment.

In this paper I have estimated that the rate of return on public investments in one of the most *successful* ventures of the past has been very high. This may give support to our intuitive feeling that the returns to such ventures in general have been quite high and to our feeling that "research is a good thing." But that does not mean that we should spend any amount of money on anything called "research." The moral is that, though very difficult, some sort of cost-and-returns calculation is possible and should be made. Conceptually, the decisions made by an administrator of research funds are among the most difficult economic decisions to make and to evaluate, but basically they are not very different from any other type of entrepreneurial decision.

A CORRECTION

I am indebted to T. D. Wallace of North Carolina State University and R. C. Lindberg of Purdue University for pointing out an error in the formula for Loss 2 on p. 374 of my article on "Research Costs and Social Returns." The correct formula is $kP_1Q_1[1 + (\frac{1}{2})k/n]$ and not $kP_1Q_1[1 + (\frac{1}{2})kn]$ as in the text. This changes the estimated ratio of Loss 2 to Loss 1 from 1.07 to 1.13, which is still a very minor difference.

In addition, however, they have raised the question whether the difference between these Losses is due merely to different assumptions about the supply elasticity. Would not the area defined as $P_1P_2P_2'P_1''$ be a more relevant measure than the area $Q_2P_2'P_1''Q_1$ in Figure 2 which I actually used? The ratio of Loss 2 so defined to Loss 1 would be on the order of the reciprocal of the elasticity of demand, and thus larger than 1 for all of the relatively inelastic demand situations considered in the paper.

It is true that, in defining these Losses, I mentioned consumer surplus, and that as defined Loss 2 does not take all of the consumer loss into account. To that extent the original text is in error. But the actual definition of Loss 2 as used in the paper is the more sensible of the two. It is simply the gain (or loss) in output due to hybrid corn valued at average (pre and post hybrid) prices. The objection to the alternative suggestion can be illustrated by considering the case of an infinitely elastic demand function. The suggested definition would indicate no social gain from hybrid corn, which is clearly wrong, whereas the definition I used would still value the increase in output at the constant price.

In general, refinements in valuing the social gain are probably not worth the confusion they may create. As far as the substantive issues are concerned, the above reservations only reinforce the conclusion that if anything, the estimated social gains are on the low side.

24. Public Purpose in Agricultural Research and Education*

EARL O. HEADY[1]

American society has been an active participant in economic development of agriculture. Aside from the ownership of productive units in farming, no other nation has had a more direct and effective participation of the public sector in technical development and progress of agriculture. Development of agriculture has not been left to the free market. Society has invested heavily, and reaped high returns, from its direct intervention in promoting progress in the industry. It has had purposeful and well administered public facilities for doing so. These facilities are represented by the agricultural colleges of the Land Grant Universities, and the corresponding activities of the U.S. Department of Agriculture. Like post offices, they are socialized services and facilities.

* From the *Journal of Farm Economics*, vol. 43, pp. 566–581, August, 1961, with omissions. Reprinted by permission of the American Farm Economics Association and the author. The author is professor of economics at Iowa State University.

[1] Journal paper J-4105 of the Iowa Agricultural and Home Economics Experiment Station, project 1135; the Center for Agricultural and Economic Adjustment Cooperating.

In contrast to the post office system, however, where firms and consumers pay some price for the services used, the supply of services from the agricultural colleges is largely unrelated to the pricing and market system. The services to be produced, the funds to be used and the distribution of the product are determined by administrators who are public employees and by legislators who are public representatives. The creation and distribution of the services of the agricultural colleges respond only remotely to the pricing mechanism, and no more so than do the public sector products represented by other governmental services. It is therefore appropriate that the products of the agricultural colleges be analyzed and given direction in terms of the national purposes which are paramount in our society and for agriculture. Certainly the agricultural colleges have been and are an extremely important element of public policy relative to the industry.

PUBLIC INTERVENTION IN AGRICULTURAL DEVELOPMENT

Since its infancy as an independent nation, the American public has not stood back, in laissez-faire stance, allowing agriculture to develop through play of free markets alone. First it acquired, mainly through public purchase and action, the land resources necessary for agriculture. Then, rather than using private firms for distribution, it developed public mechanisms and allocated land to farmers at very specific prices; prices for resources which were as purposeful as specific product price supports of recent decades. Along with this direct policy to get lands settled and developed, it promoted other services directly related to development and economic progress in agriculture. One such definite policy to catalyze agricultural development was land grants to railroads in order to extend transportation facilities and encourage improvement of factor and product markets.

Until spatial restraint fell upon the nation, the main public policy for agricultural development rested on acquisition of land and the distribution to farmers. After the public domain became fully settled, society turned in other directions in continuing its direct and non-market participation in development of agriculture. The United States turned to publicly-operated research and education, lessening the real price of these resources and improving their quality. This was the second major stage in furthering agricultural development. Creation of the agricultural colleges and the U.S.D.A. spurred resource productivity in the agricultural sector. Auxiliary public actions, further lessening the real cost of resources and catalyzing development, included investments in irrigation and reclamation and credit facilities to lessen the cost of capital. In the latter sense, public investment of SCS[2] technical assistance and

[2] Soil Conservation Service.

ACP[3] monetary payments lowers the real costs of resources and practices which give rise to greater yields. These social or non-market activities have been extremely influential in developing agriculture, in extending the productivity of agricultural resources and in augmenting the agricultural supply function. Augmentation of the supply function simultaneously has diminished the relative resource demand function, notably for labor. Farm labor requirements have been cut in half since the 1920's. But even in earlier years, public agricultural development diminished the relative demand for resources. Technical improvement caused input/output coefficients to decline and demand for resources shrunk below the level otherwise needed. . . .

The effectiveness of public participation in agricultural development is now legend. Remarkable progress, measured in the absolute increase in the product supply function and the relative decline of the factor demand function, serves as a norm for other nations and a goal which most would like to approach. The extremely effective component of public participation in agricultural progress over the last half century has been investment in research and education for technical improvement. The agricultural colleges have been relatively free from political manipulation and have been efficiently administered. Using economic development and technical advance as the criteria, they have been exceptionally successful and society has had immense benefit.

But with the nation's attainment of great wealth and a high absolute level of economic progress (with associated changes in per capita incomes, occupational distribution of the population and preference patterns of consumers), it is appropriate that the framework within which American society invests in technical advance and economic progress of agriculture be examined in terms of the consistency of its several elements. This procedure would be unnecessary if the relative demand for various commodities and services of the economy remained constant over time. But given the degree of affluence attained by American society and the current and prospective shift in the "urgency" which consumers attach to different goods and services as they become wealthier, it is appropriate that publicly produced research and education be reviewed in a developmental complex consistent with the nation's current attainment. As will be shown later, this appraisal calls not for less public investment in these activities; investments which have made great direct contribution to agricultural improvement, and even greater indirect contribution to national purposes and the non-farm society. It could call for more public investment considering (a) the growth of American society, (b) its more complex and urgent role in world affairs and (c) the potential role which Land Grant Universities might play in this complex.

[3] Agricultural Conservation Program.

Another reason also exists, causing this reexamination to be possible and relevant. The private sector of the economy now is extremely important and efficient in development and production of new agricultural technology. Likewise, it is efficient in communicating this knowledge to farmers; appropriately so, because farmer knowledge is necessary for productive use of material resources sold by private firms. Investment by private firms in communication (including salesmen, advertising and public relations) far exceeds that of extension agents and printed materials by the colleges. If measurement extends far enough into fundamental research, the private sector investment in research for new farm technology now exceeds the public investment. For this reason, underdeveloped countries cannot merely reproduce the U.S. public facilities for research and education, represented in the agricultural colleges and the U.S.D.A., and expect development results comparable to those in this country over recent decades. Basic innovations in machinery, ration supplements, fertilizers, improved seeds and even certain aspects of livestock breeding (e.g., chickens), have come to flow largely from the private sector. The private sector also has illustrated greatest ability in applied research, especially in adapting fundamental findings to applicable forms for marketing as materials. Because of growing private sector contributions, public institutions for agriculture have opportunity to evaluate the relative economic urgency of their contributions under economic growth and to divert effort towards those products or services of knowledge (a) apparently still subject to decreasing costs not realized in the private sector, (b) most consistent with the income and growth status of the U.S. economy, (c) not adapted for "package and sale" by private firms but of extreme importance for further progress in agriculture, and (d) consistent with the actual economic impact of research and education on the various segments of society.

GOALS OF PUBLIC RESEARCH AND EDUCATION

It is highly appropriate that the Land Grant College make a systematic analysis of the effects of conventional research and educational programs on income and welfare in both the farm and non-farm sectors of society; then, after this picture is more precisely established, outline the appropriate role of future research and education in a wealthy and progressing economy. Unfortunately, this role is quite different from that of a century ago and from what many Land Grant College staff members still believe it to be. A vigorous and well supported research and educational program will always be needed and the returns over the next several decades can be relatively as high as those over the previous century. But the support for this continued investment is most likely to be forthcoming if Land Grant College personnel better understand the actual effects of their efforts and develop programs which are more complete and systematic in terms of these effects. They will be better able to appeal for support to those segments of society who actually are the chief beneficiaries of the research; in contrast to the existing situation wherein benefit accrues largely to consumers but appeal for financial support is made mainly to farmers.

Some Alternatives

Numerous goals for research and education can be outlined. Some were appropriate in the first half of the last century, but are now less so. Some appropriately received less focus a half century back but now are crucial and consistent with the state of economic development in the U.S. Some of the goals which can be listed and which have been or are relevant are these:

Increase farm income. This is an apparently simple goal and the one held by the majority of agricultural college personnel over the past. It was the relevant goal a century past when society was largely agricultural, per capita incomes were low, population was increasing rapidly and demand elasticities were at levels allowing increased output to fetch larger total farm revenue. But this realm clearly ended some decades back. The farm industry in aggregate is no longer the recipient of the gains from continuous and rapid technological improvement. Demand elasticities have declined greatly with a century of national economic progress. Well-fed consumers are not attracted by a greater physical quantity of food. Thus the income elasticity of demand for food in physical magnitude, the percentage increase in per capita food consumption accompanying a one percent increase in income, has dropped effectively to zero. Food demand in total poundage increases not with further growth in income but only with growth in population. Effectively, farm prices can be maintained only if output or supply of farm products grows at the rate of the population, given the level of foreign demand. Perhaps more important to farmers in the short-run, the price elasticity of demand for major farm products, indicating the percentage by which price declines as output increases, is so extremely low that a larger output returns a smaller aggregate revenue than a smaller output. Hence, research and education leading to greater output in agriculture currently cannot have increased aggregate farm income as its basic goal. Total income to the industry will, in fact, increase if output is diminished.

With present price elasticities, then, it is consumers who gain as technology and output rates are pushed ahead more rapidly than population growth. Farm producers in aggregate bear the costs of these consumer gains. Consumers' total expenditure for food is lessened, compared to what it would be without increased output, and they have more of their budget to allocate for non-farm goods and services. Public research and education for technological improvement in its present form is food policy element, not farm policy element.

Maintenance of competitive position. It can be argued that technological advance in each state and region is necessary to meet the competition of other states and regions. (The same argument can be used for one farmer against all others.) With low price elasticities of demand and aggregate output increases accompanied by decreased industry revenue, producers in one state who fail to innovate and increase output can have their revenue decreased further than if they do not innovate, as long as producers in other regions innovate and increase output. This logic would also apply to individual agricultural colleges if they considered themselves to be independent competitors with all others; but not if they considered themselves as part of a unified system where policy might be determined jointly.

Avert starvation. This reason had important basis a century back when the stock of undeveloped land had become fully settled and the population was increasing by a fourth each decade. Technological improvement became a substitute for land; increasingly so and our land supply, effectively and relatively is now greater than at any time in the last 75 years. The starvation reason has no short-run relevance in light of current surplus stocks. It lacks long-run relevance in the sense that our attained level of affluence and real income will never allow us to have consumption drawn down to the level of subsistence. The American consumer is wealthy enough to, and would, bid large amounts of resources into agriculture for technological adaptation and intensive cultivation. He would reward additional resources handsomely, if this condition ever threatened. Subsistence possibility for domestic population growth is not the important issue in the next half century. The concern is ability to meet growing food requirements without the necessity of drawing large quantities of resources into agriculture, permitting them instead to be used for producing commodities to which consumers with high incomes attach greater marginal urgency. Research and education for technological improvement are needed, for attainment of this end. This is an honorable argument since consumption and well being of the consumer are the goal while production is only a means. Farmers in aggregate would have, under the magnitudes of price elasticity which prevail for food, greater revenue if population and food demand continuously pressed hard against output and supply.

Research in the 1960's, as defense against subsistence diets, is not for the present generation of well-fed consumers, but for those who will exist in the year 2000. It needs to be justified accordingly.

Promotion of economic growth. The above leads to a more precise and relevant goal for public improvement of agriculture. Under high per capita incomes and very low demand elasticities, traditional research and education in improved technology contribute to growth in the economy generally, but not to increased aggregate income of agriculture under the widespread short-run condition where resources of low mobility remain in the industry to produce more at a lessened income. While the aggregate short-run effect of technological improvement is not increased revenue of agriculture, it does allow food requirements to be produced with fewer resources. Hence, more resources are available for commodities to which well-fed consumers attach greater marginal value, those with high income elasticities of demand, as their incomes grow further. Clearly, this is the major and outstanding contribution of conventional public research and education for agriculture. It, rather than revenue increase for the agricultural industry, has been the actual mass accomplishment of agricultural colleges over recent decades. It is a truly significant and important accomplishment on behalf of consumers rather than aggregatively and specifically for agricultural producers, except as recipients of general economic progress. It is one which Russia and less developed countries strive to duplicate. But, unfortunately, the Land Grant Universities have not held this image of their accomplishments and, therefore, have not always had programs which were complete and consistent with this significant and broadly justifiable national goal. The future of the agricultural colleges partly revolves around an understanding of this goal and its importance; with research and education geared in directions which continue or further it but at the same time allow direct economic gain to farm producers for their contribution to it. Crystallization of this image, and appropriate extension and adaptation of research and education, will mean a broader role and opportunity for the agricultural colleges. Failure to do so may require a retreat in the function and resources open to them, at least relative to growth in the total economy and its attendant research and educational efforts and interests.

Increase knowledge. A goal, of lesser utilitarian appeal, is research and education to increase knowledge *per se*. Although quantitative data are not available for verification, a likely hypothesis is that as societies grow richer they come more nearly to look upon knowledge as an ultimate end or semi-consumption good and to invest accordingly. But to the extent they do so, emphasis is more likely to be on fundamental research and knowledge, and these particularly as they contribute to general economic advance in the more exotic realms of man's quest to create and satisfy his wants. While society may invest some quantity in public research institutions for this as an end *per se*, it is apparent that most of fundamental research has to serve as a means to ends such as those above which are more ultimate to it.

ORDERING OF RESEARCH AND EDUCATION

Research and education are not purely stochastic phenomena, with chance occurrence relative to their initiation and outcome. They need not serve as exogenous variables, with their direction predetermined by conventions of the past or as by-products of a previous organizational structure. They can be geared to the present and prospective economic or developmental status of a nation, even to bring distribution of gain from progress to producers as well as consumers. The probability of scientific discovery for a particular product, function, or service depends on the quantity and quality of research resources allocated to it. Quantitative guides, if recognized and used in the administration of research, exist even for gearing physical and biological sciences to the emphases specified by economic growth. . . .

25. Reflections on Economic Development Policy*

ALBERT O. HIRSCHMAN

A few years ago I wrote a comment on a paper entitled "Noneconomic Factors in Economic Development" in which Bert Hoselitz laid much stress on the importance of minorities and other deviants for the emergence of able and vigorous entrepreneurs. My criticism which, I believe, is also applicable to the interesting turn Hagen has given to this idea took the form of two questions: First, is the relationship reliable? In other words, aren't there some deviants, for example, homosexuals or ex-convicts, who have not shown particularly strong entrepreneurial inclinations? Must social scientists perhaps entertain the Toynbee-type hypothesis of "optimum deviancy," with all the attendant conceptual difficulties of defining the optimal point?

* From *Development of the Emerging Countries: An Agenda for Research*, The Brookings Institution, 1962, pp. 39–43, with omissions. Hirschman's comments were published as a discussion of E. E. Hagen's paper, "A Framework for Analyzing Economic and Political Change." Hirschman's comments are reprinted with the exception of the first paragraph under the new title above. Copyright 1962 by The Brookings Institution. Reprinted by permission of The Brookings Institution and the author. The author is professor of international economic relations, Columbia University.

My other question relates to the direction of the causal nexus. Hoselitz' deviants or Hagen's ejected groups may well make for economic development, but development in turn creates an *esprit de corps* among its principal agents and welds them into an identifiable group, with a personality and perhaps an ideology of its own. *Ex post,* it may look therefore as though the separateness of the group was a cause of development when in actual fact it was its result. Historical examples of this type of relationship can easily be given.

I am glad, in any event, that Hagen specifically warns against taking lantern in hand and looking for the deviants and putting them in charge. Yet the logic of his argument certainly implies that the transfer of capital alone would not work unless the ground is prepared through the presence of some such group. In this sense, then, Hagen's analysis is an extension of W. W. Rostow's preconditions. He does not say whether he proposes to substitute his set of preconditions for Rostow's or whether he considers his set as pre-preconditions to Rostow's preconditions. I am anxious and, what is more, I am worried. For when one adds to the number of preconditions, one lengthens, by the same token, the list of potential obstacles to development. The discovery of such obstacles comes in waves, usually after something has gone wrong. It is not surprising that after the Congo, Cuba, and Laos, all three recipients of large amounts of public or private capital in the past, the United States should be riding the crest of such a wave.

The most articulate reflection of a new mood of disillusion with past reliance on capital plus technical assistance is the recent article in *Foreign Affairs* by Ambassador John Kenneth Galbraith.[1] Readers are told that the development process can hardly be expected to be brought under way and that an infusion of financial aid and experts will be useless unless there be present in the to-be-aided society (1) "a substantial degree of literacy" and an "educated elite of substantial size"; (2) "a substantial measure of social justice"; (3) "a reliable apparatus of government and public administration"; and (4) "a clear and purposeful view of what development involves."

This is a counsel of perfection. In no advanced industrial country were these four conditions realized *prior* to industrialization. Moreover, if these four conditions were found to be present in any country today, that country could easily dispense with foreign financial and technical assistance; in fact, it should probably be an exporter of such assistance, with the United States as a recipient!

The Galbraithian conditions should supply, therefore, a final *reductio ad absurdum* of one approach to foreign aid that has dominated American thinking during the whole postwar period: the "will to believe"—

---

[1] Vol. 39 (April 1961), pp. 445–46.

rooted perhaps in the need to so persuade the Congress—that foreign aid is the "missing component," the "catalyst" whose addition will surely bring the alchemy of the development process to its climactic reaction: self support, "take-off," or bliss in general. The search for the components that have to be in place so that foreign capital and technical assistance from abroad can play this sure-fire role has focused successively on monetary stability, on a "favorable investment climate," on "integrated development programs," and lately on land and tax reforms. The diagnosis of "the experts" has thus fluctuated wildly, in line with the ideological preferences of the moment and with the lessons of the latest disaster.

If only as much attention had been devoted to the successes as to the failures, we should have noticed that whenever development occurs, it does so invariably in the absence of one or several of these "required" components or preconditions. In nineteenth century Germany, it occurred without much primitive accumulation of capital and in Italy without the Protestant ethic, to mention some of the earlier theories on prerequisites; and during the postwar period, Brazil experienced development in the absence of monetary stability, and Colombia even in the absence of public order, not to speak of land reform.

These experiences cast great doubt on the whole notion of preconditions or prerequisites. In fact, I believe with Gerschenkron that the only generalization one can make about the development of late comers is that they will not follow the sequence of their predecessors, but will insist on changing it around or on skipping entirely some stages as well as some "preconditions." Therefore, I continue to advocate that in their research, the experts pay special attention to the emergence and possible rationality of new or inverted sequences. When they discover an "obstacle," such as poor public administration or uneconomic land use, their job does not consist in merely advising its removal; they ought to explore also how, by moving the economy forward elsewhere, additional pressure (economic and political) could be brought on the obstacle to give way. The analysis of sequences I have in mind should be as comprehensive as possible and describe the interplay of economic, political, and cultural factors.

I am at present engaged, with the support of the Twentieth Century Fund, in the detailed analysis of sequences in economic policy-making around particular problems such as land reform or inflation or regional imbalance in five Latin American countries. In each case I am seeking answers to the question: At what particular point, under what combination of pressures, after what kind of learning process, are new insights about the nature of the problem acquired? When and why does it suddenly become possible to take effective action after decades of ineffective legislation and tinkering? I would be very interested to find out if similar efforts have been or are being undertaken by other social scientists.

But let me return to my theme. The American people might as well reconcile themselves to the fact that they will never be called on to give aid to a country unless it is afflicted with many, more or less loosely interrelated, facets of backwardness or obstacles to development. In this view, aid is a way of getting involved in the recipient country's battle against these obstacles. At first, the best the United States can do when joining the battle is often to follow Napoleon's maxim *"on s'engage; puis on voit."* Little by little, after getting committed and "seeing," that is, learning about the country's problems, some hypotheses should emerge about the sequence in which a country is likely to attack successfully the multifarious obstacles. In the search for the best hypothesis, those who administer aid programs should use what Dr. Carl Rogers, already aptly quoted by Hagen, calls "client-centered therapy." The well-known similarity in characteristics exhibited by underdeveloped countries at any one stage of development is matched only by the far less noticed variety of sequences and processes through which they move from one stage to the next. For example, the wide range of means by which one particular obstacle can be overcome was strikingly if somewhat inadvertently illustrated by Frank Tannenbaum when he wrote recently that Mexico acquired a feeling of pride in its own identity and achievements through its protracted revolution, whereas Brazil achieved similar confidence in its own destiny through the publication of a book, namely, Freyre's classic *Masters and Slaves.*

But there remains a serious question that is really the basic one to which Ambassador Galbraith was addressing himself. What if we have acquired the conviction that no further progress is possible unless a corrupt government gets ousted or a thorough-going land reform is instituted? Far be it from me to say that such situations are inconceivable. But perhaps Americans today are a little too ready to jump to this kind of conclusion. In reaction to the Cuban events they wish to rid themselves in a hurry of what Robert Heilbroner has recently called "American ostrichism," by which he means the earlier lack of attention to the social struggles and tensions that have so important a bearing on the course of development. At last, Americans have become painfully aware that it may be impossible to effect significant economic progress as long as aid actually strengthens those who are opposed to the social changes without which economic advance is impossible or meaningless.

Naturally, if the situation is the one depicted in the Communist textbook where the government is entirely the expression of one homogeneously reactionary and parasitic ruling clique while the country's popular energies and developmental resources wait to be unshackled through revolution, little can be said in favor of making aid available until the revolution has taken over. If this is the situation, the best thing for the United States Operations Mission to do is to join the rioting students or the backbush guerillas. But ordinarily reality is not that simple: the government in question may be unwilling to decree (or its parliament may be unwilling to vote) certain reforms that the United States Mission thinks are desirable; at the same time it may be anxious to undertake a variety of unexceptionable tasks of economic development. If the reforms are as central to further progress as the American experts think they are, these other tasks will either be impossible to carry out in the absence of the reforms, or they will make the need for the reforms even more compelling than before. Both eventualities bring the reforms closer, for they either force the hand of the government or hasten its downfall.

In this perspective, financial or technical help is justified, provided we Americans realize the kind of difficult game in which we are involved and are not caught unaware by the outbreak of crisis. By helping in peripheral tasks of economic development or by proving that such ventures are bound to fail within the existing socio-economic framework, one is waging a kind of guerilla warfare against the holdouts of reaction and backwardness at the center. From this point of view even the failure of a technical assistance mission can have its uses: nothing demonstrates as clearly the need to undertake thoroughgoing land reform as the failure of an attempt to establish an equitable land tax system.

Foreign aid does not necessarily always work to the benefit of the group that happens to be in power. It is desired by governments to enhance their prestige, but may turn out to undermine it. Frequently, foreign aid is requested to stave off reforms, but it may be made to accelerate them. The exploration and utilization of such disruptive and subversive potentialities of aid are perhaps particularly important for the United States as long as it is neither much given to guerilla warfare proper nor apparently very good at it. In order to be able to use aid in this fashion and not to be unduly surprised by the explosive consequences, the United States should devise ways of giving aid in a fashion that does not imply a wholesale endorsement of the programs, objectives, and values of the recipient government. It should learn—it has already done so in some cases, but is rather shamefaced about it— to cooperate with other governments in a variety of tasks, fully aware that the governments giving and receiving aid are pursuing objectives that overlap initially only to a very small extent. This way of using financial and technical assistance implies techniques quite different from those toward which the United States is now gravitating. To underwrite a development program—which appears to be the new formula, to be applied the world over—may be the appropriate technique when there is a rather complete meeting of minds. But not to underwrite a development program may be just as important at times; and it need not mean the absence of an over-all design on the part of the United States, or resignation to having just a collection of random projects. It may be a deliberate choice to remain aloof from full co-operation while giving support to certain aspirations. Perhaps research can help identify different types of aid policies appropriate to different constellations so that we will stop looking for the one best policy applicable to all possible circumstances.

SELECTED BIBLIOGRAPHY

PART 1. AGRICULTURE AND ECONOMIC DEVELOPMENT IN HISTORICAL PERSPECTIVE

Boserup, Mogens: "Agrarian Structure and the Take-off," International Economic Association, Konstanz Conference, 1960.

Johnston, Bruce F.: "Agricultural Productivity and Economic Development in Japan," *Journal of Political Economy*, vol. 59, December, 1951.

―――― and John W. Mellor: "The Role of Agriculture in Economic Development," *American Economic Review*, vol. 51, pp. 566–593, September, 1961.

Loomis, Ralph A., and Glen T. Barton: *Productivity of Agriculture, United States, 1870–1958*, U.S. Department of Agriculture Technical Bulletin 1238, April, 1961.

Ranis, G.: "The Financing of Japanese Economic Development," *Economic History Review*, vol. II, 1959.

Smith, Thomas C.: *The Agrarian Origins of Modern Japan*, Stanford University Press, Stanford, Calif., 1959.

Tang, Anthony: *Economic Development in the Southern Piedmont 1860–1950; Its Impact on Agriculture*, The University of North Carolina Press, Chapel Hill, N.C., 1958.

PART 2. MEASUREMENT PROBLEMS IN THE AGRICULTURAL SECTOR

Bellerby, J. R.: *Agriculture and Industry: Relative Income*, St. Martin's Press, Inc., New York, 1956.

Bennett, M. K.: "Intenational Disparities in Consumption Levels," *American Economic Review*, vol. 41, September, 1951.

Fano, Enzo: "Stima Della Producttivita Degli Investimenti in Agricoltura," *Bancaria*, Rome, Italy, November–December, 1961.

Farnsworth, Helen C.: "Defects, Uses and Abuses of National Food Supply and Consumption Data," *Food Research Institute Studies*, vol. 2, pp. 179–201, November, 1961.

Houthakker, H. S.: "An International Comparison of Household Expenditure Patterns Commemorating the Centenary of Engel's Law," *Econometrica*, vol. 25, October, 1957.

Hunt, K. E.: *The Organization of Field Work,* Colonial Research Publication 22, London, 1957.

Johnson, Glenn L.: "The State of Agricultural Supply Analysis," *Journal of Farm Economics,* vol. 42, December, 1960.

Morgan, T.: "The Long-run Terms of Trade between Agriculture and Manufacturing," *Economic Development and Cultural Change,* vol. 8, October, 1959.

Mukherjee, P. K.: *Economic Surveys in Under-developed Countries,* Asia Publishing House, New York, 1959.

O'Loughlin, Carleen: "The Measurement and Significance of Agricultural Sector Statistics in National Accounting," *Social and Economic Studies,* vol. 6, September, 1957.

Panikar, P. G. K.: "Rural Savings in India," *Economic Development and Cultural Change,* vol. 10, October, 1961.

Ruttan, Vernon: "Research on the Economics of Technological Change in American Agriculture," *Journal of Farm Economics,* vol. 42, November, 1960.

U.S. Department of Agriculture: *Major Statistical Series of the United States Department of Agriculture: How They Are Constructed and Used,* 1957.

PART 3. THEORETICAL ASPECTS OF AGRICULTURE IN ECONOMIC DEVELOPMENT

Eckaus, R. S.: "The Factor Proportions Problem in Underdeveloped Areas," *American Economic Review,* vol. 45, September, 1955.

Enke, Stephen: "Food Constraints on Industrial Development in Poor Countries," *Southern Economic Journal,* vol. 27, April, 1961.

———: "Industrialization through Greater Productivity in Agriculture," *The Review of Economics and Statistics,* vol. 44, February, 1962.

Jorgenson, Dale W.: "The Development of a Dual Economy," *Economic Journal,* vol. 71, June, 1961.

Lewis, Arthur: "Economic Development with Unlimited Supplies of Labor," *The Manchester School,* vol. 22, May, 1954.

Mellor, John W. and Robert D. Stevens: "The Average and Marginal Product of Farm Labor in Underdeveloped Countries," *The Journal of Farm Economics,* vol. 38, August, 1956.

Nicholls, William H.: "Industrialization, Factor Markets, and Agricultural Development," *Journal of Political Economy,* vol. 59, August, 1961.

———: "An Agricultural Surplus as a Factor in Economic Development," *Journal of Political Economy,* vol. 71, February, 1963.

Ohkawa, Kazushi: "Balanced Growth and the Problem of Agriculture—With Special Reference to Asian Peasant Economy," *Hitotsubashi Journal of Economics,* vol. 2, September, 1961.

PART 4. SOME ASPECTS OF THE PROCESS OF CHANGE IN AGRICULTURE

Agricultural Production Team of the Ford Foundation: *Report on India's Food Crisis and Steps to Meet It,* New Delhi, April, 1959.

Aktan, Resat: "Mechanization of Agriculture in Turkey," *Land Economics,* vol. 33, November, 1957.

Balogh, T.: "Agricultural and Economic Development," *Oxford Economic Papers,* vol. 13, February, 1961.

Barlowe, Raleigh: "Land Reform and Economic Development," *Journal of Farm Economics,* vol. 35, May, 1953.

Barter, P. G. H.: "Special Problems of Agricultural Planning," *Monthly Bulletin of Agricultural Economics and Statistics,* vol. 2, June, 1962.

Bennett, Merrill K.: "Longer and Shorter Views of the Malthusian Prospect," *Food Research Institute Studies,* vol. 4, February, 1963.

Bonnen, James: "Land Grant Colleges: Some Observations on the Organizational Nature of a Great Technological Payoff," *Journal of Farm Economics,* vol. 44, December, 1962.

Brewster, John: "The Machine Process in Agriculture and Industry," *Journal of Farm Economics,* vol. 32, February, 1950.

Chang, Pei-Kang: *Agriculture and Industrialization: The Adjustments That Take Place as an Agricultural Country is Industrialized,* Harvard University Press, Cambridge, Mass., 1949.

Crawford, John: "Using Surpluses for Economic Development," in *Proceedings of the International Conference of Agricultural Economists,* London, 1963.

Dewey, Alice: *Peasant Marketing in Java,* The Free Press of Glencoe, New York, 1962.

Edwards, David: *An Economic Study of Small Farming in Jamaica,* Institute of Social and Economic Research, University College of the West Indies, Kingston, Jamaica, 1961.

Flores, Edmundo: *Tratado de Economia Agricola,* Fondo de Cultura Economica, Buenos Aires, 1961.

Froehlich, Walter (ed.): *Land Tenure, Industrialization and Social Stability: Experience and Prospects in Asia,* Marquette University Press, Milwaukee, Wis., 1961.

Gadgil, D. R.: "Integration of Land Settlement Policies into the Economic and Social Development of Countries," *Monthly Bulletin of Agricultural Economics and Statistics,* vol. 8, October, 1959.

Hathaway, Dale: *Government and Agriculture: Economic Policy in a Democratic Society,* The Macmillan Company, New York, 1963.

Heady, Earl O.: *Agricultural Policy Under Economic Development,* Iowa State University Press, Ames, Iowa, 1962.

Hillman, Jimmye: "Problems of Increasing Agricultural Productivity in Less Advanced Countries," *Journal of Farm Economics,* vol. 43, May, 1961.

Hoselitz, Bert F.: "Agriculture in Industrial Development," in *Food—One Tool in International Economic Development,* Iowa State University Press, Ames, Iowa, 1962, pp. 125–147.

Iowa State University Center for Agricultural and Economic Adjustment, *Food—One Tool in International Economic Development,* Iowa State University Press, Ames, Iowa, 1962.

Johnston, Bruce F.: "Agricultural Development and Economic Transformation: A Comparative Study of the Japanese Experience," *Food Research Institute Studies,* vol. 3, November, 1962.

Katz, Saul M. and Frank McGowan: *A Selected List of U.S. Readings on Development,* Agency for International Development, Washington, D.C., 1963.

Long, Erven: "The Economic Basis of Land Reform in Underdeveloped Economies," *Land Economics,* vol. 37, May, 1961.

Maddox, James: "Economic Growth and Revolution in Mexico," *Land Economics*, vol. 36, August, 1960.

Mellor, John W.: "The Process of Agricultural Development in Low-Income Countries," *Journal of Farm Economics*, vol. 44, August, 1962.

————: "The Use and Productivity of Farm Family Labor in Early Stages of Agricultural Development," *Journal of Farm Economics*, vol. 45, August, 1963.

Mosher, Arthur: *Technical Cooperation in Latin American Agriculture*, The University of Chicago Press, Chicago, 1957.

Oluwasanmi, H. A.: "Land Tenure and Agricultural Development in Tropical Africa," *Journal of Farm Economics*, vol. 39, August, 1957.

Oshima, Harry T.: "A Strategy for Asian Development," *Economic Development and Cultural Change*, vol. 10, April, 1962.

Parsons, Kenneth: "Land Reform in the Postwar Era," *Land Economics*, vol. 33, August, 1957.

Perkins, Maurice and Lawrence Witt: "Capital Formation: Past and Present," *Journal of Farm Economics*, vol. 43, May, 1961.

Raup, Philip: "The Contribution of Land Reform to Agricultural Development: An Analytical Framework," *Economic Development and Cultural Change*, vol. 12, October, 1963.

Ruttan, Vernon W.: "Research on the Economics of Technological Change in American Agriculture," *Journal of Farm Economics*, pp. 735–754, vol. 42, November, 1960.

Schickele, Rainer: "Resettlement Problems and Policies," *Netherlands Journal of Agricultural Science*, vol. 5, November, 1957.

Schultz, Theodore W.: "The Supply of Food in Relation to Economic Development," *Economic Development and Cultural Change*, vol. 4, December, 1952.

————: *The Economic Organization of Agriculture*, McGraw-Hill Book Company, Inc., New York, 1953.

————: "Value of U.S. Farm Surpluses to Underdeveloped Countries," *Journal of Farm Economics*, vol. 42, December, 1960.

————: *The Economic Value of Education*, Columbia University Press, New York, 1963.

————: *Transforming Traditional Agriculture*, Yale University Press, New Haven, Conn., 1964.

Sen, S. R.: *The Strategy for Agricultural Development*, Asia Publishing House, Bombay, India, 1962.

Shorter, Frederic: "Foodgrains Policy in East Pakistan," in *Public Policy—A Yearbook of the Graduate School of Public Administration*, Harvard University Press, Cambridge, Mass., 1959.

Stern, R. M.: "A Century of Food Exports," *KYKLOS*, vol. 13, fasc. 1, 1960.

Swerling, Boris: "Some Interrelationships Between Agricultural Trade and Economic Development," *KYKLOS*, vol. 14, fasc. 3, 1961.

Timmons, John F.: "Land and Water Resource Policy," *Journal of Farm Economics*, pp. 95–108, vol. 45, February, 1963.

Tostlebe, Alvin: *Capital in Agriculture [American]: Its Formation and Financing Since 1870*, National Bureau of Economic Research, New York, 1957.

U.S. Department of Agriculture, Economic Research Service: *Agrarian Reform and Economic Growth in Developing Countries*, 1962.

United Nations Department of Economic and Social Affairs: *Measures for the Economic Development of Underdeveloped Countries*, New York, 1951.

United Nations Department of Economic and Social Affairs: *Instability in Export Markets of Underdeveloped Nations,* New York, 1952.

United Nations Department of Economic and Social Affairs: *International Compensation for Fluctuations in Commodity Trade,* New York, 1961.

Wald, Haskell: *Taxation of Agricultural Land in Underdeveloped Economies: A Survey and Guide to Policy,* Harvard Law School International Program in Taxation, Harvard University Press, Cambridge, Mass., 1959.

Wharton, C. R., Jr.: "Marketing, Merchandising, and Money Lending: A Note on Middleman Monopsony in Malaya," *Malayan Economic Review,* vol. 7, October, 1962.

Wickizer, V. D.: "The Smallholder in Tropical Export Crop Production," *Food Research Institute Studies,* vol. 1, February, 1960.

Witt, Lawrence and Carl Eicher: "The Effects of United States Agricultural Surplus Disposal Programs on Recipient Countries," *Michigan State University Experiment Station Research Bulletin 2,* 1964.

Abdel-Rahman, I. H., 336n.
Agarwala, A. N., 127n.
Aktan, Resat, 400
Angell, J. W., 314
Anschel, K. R., 129
Arutunian, I. V., 257n.
Ashby, A. W., 309

Bachmura, F. T., 223n.
Bailey, M. J., 369n., 378n.
Balassa, Bela, 181n.
Baldwin, K. D. S., 300n.
Baldwin, R. E., 10, 72n., 206, 207, 238
Balogh, T., 401
Barber, W. J., 133n., 141
Barlowe, R., 401
Barone, Enrico, 160, 163
Barter, P. G. H., 401
Barton, G. T., 399
Bator, F. M., 364n.
Bauer, P. T., 33n., 38, 39n., 241n., 318,
    360n., 361n., 364
Baumol, W. J., 228n.
Beal, G. M., 225n.
Bellerby, J. R., 99, 399
Bennett, M. K., 99, 399, 401
Berg, Elliot J., 204
Betz, George W., 8n.
Binns, Bernard, 282
Bishop, C. E., 220, 221
Black, J. D., 152n.
Blau, Gerda, 209, 322
Boeke, J. H., 127
Bogue, D. J., 218
Bohannan, P., 204n.
Bohr, Niels, 147
Bonnen, James, 4, 212n., 401
Booth, C., 81n.

Boserup, Mogens, 399
Bowles, Gladys K., 215n., 218n.
Brahmananda, P. R., 38, 39
Breshkovskaia, Katerina, 154n.
Brewster, John, 401
Bublot, G., 81n.
Buck, J. Lossings, 130, 141
Burch, Thomas A., 223n.
Butler, C. P., 223n.

Cahen, Mme., 81n.
Carrillo-Flores, A., 336n.
Chang, Pei-Kang, 401
Charlton, J. L., 223n.
Chenery, H. B., 168n.
Cheng, K. C. I., 220, 223
Childe, V. G., 163n.
Cho, Yong Sam, 142
Choudhry, N. K., 8n.
Clark, Colin, 67n., 81n., 99, 232
Cleland, W., 294, 295
Clough, M., 373n.
Coale, A. J., 14n., 15, 37, 140n.
Cochrane, W. W., 366n.
Collins, N. R., 210, 359, 365n.
Conrad, A. H., 76n.
Crawford, J. G., 336n., 351, 401

Dales, J. H., 206, 235
Dalton, G., 204n.
Dandekar, V. N., 127, 134, 142, 169,
    343n.
Delewski, J., 154n.
Denison, E. F., 101n.
Dewey, Alice, 401
di Nardi, G., 168n.
Domar, E. D., 125
Dore, R. P., 53n., 60n.

Dovring, F., 10, 78, 206
Ducoff, L. J., 224
Duesenberry, J. S., 74n., 125, 248n., 250n.

Eccarius, J. G., 152n.
Eckaus, R. S., 129, 131–133, 142, 400
Eckstein, Alexander, 4
Edwards, David, 100, 401
Eicher, Carl, 129, 340n., 346n., 403
Ellis, H. S., 364n.
Engels, F., 149n., 151, 164n.
Enke, Stephen, 126, 133n., 142, 400
Ewell, R. H., 381
Ezekiel, Hannan, 142
Ezekiel, Mordecai, 343

Fabrizi, Carlo, 359n.
Fano, Enzo, 399
Farnsworth, Helen C., 100, 399
Fay, C. R., 241n.
Fei, J. C., 128, 133n., 142, 143, 181, 200, 202
Fisher, Franklin M., 355
Fisher, J., 70n.
Flores, Edmundo, 401
Foner, Philip S., 161n.
Foote, R. J., 373n.
Fox, Karl, 341n., 355n.
Frankel, S. Herbert, 142
Freyre, Gilberto, 396
Froehlich, Walter, 401

Gad, H., 81n.
Gadgil, B. R., 130, 401
Gaitskell, A., 305n.
Galbraith, J. K., 77, 212, 360n., 394
Gatti, G., 150n.
Georgescu-Roegen, N., 20n., 21n., 24n., 25n., 42–44, 126, 127, 132, 134, 142, 144, 166n., 169–173, 175, 177, 179, 180
Gerschenkron, A., 4, 8, 212, 395
Ginor, F., 346, 347
Giusti, U., 81n.
Goering, T. J., 349n.
Goldman, M., 269n.
Goldsmith, R. W., 229
Goodrich, C., 218n.
Greaves, I. C., 243n.
Griliches, Z., 210, 234, 369
Grosse, R., 250n.
Gudin, E., 313
Gunton, G., 161n.
Gustafson, R. L., 234
Gutman, G. O., 125, 126

Habbakkuh, H. J., 9
Haberler, G., 132, 142

Hagen, E. E., 125n., 212, 393, 394, 396
Hagood, Margaret J., 218
Hamilton, C. Horace, 218n.
Hanau, A., 208n.
Harberger, A. C., 77n., 369n.
Harrod, R. F., 125, 228
Hart, Albert G., 336n.
Hart, J. F., 218n.
Hathaway, Dale, 205, 208n., 211, 214, 358n., 401
Heady, Earl O., 3, 212, 386, 401
Heilbroner, Robert, 396
Helper, H. R., 75n.
Herzen, Alexander, 153n.
Higgins, Benjamin, 15, 16, 33–36, 41, 42n., 127
Hillman, J. S., 340n., 401
Hirschman, Albert, 4, 15, 125, 212, 360n., 393
Holton, R. H., 210, 359, 360n., 368n.
Hoover, Calvin B., 166n.
Hoover, E. M., 14n., 15, 37, 70n., 140n.
Hoselitz, Bert F., 4, 125n., 194, 393, 394, 401
Houthakker, H. S., 99, 399
Hsieh, Chiang, 142
Hsieh, S. C., 199
Hubbard, L. E., 156n.
Hunt, K. E., 400

Jacoby, N., 199
Jamison, J. A., 365n.
Jasny, Naum, 260n.
Jenkins, M. T., 371n.
Johnson, D. Gale, 23n., 204, 234
Johnson, Glenn L., 99, 101, 120, 400
Johnson, Gwendolyn, 117n.
Johnson, Sherman E., 38n.
Johnston, Bruce F., 9, 19n., 22n., 23n., 24n., 27n., 28n., 163n., 197n., 199, 399, 401
Jones, Edwin F., 198n., 199
Jones, William O., 135, 142, 204
Jorgenson, Dale W., 128, 400

Kahan, Arcadius, 23n., 100, 206, 207, 251, 256n., 257n.
Kahn, A. E., 15, 168n., 346n., 348
Kaldor, N., 125, 202
Kannappan, Subbiah, 4
Kao, Charles H. C., 129
Katz, Saul, 4, 401
Kautsky, Karl, 146, 148n., 149n., 150n., 151n., 160n., 162n.
Kawano, S., 81n.
Kenadjian, B., 132, 139, 142
Khan, Nasir Ahmad, 126n., 142
Khatkhate, D. R., 352

Kiser, Clyde, 117n.
Klein, J. W., 373n.
Koestner, N., 131, 142, 293–296
Krishnamurti, 287
Kuznets, S., 7, 8n., 29n., 65, 99, 100, 102, 105, 116, 160, 206, 254, 312n.

Lee, T. H., 199
Leibenstein, H., 15n., 16n., 127n., 129, 130, 132, 134, 142, 157n., 171–173, 194, 353n.
Lenin, V., 152n., 153n.
Leontief, W. W., 239
Lewis, W. A., 12n., 28n., 29, 34–36, 41, 127, 129, 130–132, 133, 142, 158, 181, 182, 187–188, 194, 201, 205, 207, 212, 246n., 299, 309–310, 400
Li, Choh-Ming, 66n.
Lindberg, R. C., 385
Long, E., 401
Loomis, R. A., 399
Lucchi, O., 81n.
Luebke, B. H., 218n.
Luxemburg, Rosa, 154n.

McCarthy, T., 147n.
McElveen, J. V., 221n.
McGowan, F., 401
Maddox, J., 402
Madgearu, V., 156n.
Malenbaum, W., 4, 29, 30n., 32
Mandelbaum, K., 142, 243n.
Mantoux, P., 19n.
Martin, J. A., 218n.
Marx, K., 8n., 43, 147–153, 155n., 157n., 160n., 161, 162n.
Mason, E. S., 356
Mazumdar, D., 142
Mehren, G. L., 366n.
Meier, G. M., 71n.
Mellor, J., 3, 4, 9, 129, 132, 135, 136, 143, 197–198n., 199, 399, 400, 402
Menzie, E. L., 340n.
Metzler, W. H., 223n.
Meyer, J. A., 76n.
Mighell, R., 381n.
Mikesell, R., 343n.
Mints, L. E., 255n.
Mitrany, D., 151n., 152n., 153, 154
Montias, J. M., 181n.
Moore, W. E., 156n., 243n., 294
Moorti, T. V., 199
Morgan, T., 8n., 400
Mosher, A., 3, 4, 211, 402
Mosk, S. A., 247n.
Mueller, W. F., 364n.
Mujumdar, N. A., 137, 138, 143

Mukherjee, P. K., 100, 400
Myint, H., 247n.

Nasu, S., 52n.
Navarrete, A., 130, 143
Navarrete, I., 130, 143
Nerlove, M., 374n.
Nicholls, W. H., 3, 5, 8–9, 11, 18n., 34n., 211, 212n., 400
North, D. C., 9, 10, 69, 70n., 71n., 74n., 99
Nurkse, R., 126, 129–132, 134, 135, 143, 192n., 194, 201, 208–209, 242n., 282, 292, 311

Ogg, W. E., 225n.
Ohkawa, K., 9, 45, 46–50n., 52–59n., 61n., 63n., 65n., 99, 115n., 400
Ohlin, G., 8n.
Ojala, E., 67n.
O'Loughlin, Carleen, 400
Oluwasanmi, H. A., 402
Oshima, H. T., 9, 128, 135n., 136, 143, 195, 197, 199, 200–202, 211, 402

Paish, F. W., 318
Panikar, P. C. K., 208, 400
Papandreou, A. G., 359n.
Parish, Ross, 233
Parsons, Kenneth, 402
Parthasaratry, Gogula, 143
Patel, K. R., 143
Pepelasis, Adam A., 140, 141, 143
Perkins, Maurice, 402
Pim, A., 241n.
Pond, Martin, 5
Posthuma, S., 336n.
Prebisch, R., 209

Quesnay, F., 163
Qureshi, M. L., 336n.

Ranis, Gustav, 61, 62n., 128, 133, 142, 143, 181, 194, 200, 202, 399
Rashin, A. G., 81n.
Raup, Philip, 5, 207, 402
Renshaw, E. F., 378n.
Roberts, L. H., 154n.
Robinson, Joan, 129, 130, 135, 143
Rogers, Carl, 396
Rogers, Everett M., 210
Rosenstein-Rodan, P. N., 130, 138, 139, 143, 201, 340n., 364n.
Rosovsky, H., 9, 45, 64n., 99, 115n.
Rossi-Doria, M., 359n.
Rostow, W. W., 7, 8, 70n., 77, 186n., 194, 394

Ruttan, V. W., 10, 210n., 223, 341, 400, 402

Saito, M., 52n.
Schickele, R., 402
Schiller, O., 24n., 25n.
Schultz, T. W., 2, 3, 5, 70, 71, 73n., 77, 78n., 130–132, 139, 140, 143–144, 157, 158n., 204, 205, 206, 208n., 212, 227, 229, 231–234n., 245n., 340n., 352n., 356n., 369n., 380, 402
Schwartz, H., 20n., 21n., 22n., 23n., 24n.
Sen, A. K., 144
Sen, S. R., 211, 351, 352, 402
Shorter, F., 402
Singer, H. W., 209, 247n.
Singh, S. P., 127n.
Singh, T., 144
Sitton, G. R., 197–198n., 200
Smith, A., 71
Smith, T. C., 50n., 399
Smith, T. L., 117n.
Smithies, A., 125
Solow, R. W., 125
Sonin, M. I., 255n., 256n.
Sovani, N. V., 144
Spengler, Joseph J., 227n., 235n.
Spengler, Oswald, 149n.
Stam, Jerome, 355n.
Stern, Robert, M., 204, 402
Stevens, R. D., 136, 143, 197n., 199, 400
Stigler, George, 71, 77, 366n.
Strassman, Paul, 5
Strumilin, S. G., 81n.
Sweezy, Paul M., 154n.
Swerling, Boris, 402

Taeuber, Conrad, 216n., 217n.
Tang, Anthony, 70n., 399

Tannenbaum, F., 396
Tarver, James D., 224n.
Telser, L. G., 369n.
Thaden, J. F., 216n.
Thurnwald, Richard, 167n.
Tiebout, Charles, 71n.
Timmons, J. F., 402
Tinbergen, Jan, 212
Tobata, S., 49n., 50n., 60n., 81n.
Tobin, James, 125
Tostlebe, Alvin S., 110n., 208, 402
Tschajanov, A., 154, 155n.
Tsunematsu, S., 62

Umemura, M., 202

Vakil, C. N., 38, 39
Veblen, Thorstein, 150
Viner, Jacob, 15, 130, 132, 144
Volin, Lazar, 24n.

Wald, Haskell, 403
Wallace, T. D., 385
Walras, Leon, 160
Warriner, Doreen, 130, 131, 144, 156n., 157n., 207, 272
Weulersse, J., 274
Wharton, C., 100, 403
Wheeler, Richard, 348n.
Wickizer, V. D., 207, 241n., 403
Witt, Lawrence W., 209, 339, 340n., 341n., 346n., 348n., 349n., 402, 403
Wonnacott, Paul, 144
Woytinsky, E. S., 145n., 161n.
Woytinsky, W. S., 145n., 161n.

Yamey, B. S., 360n.
Yotopoulos, P. A., 140, 141, 143
Young, Arthur, 287
Youngson, A. J., 8n., 71n., 77n.

SUBJECT INDEX

Additionality (*see* Public Law 480)

Agents, human, improvement in, 123, 124

Agrarian economics, 145, 154, 155, 163–167

Agrarian question, 150, 151

Agrarian reform, 20–22, 170, 171 ,174–180
  (*See also* Land reform)

Agrarian structure, 50–52, 60, 61, 277, 278

Agreements, international commodity (*see* International commodity agreements)

Agricultural adjustment as consequence of development, 2, 3

Agricultural change, process, 3, 4, 203–398

Agricultural contribution to development, 17
  ambiguities in, 104, 105
  (*See also* Factor contribution of agriculture; Market contributions of agriculture; Resources, underutilized)

Agricultural development, complexities, 213
  Eastern Europe, 20, 21, 162–167
  history, 3, 7–11, 16–98
  India, 15, 30, 33–40
  Japan, 26–29, 45–69
  lessons from Western experiences, 24–26
  policies, 4, 11, 12, 33–36, 203, 210–213, 339–344, 354–359, 386–393
  role of, in Asia, 26–40
  two-sector models, 127, 128, 182–192

Agricultural development, U.S.S.R., 20–25, 206, 207, 251–271
  (*See also* Agriculture, in development; Development)

Agricultural efficiency and land reform, 273

Agricultural export surpluses (*see* Exports, of agricultural surpluses; Public Law 480)

Agricultural exports (*see* Exports, agricultural)

Agricultural investments, 52–54, 243–245, 247–249, 268–270, 387–389

Agricultural population changes, 10, 78–98, 215, 216

Agricultural productivity, capital formation, 23
  changes in, 46–54, 55–61, 189–192
  industrial contribution to, 13, 14, 109–111
  international implications, 65–67, 113, 114
  open and closed economy, 12, 13
  prior to development, 8, 9
  relative to population, 18
  support of development, 12–14

Agricultural research (*see* Research in agriculture)

Agricultural retardation, 23, 24, 31, 35, 36, 58, 60, 61

Agricultural savings, 208

Agricultural sector changes, 211, 393–398

Agricultural sector neglect, 2, 182

Agriculture, capital formation, 114–117, 208, 243–245, 247–249, 263, 268–270
  dangers in restructuring, 25, 26

Agriculture, delivery quotas, 22, 115, 259
  in development, in Communist China,
      29–33
    in Japan, 9, 26–29, 45–69
    theory, 3, 9, 125–202
    in Western Europe, 16–20
  diminishing returns in (see Diminish-
      ing returns)
  effect, of industrialization, 13, 14
    of migration, 219–223
  exploitation of, 276
  growth rates compared (see Growth
      rates)
  and industry, growth rates, 77
    interrelations, 1–3, 12–14, 192–194
    priorities, 15, 34, 35
    scale of production, 149–151
    (See also Terms of trade)
  labor force proportions, 10, 78–98
  large-scale (see Large-scale agricul-
      ture)
  migration from, 205, 214–226
  peasant (see Peasant agriculture)
  plantation (see Large-scale agricul-
      ture)
  process of change, 203–398
  and regional growth, 10, 69–78
  socialization of (see Socialization of
      agriculture)
  structural changes in, 103, 104, 110,
      219–225, 267–270
  in takeoff, 69, 77, 181, 182, 192
  taxes (see Taxes)
Analysis, macroeconomic, dangers of
    overemphasis, 41, 42
  marginal, shortcomings, 42–44
  (See also Marginal principles)
Applicability of Communist model, 31–
    33
Applying Soviet experience in China, 26
Argentina, 17, 18, 25, 26, 35, 320–322
Australia, 17, 35, 276

Backward-sloping supply curve, 204
Balanced bargaining, commodity agree-
    ments, 325, 326
Balanced growth, 14, 15, 58, 182, 192–
    194
Barter (see Public Law 480)
Belgium, 83, 84
Big-push industrialization, 15, 16, 36–39
Bolivia, 279, 280
Brazil, 17, 18, 396
Buffer funds, 315–320
  (See also International commodity
      agreements)

Buffer stocks, 313–315, 327, 328
  (See also International commodity
      agreements)
Bulgaria, 277, 278

Calvary of capitalism, 161, 162, 164
Canada, 17, 276
Capital, human, 204, 205, 235
  social overhead, 15, 27, 258
Capital formation, 23, 114–117, 208
Capital imports, financed by farm exports,
    21, 49, 50, 73, 74, 208
Capital investments, 244, 245, 248, 249,
    268–270, 287, 303, 304
Capitalism, impact on agriculture, 165
  and Socialism compared, 162–164,
      170, 178–180
China, Communist, 26
  applying Soviet experience in, 26
  development summarized, 29–33
Collective farms, 253–262, 264–266, 304
  characteristics, 253, 254
  compared with state farms, 267
  as cooperatives, 253
  future, 271
  incentives to members, 254, 265, 266
  increase in size, 270, 271
Collectivization, 22–24, 252–254
Colombia, Public Law 480 in, 348, 349
Colonization (see Land settlement)
Commercial trade and export surpluses,
    347, 349, 351–352, 355, 356
Commercialization point, 189–191, 196,
    197
Commodity agreements, international
  (see International commodity agree-
      ments)
Communism and overpopulation, 165–
    167
Communist model, applicability to Asia,
    31–33
Comparative advantage, changes in, 34,
    35, 74–76
Compensation in land reform, 285, 286
Compensatory financing for export earn-
    ings, 335–338
Concessional sales (see Public Law 480)
Consumption, conspicuous, 287
  controls on, 259–262
Contribution to development, agriculture
  (see Agricultural contribution to
      development; Factor contribution of
      agriculture; Market contributions of
      agriculture; Product contribution of
      agriculture)
Cooperatives in land reform, 177–180,
    288, 289
Corn, hybrid (see Hybrid corn)

Costs, social and political, in China, 31
Counsels of perfection in development, 394, 395
Credit in land reform, 288, 289
Critical minimum effort, 182
Czechoslovakia, 88, 89, 288

Defining tasks of development, 31
Delivery quotas (see Agriculture, delivery quotas)
Demand elasticities for exports, 320, 321
(See also Elasticity)
Denmark, 85, 86, 155, 156
Development, agricultural support of, 12–14
    consequences for agricultural adjustment, 2, 3
    diminishing returns limits, 69, 70, 231, 233
    dualistic economy and, 26, 127, 128
    food prices and, 19, 28, 354–357
    institutional change and, 278–279, 286, 287
    labor migration in, 117–119, 224, 225
    land reform and, 207, 272–298
    land settlement pattern and, 206, 238–251
    measurement problems, 3, 98–124
    need of patience, 395, 396
    policy, counsels of perfection, 394, 395
    preconditions, 394, 395
    production functions and, 206, 238–251
    role of deviants, 393
    stages of, 4, 7, 8, 181
    strategy of, 362, 363, 396–398
    substitutes for prerequisites, 4, 8, 395
    tasks of, defining, 31
    theory of agriculture in, 125–202
    wages during, 185, 187–192
    (See also Agricultural contribution to development; Agricultural development; Agricultural productivity; Agriculture, and industry; Agriculture, in development; Capital formation; Exports, agricultural; Natural resources; Role of agriculture; Taxes; and under individual countries)
Deviants, role in development, 393
Diffusion of technology, 210, 369–386
Diminishing returns, 69, 70, 121, 227, 228, 231–233
Disguised unemployment, 126, 129–144, 201, 292
    bibliography, 141–144
    criticism, 131, 132
    definition, 130–135

Disguised unemployment, diagram, 184, 185, 197, 198
    in Eastern Europe, 130
    empirical studies of, 130–132, 135–141
    in Greece, 126, 140, 141
    in India, 126, 130, 137–139, 140
    in Italy, 126, 138, 139
    in Thailand, 126, 136
    theory, 132–135
    (See also Labor, redundant; Zero marginal productivity of labor)
Distribution of income, Japan, 65, 66
Distribution as a lagging sector, 269, 359–369
    economies of scale in, 364, 365, 368
    goals for, 361, 362
    innovations, 364, 365, 367
    obstacles to change, 363–366
    programming, 366–369
    shortages of managerial talent, 364, 365
    strategy, 362, 363
Dominant social groups, 17–19
Dualism, 26, 127, 128

Economic development (see Development)
Economies of scale, 252, 270, 284, 364, 365, 368
    (See also Scale of farming)
Egypt, 275, 280, 294
Elasticity, of demand, exports, 320, 321
    income, of food, 48, 49, 57, 77, 78, 99, 100, 126
    price, implications, 390, 391
    of supply, 265, 266, 317, 318
Emigrants, 17, 19, 20
    (See also Migration)
Employment, growth, nonagricultural, 92–94
England (see Great Britain)
Europe, Eastern, 20, 21, 130, 156
    effects of commercialization on, 162–166
    Western, 276
    development summarized, 18–20
European Common Market, 332–335, 341
Export dominance, consequence, 70, 71
Export earnings, instability, 311–313
    proposals to stabilize, 313–330, 335–338
Export markets, 35
Export restriction, 328–330
Export tax policies, compared, 320–322
Export trade, comparisons, 312
Exports, agricultural, and development, 10, 49, 50, 69–78, 113, 114, 208, 238–251, 311–322

Exports, of agricultural surpluses, 17, 21, 209, 210, 332–334
(*See also* Public Law 480)
farm products, finance capital imports, 21
supply elasticity, 317, 318
prime mover in development, 70, 71
underdeveloped countries, problems, 333–335
Extension and research services, 27, 212, 389–393

Factor contribution of agriculture, 100, 114–119, 206, 254–258, 264, 265, 267–270
(*See also* Market contributions of agriculture; Product contribution of agriculture)
Factors in land settlement, 299–309
Family farms, 43, 72, 73, 75, 206, 241, 242, 276, 310
Farm size, 284
(*See also* Family farms)
Feudal agriculture, 25, 28, 173, 174, 278–279
Field surveys, 100
Finland, 84, 85, 288
Food, income elasticity (*see* Elasticity)
Food balances, 100
Food crisis, 36–38, 58
Food grants (*see* Public Law 480)
Food imports and industrialization, 19
Food prices, 19, 152
stability of, 28
Food requisition (*see* Agriculture, delivery quotas)
Food for wages, 352, 353, 357
Foreign aid, 395–398
France, 25, 86, 87, 284
Freehold and tenure, 306, 307

Gezira irrigation program, 305
Ghost inputs, 121–124
Great Britain, 25, 82–84, 276, 284
development summarized, 18–20
Greece, 126, 140, 141
Growth, and agricultural exports, 113, 114
balanced (*see* Balanced growth)
nonfarm employment, 92–94
(*See also* Development)
Growth rates, 54–56, 61, 62
comparisons, 46, 48–50, 67, 68, 80–94

Havana Charter, 324, 325, 328, 329
Human agents, improvement in, 123, 124
Human capital, 204, 205, 235

Hungary, 165, 277, 278
Hybrid corn, 369–386
research expenditures, 370–372
value of, 372–377, 385, 386
Hybrid sorghum, 382, 383
Hyper-inflation and turning point, 196, 197, 200, 201

Immigration, 17
(*See also* Migration)
Imports, 19, 57–61, 74, 209, 245, 261, 262
Incentives to farmers, 53–54, 58, 59, 254, 265, 266, 308
effect of Public Law 480 on, 346, 347, 349
Japan, 53, 59
U.S.S.R., 254, 266
Income distribution, 65, 66, 243, 244, 248, 249, 284
Income elasticity, food (*see* Elasticity)
Income levels, 99, 266
India, 15, 30, 126, 130, 279, 280, 287, 288
development summarized, 33–40
disguised unemployment, 137–140
effect of Public Law 480, 350–352
Industrialization, big-push, 15, 16, 36–39
Industry and agriculture, growth rates, 77
priorities, 15, 34, 35
relationships, 1–3, 12–14, 19, 109–111, 152, 192–194, 224, 225
scale, 27, 28, 31, 245–249
Innovations, 210, 364, 365, 367, 370–380
Inputs, ghost, 121–124
nonconventional, 100, 101, 120, 124
Instability of export earnings, 311–313
Institutional change and development, 278, 279, 286, 287
Institutional monopoly and population, 283, 284, 297, 298
Institutional wage, 184, 185, 197–199, 201
Interdependence, 1–3, 100, 102–119
International commodity agreements, 209, 318, 322–329
balancing bargaining, 325, 326
objectives, 323, 324
possible role, 338, 339
principles, 324, 325, 328, 329
stabilizing export earnings, 323–330
types of, 326–330
International sugar agreement, 329
International terms of trade (*see* Terms of trade, international)
International tin agreement, 328

International wheat agreement, 326, 327
Investment in knowledge, 14, 27, 53, 73, 103, 270
Irrigation, Gezira program, 305
Israel, effects of Public Law 480, 346–348
Italy, 86–89, 126, 138, 139, 287, 294

Japan, 9, 35, 90–92, 115, 276, 320–322
  development, role of agriculture in, 45–69
  summarized, 26–29

Knowledge, investment in (see Investment in knowledge)
Kulaks, elimination of, 22, 157, 254, 255

Labor, agricultural, efficiency of, 24
  proportions, 10, 78–98
  contributions of agricultural (see Factor contribution of agriculture)
  redundant, 183–188, 197–199, 201
    (See also Disguised unemployment)
  sub-subsistence wage, 171–173
    (See also Disguised unemployment; Zero marginal productivity of labor)
Labor market functioning, 204
Labor migration in development, 117–119
Labor mobility, structural relations, 256, 257
Land, substitution for, 267, 268
  (See also Natural resources)
Land (as factor), 27, 39, 227–233
  (See also Natural resources)
Land payments, 308, 309
Land quality, 300
Land reform, 207, 272–298
  arguments for, 285–290
  compensation in, 285, 286
  defined, 272, 273
  historical perspective, 275–280
  (See also Agrarian reform)
Land settlement, 206, 207, 238–251, 299–310
  appropriate tenure rules, 307–309
  capital in, 303, 304
  factors in success, 299–309
  size of farm, 306
Land settlers, characteristics, 300–302
Land taxes (see Taxes)
Large-scale agriculture, 17–19, 21–25, 72–75
  large estates, 283–285
  latifundia, 279, 283, 290, 296, 297
  plantations, 206, 207, 240–242
Latin America, 18, 211, 393–398

Leisure, unwanted, 43, 44, 159–162
Local currency (see Public Law 480)
Longrun planning, dangers of overemphasis, 41, 42

Macroeconomic analysis, problems, 41, 42
Malaya, 299
Managerial skill, 122, 123, 364, 365
Marginal analysis, shortcomings, 42–44
Marginal principles, profit maximization, 20, 21, 146, 147, 162–165
Marginal productivity of labor (see Zero marginal productivity of labor)
Market contributions of agriculture, 100, 109–114, 210, 359–369
  (See also Factor contribution of agriculture; Product contribution of agriculture)
Market supply curve, 204
Marketing (see Distribution as a lagging sector)
Marketing boards, 318
  (See also International commodity agreements)
Marxist economic doctrine, 149, 150, 251
Marxist theory, 146, 147, 149–153, 158, 161, 162
Marx's scorn of peasant, 151
Measurement problems, 3, 98–124, 236–238
Mexico, 279–280, 288, 289, 297, 396
Migrants, characteristics of, 216–219
Migration, from agriculture, 50–52, 60, 205, 214–226, 255–257
  effects of, 21, 117–119, 168, 219–224
Migration policy, 214–216, 224–226, 258
Multilateral contract, 326, 327
  (See also International commodity agreements)

Narodniki, 153, 154
Natural resources, 72, 73, 205, 206, 227–238
  (See also Land [as factor])
Netherlands, 83, 84
New Zealand, 276
Nigeria, 299, 300, 306–308
Nonconventional inputs (see Inputs, nonconventional)
Norway, 85, 86

Overpopulation, 21, 24–26, 154, 155, 158, 165–167, 170–174, 292, 294
  concepts of, 155–159, 291, 292
  evidence for, 156, 157, 293–295
  (See also Population; Zero marginal productivity of labor)

Pakistan, 279, 280
  effects of Public Law 480, 350
Peasant agriculture, 22, 23, 42, 50–52,
    144, 145, 151, 153, 154, 165, 166,
    176, 177, 207, 252, 276, 287, 288,
    294
  concepts of, 148–150
Planning, 41, 42, 350, 351
Plantation agriculture (see Large-scale
    agriculture)
Poland, 288
Policies (see Agricultural development;
    Development; Export tax policies;
    International commodity agree-
    ments; Public Law 480; Taxes)
Population, growth rates, 46, 48–50, 80–
    94
  and land reform, 274, 290–298
  structure (see Overpopulation)
Population changes, 10, 78–98
Population pressures and emigrants, 19,
    20
  (See also Migration)
Portugal, 86–89
Preconditions in development 394, 395
Prerequisites, substitutes for, in develop-
    ment, 4, 8, 395
Price elasticity (see Elasticity)
Private agriculture, U.S.S.R., 260, 261,
    266, 267
Product contribution of agriculture, 100,
    105–109, 206, 258–262, 265, 266
  (See also Factor contribution of ag-
    riculture; Market contributions of
    agriculture)
Production functions, 120, 121, 206, 234,
    235, 238–251
Productivity (see Agricultural produc-
    tivity; Zero marginal productivity
    of labor)
Profit maximization (see Marginal prin-
    ciples)
Prussia, 276
Public Law 480, 209, 210, 339–359
  definition of terms, 341, 342
  described, 339–341
  general evaluation, 354–357
  mechanics, 344–346
  monetary effects, 351, 352, 354–357
  rationale, 342–344
Puerto Rico, 304

Redundant labor, diagram, 184–188,
    197–199, 201
  (See also Disguised unemployment)
Regional growth and agriculture (see
    Agriculture, and regional growth)

Requisition of farm products (see Ag-
    riculture, delivery quotas)
Research in agriculture, 27, 212, 369–
    372, 380–382, 384–393
Resources, underutilized, 30
  (See also Land [as factor]; Natural
    resources)
Retardation hypothesis, 70–77
Role of agriculture, 9, 11–44, 46–54, 68,
    69, 74, 77, 100, 102–119
  (See also Factor contribution of ag-
    riculture; Market contributions of
    agriculture; Product contribution
    of agriculture)
Rumania, 156, 157, 165, 288
Russia, 20–25, 156, 165
  (See also U.S.S.R.)

Savings, agricultural, 208
Scale of farming, 149–151, 243–252,
    284, 306
  (See also Economies of scale)
Serfdom, 20, 21, 278
Shortage point, 189–191
Site preparation, 302, 303
  (See also Land settlement)
Small-scale industry, 27, 28, 31
Social equality and land reform, 273
Social groups, dominant, 17–19
Social movements, 153, 154, 396
Social overhead capital (see Capital,
    social overhead)
Socialism and capitalism compared, 162–
    164, 170, 178–180
Socialist party, Agrarian Question, 150,
    151
Socialization of agriculture, 167–169,
    206, 207, 252–254
Soil exhaustion, land reform, 292, 293
Sorghum, hybrid, 382, 383
Soviet experience applied in China, 26
Soviet Union (see Russia; U.S.S.R.)
Spain, 86, 87
Stages of development, 4, 7, 8
Standard theory, 145–148, 164
State farms, 252, 253, 267
Statistics, U.S.S.R., 31
Strategy in development, 362, 363, 396–
    398
  (See also Agricultural development;
    Balanced growth; Development;
    Export tax policies; International
    commodity agreements; Public
    Law 480; Taxes)
Structural changes (see Agriculture,
    structural changes in; Agricultural
    change)

Structural interdependence, 49, 50, 60, 61, 100, 102–119, 256, 257
Structural relations in agriculture, 267–270
Structural surpluses, 332–334
Structure of population change, theory, 95–98
Structures, agricultural (*see* Agrarian structure; Land reform)
Substitute for requisites, 4, 8, 212, 213, 395
Sugar agreement, international, 329
Supply elasticity (*see* Elasticity, of supply)
Surpluses, agricultural export (*see* Exports, of agricultural surpluses; Public Law 480)
Surveys, field, 100
Sweden, 84, 85, 284
Switzerland, 83, 84, 276

Taiwan, 31
Takeoff, agriculture in (*see* Agriculture, in takeoff)
Taxes, on agriculture, 30, 53, 54, 62–64, 114, 115, 263, 264
  on exports, 320–322
  on land, 28, 115
Technological changes, theory, 121, 122
Technology, diffusion of, 210, 369–386
Tenure rules, 306–309
Terms of trade, adverse to development, 209, 311, 312, 322, 339
  agricultural-industrial, 22, 49, 59, 60, 187, 191, 192, 196, 252, 259, 263 265, 266
  international, 14, 209, 311–322, 323–339
  fluctuations in, 208, 209, 311–322
Thailand, 126, 136
Theory, disguised unemployment, 132–135
  economic development, 181–202
  agriculture in, 3, 125–202
  Marxist (*see* Marxist theory)
  Standard, 145–148, 164
  technological changes, 121, 122
Tin agreement, international, 328
Tropical products, surpluses, 333, 334

Tunisia, 352, 353
Turkey, 368
Turning point, 187, 188, 196, 197, 200, 201
Two-sector models, 127, 128

Unbalanced development, 282, 289
Underdeveloped, defined, 281, 282
Underdeveloped nations' export problems, 333–335
Underemployment and marginal analysis, 42–44
Unemployment, disguised (*see* Disguised unemployment; Zero marginal productivity of labor)
U.S.S.R., 31, 35, 90, 91, 115, 206–208
  agricultural development, 251–271
  development summarized, 21–25
  (*See also* Russia)
United States, 17, 75, 89–91
  migration from farms, 214–226
  regional growth, 69–78
  surplus export policies, 339–359
Unlimited supply of labor (*see* Labor, redundant; Disguised unemployment)
Unwanted leisure (*see* Leisure, unwanted)

Vicious cycle, 282, 289, 290

Wages, institutional, 184, 185, 197–199, 201
  paid in food, 352, 353, 357
  rise during development, 185, 187–192
West Indies, 299
Wheat agreement, international, 326, 327
World Food Program, 341

Yugoslavia, 155, 156, 287

Zero marginal productivity of labor, 130, 166, 183, 197
  bibliography, 141–144
  related, to overpopulation, 157–159, 294–298
  to unwanted leisure, 42–44
  theory, 132–135, 171–173
  (*See also* Disguised unemployment)